Practical Techniques of Electronic Circuit Design

PRACTICAL TECHNIQUES OF ELECTRONIC CIRCUIT DESIGN

Second Edition

ROBERT L. BONEBREAK

A Wiley-Interscience Publication

JOHN WILEY & SONS

New York · Chichester · Brisbane · Toronto · Singapore

Library of Congress Cataloging in Publication Data:

Bonebreak, Robert L., 1921–
Practical techniques of electronic circuit design.

  "A Wiley-Interscience publication."
  Bibliography: p.
  Includes index.
  1. Electronic circuit design.   I. Title.

TK7867.B63 1987   621.3815'3   86-23382
ISBN 0-471-85244-9

Printed in the United States of America

10   9   8   7   6   5   4   3   2   1

To my wife, Mary

Preface

This book is written to serve those who are faced with practical electronic circuit design problems in their work. Perhaps one of the most direct areas of application is in the work of the large number of engineers who are highly trained as computer specialists without the initial intention of becoming hardware designers. The practical world has a way of forcing an expansion of capabilities so that the computer and hardware specialists must each gain a good insight into the other's skills.

Some familiarity and experience with electronic circuits are assumed, so that the book is not a beginner's text. It is, however, directed toward the straightforward design of electronic circuits by those who lack a strong background in electronic circuit design. This book is more concerned with facts and correct procedures than with proofs or derivations.

The electronic design techniques presented are based on the most effective use of present-day components. This is a constantly shifting pattern because integrated circuits continue to replace discrete transistor circuits. For example, the design of the flip-flop, which has been a classic schoolroom project for years, has now been made virtually obsolete by the availability of monolithic circuits.

There are, however, many areas in which discrete design is and will continue to be needed.

Chapter 10 on laboratory procedures should be read first and then reread from time to time to make certain that good working techniques are followed. Chapter 1 on the basic transistor is written in engineering terms as contrasted to the usual physics approach and should be read before Chapter 2. Aside from this the chapters are largely independent and can be referred to as required.

Where practical, tables or nomographs are provided to speed the design process. This is particularly true of both passive and active filters, where the use of computers has greatly reduced the design effort for the majority of requirements.

The subjects were selected for their wide application and also because they contain information commonly misunderstood by designers with limited experience. Definitions and symbols are carefully indexed to allow the reader to study the chapters in preferred order.

The design procedure and techniques of electronic circuits vary substantially with each application. For example, consider the following classifications:

1. High-reliability and wide-temperature equipment such as military, space, and some industrial applications.

2. Very-low-cost high-production consumer-oriented products.

3. One-of-a-kind designs for obtaining data, testing other types of equipment, prototype design concepts, and providing assistance in areas not covered by available commercial products.

Although the information in this book is useful in all areas, it is specifically directed toward the last category. Here it is usually important to keep the design costs to a minimum by substituting some "after fabrication" adjustment in place of a more rigorous initial design. This is especially evident when it is realized that most important parameters have a tolerance range of 2 or 3, and often as high as 10, to 1. Indeed, many parameters that are important in a particular design may not be specified at all. Accordingly, explanation of the procedures is presented largely on an intuitive basis, with some occasional simple algebra.

Devices are generally described as ideal components so that the fundamental concepts can be emphasized. This is then followed by a detailed list and description of the deviations from the ideal case and of the circumstances under which they are important. In all cases parameters from present-day devices are used to illustrate when variations from the ideal case must be considered. To aid in this effort some data sheets are included in the text. However, for proper design it is necessary to obtain a good selection of current data sheets and publications directly from the manufacturer.

A chapter on design projects (Chapter 11) for classroom participation has been included in this text. These projects are meant to stimulate discussions and debates relating to different procedures and techniques in producing a proper design. They require detailed and extensive design, construction, and testing efforts and will be a very valuable contribution toward developing the necessary skills for competent hardware design.

Finally, Chapter 9, Circuit and Component Applications, is a collection of working designs with step by step explanations of how and why the parts used were selected.

ROBERT L. BONEBREAK

Los Angeles, California
April 1987

Contents

ONE

Transistors

This chapter is different than the rest of the book in that it provides specific background material for the succeeding chapter. The emphasis is on describing, rather than proving, the transistor properties so that useful design equations can be developed.

1.1 FUNDAMENTALS

The ideal transistor is a simple device. It is shown in Fig. 1.1 connected as collector-loaded amplifier or, as it is generally called, a common emitter circuit.

Transistor action, which results in its ability to amplify, occurs because a small change in base current results in a larger change in collector current. This is represented as

$$\beta = \frac{\Delta i_c}{\Delta i_b} \tag{1.1}$$

The base current flows into the emitter so that

$$i_e = i_b(1 + \beta) \tag{1.2}$$

The ideal transistor has these properties:

The current transfer ratio, $\beta = \infty$
The transistor output resistance, $r_o = \infty$
The transistor base resistance, $r_b = 0$
The transistor emitter resistance, $r_e = 0$
The transistor reverse gain, $h_{re} = 0$

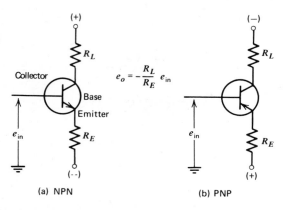

FIGURE 1.1   The ideal transistor: (*a*) NPN; (*b*) PNP.

The transistor collector-to-base leakage current, $I_{CBO} = 0$
The transistor base-to-emitter voltage drop, $e_{be} = 0$
The transistor collector-to-base capacitance, C_{cb} (or C_{CB}) $= 0$
The transistor emitter-to-base capacitance, $C_{eb} = 0$
The transistor current gain–bandwidth product, $f_t = \infty$

1.1.1 Common Emitter Connection

To evaluate the ideal transistor, let us further consider the common emitter connection shown in Fig. 1.1.

Because $\beta = \infty$, the signal current induced in the collector flows in the emitter. Also, since r_b and r_e are zero, any signal change applied from base to ground occurs across R_E. Accordingly, the signal at the collector must be R_L/R_E as great as the input signal. From this

$$\text{gain} = -\frac{R_L}{R_E} \tag{1.3}$$

This equation states that the voltage gain of the ideal transistor is independent of the transistor. R_L/R_E is the theoretical limit of the voltage gain of a transistor without positive feedback. Positive feedback, generally undesirable, promotes instability or oscillation and is caused by poor layout and decoupling techniques. In practice R_L and R_E are limited by design considerations and the gain equation will be modified by considering real transistor parameters, as illustrated in Fig. 1.2*a*.

At this time it would be well to point out that for a transistor to function properly it must have a defined DC current flowing in the collector and emitter which is developed because of a properly applied voltage and a DC base current input. These DC currents are designated as I_C, I_E, and I_B, respectively and are discussed in the section on transistor biasing. The development of the signal relations is based on the superposition of the signal currents, respectively i_c, i_e, and i_b, on the defined bias condition.

As previously stated, when an input current is directed to the base it flows through the base–emitter junction to the emitter. This allows a larger current βi_b to flow from the collector to the emitter. Accordingly, the emitter current is equal to $(\beta + 1)i_b$. From this it is apparent that R_E is $(\beta + 1)$ times as effective as R_B in limiting the base current. From this we have

$$\text{Base input resistance} = R_B + R_E(\beta + 1) \qquad (1.4)$$

Likewise, when a current is inserted in the emitter, a current flows from the emitter through the base lead that is equal to $i_e/(1 + \beta)$. Thus with respect to the gain of a transistor, a value of R_B in the base is equivalent to a value of $R_B/(1 + \beta)$ in the emitter. This is not the case in controlling other conditions such as bias stability and frequency response, which are discussed in a later section. It remains true, however, that

$$\text{Emitter input resistance} = R_E + R_B/(\beta + 1) \qquad (1.5)$$

Now in addition to the external resistors R_E and R_B the transistor has internal resistance expressed as r_e and r_b. r_e must be added to R_E and r_b must be added to R_B. As a very reasonable approximation we use β in place of $(\beta + 1)$ so that our gain equation now becomes

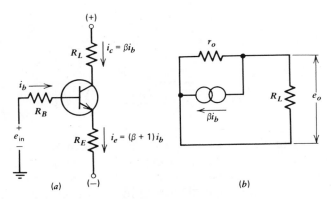

FIGURE 1.2   Common emitter amplifier.

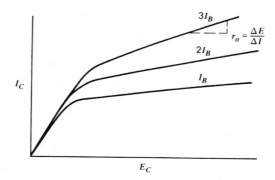

FIGURE 1.3   Transistor $E-I$ curves.

$$A_v = \frac{e_o}{e_{\text{in}}} = \frac{-R_L}{[(R_E + r_e) + (R_B + r_b)/\beta]} \qquad (1.6)$$

When the collector resistance r_o departs from the ideal and becomes finite, the gain is lowered. Referring to Fig. 1.2b, it is seen that the output of the transistor is represented by a current generator in parallel with the transistor output resistance r_o. If the load resistor R_L is connected as shown, it is seen that R_L and r_o are in parallel. From this several different expressions can be derived. First,

$$e_o = \beta i_b\left(\frac{R_L r_o}{R_L + r_o}\right) = \frac{\beta i_b R_L}{(1 + R_L/r_o)} \qquad (1.7)$$

or when $r_o = \infty$,

$$e_o = \beta i_b R_L \qquad (1.8)$$

A more general expression for the voltage gain is obtained from (1.6) by substituting r_o and R_L in parallel for R_L:

$$A_v = \frac{e_o}{e_{\text{in}}} = \frac{-R_L}{\left[(R_E + r_e) + \dfrac{(R_B + r_b)}{\beta}\right]\left(1 + \dfrac{R_L}{r_o}\right)} \qquad (1.9)$$

Another way of looking at what a finite r_o does in an amplifier circuit is shown by Fig. 1.3. $1/r_o$ is the slope of the $E-I$ curve. If a signal is put on the base in such a way as to make I_C increase, the drop across the load resistor causes the collector voltage to decrease. This in turn reduces the original current increase, which is a loss of gain.

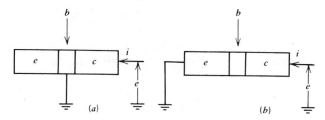

FIGURE 1.4   Transistor output resistance: (*a*) grounded base; (*b* grounded emitter.

Again, as in the case with r_e and r_b, the output resistance is seldom a known value. r_o, however, unlike r_e and r_b, is not a physical value of the transistor; it is instead a function of the transistor collector resistance r_c and the external resistors R_E and R_B. This is demonstrated as follows. Figure 1.4*a* shows an ideal grounded base configuration (See Section 1.1.2). If a signal is applied to the collector, a current flows through the collector to the base and to ground.

The output resistance r_o is e/i. In the case of the ideal grounded emitter, the current created by the applied voltage, *e*, flows through the base across the base–emitter junction. Because of the transistor action this causes the current to be multiplied, resulting in an output resistance for the ideal grounded emitter case that is $1/\beta$ times that of the ideal grounded base configuration, a very considerable reduction. In a real circuit there are always finite resistance values associated with both the emitter and the base, so that neither is a pure ground.

Figure 1.5 is a plot of the equation for the common emitter output resistance and clearly shows the relationship to the base and emitter resistances. Fortunately, r_o is generally not a major factor in determining the gain of a transistor amplifier circuit. This is especially true

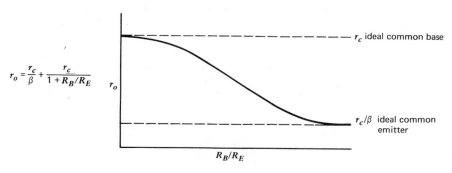

$$r_o = \frac{r_c}{\beta} + \frac{r_c}{1 + R_B/R_E}$$

FIGURE 1.5 r_o versus R_B/R_E.

in broadband amplifiers where R_L must be kept low to ensure the necessary high-frequency response.

There remains one more consideration in the low-frequency common emitter amplifier. This comes about from the fact that the output voltage has a feedback effect on the input base current. This is represented in the h parameters by h_{re}. However, h_{re} is also a function of R_E and R_B, and since the published values of h_{re} are generally for the intrinsic transistor, the information is not very useful. Happily, this effect is generally quite small and can usually be neglected.

1.1.2 Common Base Connection

In addition to the common emitter there remain two other ways in which the transistor can be connected. The common base is discussed first and is shown in Fig. 1.6, where

$$I_o = \alpha I_{\text{in}} \text{ by definition}$$

$$= I_{\text{in}} - I_B$$

$$= I_{\text{in}} - \frac{I_{\text{in}}}{(1 + \beta)} \tag{1.10}$$

$$= I_{\text{in}} \left(\frac{\beta}{1 + \beta} \right)$$

$$\therefore \alpha = \frac{\beta}{1 + \beta}$$

This circuit follows many of the rules of the common emitter circuit. For example the voltage gain is the same except that it is noninverting:

$$\frac{e_o}{e_{\text{in}}} = \frac{R_L}{[(R_E + r_e) + (R_B + r_b)/\beta] (1 + R_L/r_o)} \tag{1.11}$$

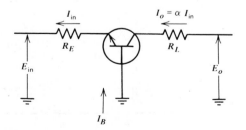

FIGURE 1.6   Common base relations.

However, the input impedance is much lower, being approximately

$$R_{in} = (R_E + r_e) + \frac{(R_B + r_b)}{\beta} \qquad (1.12)$$

resulting in less power gain. The current gain α is also very much reduced, being essentially unity [or, more precisely, $\alpha = \beta/(1 + \beta)$]. The advantages of the common base circuit are

1. Better high-frequency performance
2. Higher output resistance
3. Higher collector breakdown voltage

The superior frequency performance results from two different reasons. First, the current gain α is a function of frequency, and since $\beta = \alpha/(1 - \alpha)$ it is seen that β varies more strongly with frequency. For example if α changes from 0.98 to 0.97, a change of approximately 1%, β changes from 49 to 32, a change of 53%. Further analysis shows that

$$f_\beta(-3 \text{ dB}) = \frac{f_\alpha(-3 \text{ dB})}{\beta} \qquad (1.13)$$

The second reason is that the collector-to-base capacitance C_{cb} is isolated from the input by the common base connection. This greatly reduces the input capacitance because in the common emitter connection C_{cb} is multiplied by 1 plus the amplifier gain (see Miller effect, Appendix I) which is often the limiting factor in high-frequency performance.

The reason for the higher output resistance was given in Section 1.1.1 where r_o was discussed.

A reference to transistor data sheets shows that the collector breakdown voltage can be given in two different ways.

The first is V_{CBO} (collector-to-base breakdown with the emitter open) and the second, generally much lower, is V_{CEO} (collector-to-emitter breakdown with the base open). When the base and emitters have finite resistors to ground, the breakdown is somewhere between the two limits.

The basic breakdown might be called the V_{CBO}, but when the breakdown current begins to flow and is allowed to cross the base-to-emitter junction, as with V_{CEO}, this breakdown current is multiplied by the transistor action and its magnitude increases much more rapidly, resulting in the lower breakdown voltage.

Further details on when and why to choose between the common emitter and common base connections are given in the sections that deal more directly with transitor circuit design.

1.1.3 Emitter Follower Connection

The common collector or, as it is usually called, the emitter follower is entirely different in its function from the other two forms. The emitter follower is essentially a unity voltage gain buffer with a high-impedance input and a low-impedance output. Figure 1.7 shows a typical emitter follower. The input resistance

$$R_{in} = R_S + \frac{r_c \beta R_L}{(r_c + \beta R_L)} \tag{1.14}$$

where R_S includes r_b, and $R_L = (R_E + r_e)$.

This is about what would be expected from the previous discussions. That is, R_E is multiplied by β when transferred to the input. In addition, it is seen that the input resistance is limited by the collector resistance r_c because it is in parallel with the multiplied emitter load. r_c is usually very much larger than βR_L, and in this case the input resistance becomes $R_{in} = R_S + \beta R_L$.

The output resistance is again understandable from the earlier discussions:

$$r_o = r_e + \frac{1}{\beta} \left[\frac{r_c R_S}{(r_c + R_S)} \right] \tag{1.15}$$

Now, if $r_c = \infty$,

$$r_o = r_e + \frac{R_S}{\beta} \tag{1.16}$$

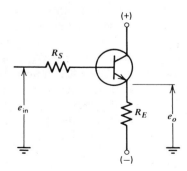

FIGURE 1.7   The emitter follower connection.

In addition, R_E is in parallel with the output, but is usually so large that it need not be considered.

A word of caution is necessary at this point. r_o is a dynamic resistance. That is, it depends on the transistor having a normal current to produce its calculated value. If the current capability of the transistor is exceeded by the load demand, the output current is limited, leading to possible transistor damage. If the load demands current from the emitter source in excess of the quiescent bias value, the transistor shuts off and the output resistance reverts to that of R_E.

Since the load current passes through the base–emitter junction, the basic transistor frequency response is limited by the same mechanism as the common emitter stage. That is, it is a β roll-off as contrasted to an α roll-off of the common base stage.

1.1.4 Transistor Data Sheets

At this point it is suggested that the reader look over a number of transistor data sheets and observe the wide variation in tolerances, many of which are unbounded on one side. Another point to observe is the lack of needed specifications. This is why it is often necessary to make approximate calculations for a design and then make readjustments after some data have been taken.

In addition, there is the natural variation in the transistor parameters as functions of the current, voltage, and temperature. Total inclusion of these variations leads to a procedure known as "worst case design." This is a complex procedure, which is really suited only for computer applications. The end result is an extremely conservative design with low performance for a given volume of hardware.

Obviously, some trade-off is necessary between this and the procedure of squeezing the last drop of performance out of a given design. The design equations and intuitive models developed in this chapter are organized to allow the direct incorporation of external passive elements into the transistor in order to obtain a given result. Historically, this manner of transistor modeling is known as **T** parameters. Figure 1.8 shows how external components are added to a **T** equivalent circuit. As previously indicated, r_o is a function of R_E and R_B, but for the low-frequency model r_e and r_b can be directly added to the external parameters.

The transistor emitter resistance consists of two parts. One is current dependent and can be directly calculated. The other is ohmic and must be obtained by measurement:

$$r_e = \left(\frac{26}{I_e \text{mA}} + R_{\text{ohmic}} \right) \Omega \qquad (1.17)$$

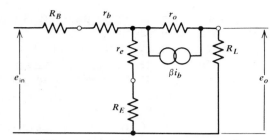

FIGURE 1.8 Low-frequency transistor **T** model.

Low frequency transistor parameters of any form are seldom given in today's data sheets. The reason for this is not at all clear, since a proper design approach is not possible without this knowledge. Occasionally a set of **h** parameters are found as shown in Fig. IV.1 for the 2N2222A transistor. The **h** parameters cannot directly combine with other circuit elements and, furthermore, there is a separate set of **h** parameters for each of the three basic transistor connections. That the **h** parameters have survived since the beginning of the transistor seems very strange.

It is, however, possible to convert the **h** parameters to **T** parameters, and this useful relationship is shown in Section I.1 with a sample calculation from data sheets of the 2N2222A transistor.

Test equipment can also be built to measure the **T** parameters. One such set of test equipment is described in Ref. [1].

1.1.5 Additional Considerations

A transistor has also a current gain and a power gain, as well as the voltage gain that has already been discussed.

The maximum current gain of grounded emitter stage is β, that of the emitter follower is β + 1, and the grounded base circuit approaches unity as a limit. In practice the current gain of the grounded emitter and emitter follower stages is reduced somewhat by the shunting effect of the base bias resistors (see Section 1.2).

The power gain is considerably more complex because it requires careful impedance matching to produce efficient results. Fortunately, many circuits do not require optimum power gain and are designed primarily to emphasize voltage gain and bandwidth, using emitter followers as buffer stages when needed.

Power stages and sometimes the drivers of the power stages often require direct matching. High-frequency power transistors generally contain power gain data with complex impedance information for the inputs and the outputs. Chapter 5 on transformers and Chapter 9 on circuit and component applications give additional information on coupling methods.

Appendix I contains tables of both accurate and approximate formulas for amplifiers in all three transistor connections.

In summary, it might be stated that a first-time accurate design of a transistor stage can be impractical because of lack of information on the transistor and the large tolerance spreads allowed by the manufacturer. It is generally much more efficient in time and effort simply to approximate the design and make corrections based on measurements of the completed design. This is particularly true when high-frequency circuits are designed. The transistor model is more complex and it is also very difficult to estimate the associated stray capacitance and inductance in the circuit.

1.2 BIASING

To establish the desired current in a transistor, a bias system must be developed to inject a current into the base. In the examples that follow the characteristics of the 2N2222A transistor are used.

One of the problems that faces even the experienced designer is the profusion of symbols. To ease this problem, Appendix V lists some of the symbols. In this section we must distinguish between the small current gain, β or h_{fe}, and the β used for biasing, h_{FE}.

h_{FE} is a function of temperature and increases approximately 100% over a junction temperature range of 25 to 175°C. The second factor that sometimes affects the bias conditions is the collector-to-base leakage current. This is small at room temperature but almost doubles every 10°C. For the 2N2222A $I_{CBO} = 0.01$ μA at 25°C and about 1 μA at 100°C. In the example at hand this is not enough to affect the design but it must be considered at higher temperatures.

1.2.1 Base Biasing

The simplest biasing system is a single resistor from the collector supply, as shown in Fig. 1.9a. Estimating $h_{FE} = 120$ with a desired 10-mA collector current, we would have $I_B = 10^{-2}/120 = 83.3$ μA.

If the supply is $+25$ V, we have

$$R_B = \frac{25 - 0.6}{83.3(10)^{-6}} = 281 \text{ k}\Omega$$

With an ambient temperature rise from 25 to 100°C β would be expected to increase 50%. The original base current of 83.3 μA would

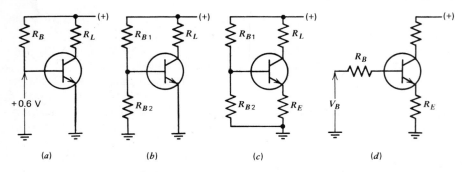

FIGURE 1.9 Transistor base biasing.

now produce 50% more collector current, which could well be above the tolerance level.

An improvement would be to add a second resistor from base to ground as in Fig. 1.9b. This is of limited value, however, because there is only 0.6 V from base to ground and consequently R_{B2} is generally too low for any worthwhile gain in stability. A more suitable method is shown in Fig. 1.9c. Not only are the bias and gain stability improved, but added control of the AC signal gain can be obtained by shunting all or part of R_E with a capacitor.

As an example, let us set $R_E = 100\ \Omega$ and $I_C = 10$ mA. This makes $I_C R_E = 10^{-2}(100) = 1$ V. Accordingly, the base-to-ground voltage $= 1.6$ V. To the required bias current of 83.3 μA let us add five times this amount of stable current and see what the result is:

$$5(83.3)\mu A = 416.5\ \mu A$$

$$R_{B2} = \frac{1.6\ V}{416.5(10)^{-6}} = 3.84\ k\Omega$$

$$R_{B1} = (25 - 1.6)/(416.5 + 83.3)\ (10)^{-6} = 46.8\ k\Omega$$

Applying Thévenin's theorem (Appendix I) to the base circuit of Fig. 1.9c, we obtain Fig. 1.9d, where

$$R_B = \frac{R_{B1}R_{B2}}{R_{B1} + R_{B2}} = \frac{(46.8)\ (3.84)}{46.8 + 3.84} = 3.55\ k\Omega$$

$$V_B = \frac{V_C R_{B2}}{R_{B1} + R_{B2}} = \frac{25(3.84)}{46.8 + 3.84} = 1.9\ V$$

We can now write the equation as $V_B = I_B R_B + V_{BE} + I_E R_E$. Since $I_E \cong I_C$ and $I_B = I_C/h_{FE}$,

$$I_C = \frac{V_B - V_{BE}}{R_B/h_{FE} + R_E} = \frac{1.9 - 0.6}{(3550/120) + 100}$$

$$= 10 \text{ mA}$$

which confirms the calculations.

If h_{FE} increases 50% to 180, we have

$$\frac{1.9 - 0.6}{(3550/180) + 100} = 10.9 \text{ mA}$$

V_{BE} has a temperature coefficient of about 2 mV/°C, the voltage decreasing with increasing temperature. For a change of 25 to 100°C we have $V_{BE} = 0.6 - 75(2) (10)^{-3} = 0.45$ V, and

$$I_C = \frac{1.9 - 0.45}{(3550/120) + 100} = 11.2 \text{ mA}$$

Unfortunately, these two effects are additive and the overall effect of the temperature change would be

$$I_C = \frac{1.9 - 0.45}{(3550/180) + 100} = 12.1 \text{ mA}$$

1.2.2 Emitter Biasing

It is often advantageous in an electronic circuit to have both $(+)$ and $(-)$ power supplies. When this occurs, there is more flexibility in the biasing system that can be used. Figure 1.10 shows how the emitter biasing system is developed. Figure 1.10a presents the most direct method. Given a desired R_L, the gain is approximately $R_L/[(R_B/\beta) + R_E]$, from which R_E is obtained. The current is then selected to establish the operating level of the collector. V_E is determined from $R_E I_C = V_E - V_e$:

$$V_E = R_E I_C + V_e \tag{1.18}$$

This, however, would require a special power supply for each V_E that is calculated, a highly impractical method. Instead a two-resistor system is employed using the normal supply voltage. It is seen that R_E must be $R_1 R_2/(R_1 + R_2)$, or

$$R_1 = \frac{R_E R_2}{R_2 - R_E} \tag{1.19}$$

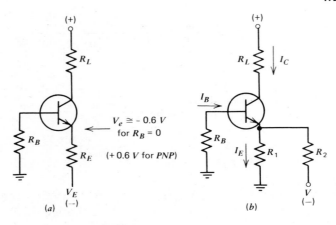

FIGURE 1.10 Emitter biasing.

Also by Thévenin's theorem, $(V)R_1/(R_1 + R_2) = V_E$, or

$$R_2 = \frac{R_1(V - V_E)}{V_E} \qquad (1.20)$$

Substituting Eq. 1.20 in 1.19, we have

$$R_1 = \frac{R_E V}{V - V_E} \qquad (1.21)$$

For example, with $R_E = 100 \ \Omega$ and $I_C = 10$ mA, with the base at ground potential, and assuming that $V = -15$ V, we have

$$V_E = R_E I_C + V_e = 100(10)^{-2} + 0.6 = 1.6 \text{ V}$$

$$R_1 = \frac{R_E V}{V - V_E} = \frac{100(15)}{15 - 1.6} = 11.9 \ \Omega$$

$$R_2 = \frac{R_1(V - V_E)}{V_E} = \frac{111.9(15 - 1.6)}{1.6} = 937.5 \ \Omega$$

For an NPN V is $(-)$ and for a PNP V is $(+)$. It should be noted that $V - V_E$ always has a magnitude less than V whether the supply is $(+)$ or $(-)$. It is also apparent that this method of biasing consumes more power than base biasing. The emitter supply furnishes

$$\frac{(15 - 0.6)}{937.5} = 14.3 \text{ mA}$$

which is $14.3 (10)^{-3}(15) = 214$ mW as compared to the basic required power of $(10$ mA$) (1.6$ V$) = 16$ mW. However, when this level of power is not important, it is a convenient method of bias.

It should be noted that these calculations state that the base is at ground potential. If there is a resistor from base to ground, the base current (I_C/h_{FE}) is flowing from ground through R_B to the base (remember that $I_E = I_C + I_B$). For example, if $I_B = 83.3$ μA and $R_B = 10$ kΩ, $E_B = -0.833$ V. Accordingly, V_E becomes $-0.6 - 0.833 = -1.433$ V and is so used in the equations above. For the equivalent PNP transistor the voltage would be $= +1.433$ V.

1.3 FIELD EFFECT TRANSISTORS

Although field effect transistors, commonly called FETs, perform a circuit function similar to that of the bipolar transistor discussed in previous sections, they require different design equations to predict their performance properly. To start with, their equivalent connections are given different names and symbols, as shown in Fig. 1.11. More importantly, the current drawn by the gate is very small and not a factor in controlling their operation.

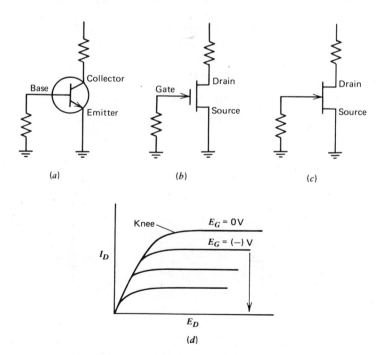

FIGURE 1.11   FET symbols and characteristics.

There are two general types of FETs—the junction FET or JFET and the metal oxide semiconductor FET or MOSFET. The JFET is described first and then the two devices are compared.

1.3.1 The Junction FET

The JFET has a current–voltage relation similar to that of the transistor. In Fig. 1.11d in the region above the "knee" it is seen that the slope is small and consequently the drain resistance is high, making it suitable for use as an amplifier. The region below the "knee" is called the linear characteristic. The knee in the transistor characteristic is generally much lower and the region below finds little use before the transistor is put into saturation. The FET behaves somewhat differently in this area and, because it covers a greater voltage range, has more applications. The principal difference is that the transistor injects a current from the base that causes a voltage drop between the emitter and collector. This is called the offset voltage. The FET in this region is really a voltage-controlled resistor. The gate voltage sets the resistance and the drain voltage determines by Ohm's law how much current will flow. The FET as an amplifier is modeled in Fig. 1.12.

The transconductance $g_m = \Delta i_d / \Delta V_{gs}$ is a measured parameter of the FET much as $\beta = \Delta i_c / \Delta i_b$ is for the transistor.

We first solve for the gain of the amplifier when $R_S = 0$, since this is very easy. $g_m V_{gs}$ is a current generator; hence

$$e_o = \frac{-Z_L r_d}{Z_L + r_d}(g_m V_{gs})$$

Because V_{gs} in this case is e_i, the gain is given by

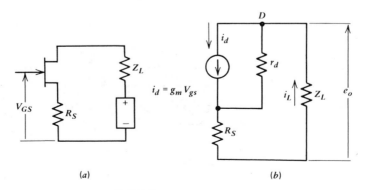

(a)   (b)

FIGURE 1.12 FET model.

$$\frac{e_o}{e_i} = \frac{-g_m Z_L r_d}{Z_L + r_d} = \frac{-g_m Z_L}{1 + Z_L/r_d} \tag{1.22}$$

It is seen that r_d is shunting current away from the load and, as r_d becomes larger, the gain approaches

$$\frac{e_o}{e_{\text{in}}} = -g_m Z_L \tag{1.23}$$

When R_S is included, the algebra becomes more involved. Because the current divides directly, as the conductance we can write the identity

$$\frac{i_L}{1/(Z_L + R_S)} = \frac{g_m V_{gs}}{1/(Z_L + R_S) + 1/r_d}$$

Solving for i_L, we have

$$i_L = \frac{g_m V_{gs}}{1 + (Z_L + R_S)/r_d} \tag{1.24}$$

Since $e_{\text{in}} = V_{gs} + I_L R_S$ or $V_{gs} = e_{\text{in}} - i_L R_S$, we can substitute in Eq. 1.24 and solve for i_L:

$$i_L = \frac{g_m e_1}{1 + g_m R_S + (Z_L + R_S)/r_d} \tag{1.25}$$

Multiplying by Z_L and solving for $e_o = i_L Z_L$, we have

$$\frac{e_o}{e_{\text{in}}} = \frac{g_m Z_L}{1 + g_m R_S + (Z_L + Z_S)/r_d} \tag{1.26}$$

If $R_S = 0$ this equation becomes Eq. 1.22. If the drain resistance becomes very large, the gain reduces to

$$\frac{e_o}{e_{\text{in}}} = \frac{g_m Z_L}{1 + g_m R_S} \tag{1.27}$$

For a source follower, $Z_L = 0$. The gain equation is derived as follows:

$$e_o = i_d \frac{r_d R_S}{r_d + R_S} \tag{1.28}$$

Since $i_d = g_m V_{gs} = g_m(e_{in} - i_d R_s)$, we can solve for i_d and substitute this in Eq. 1.28. Solving for the gain, we have

$$\frac{e_o}{e_{in}} = \frac{g_m}{1 + g_m R_s}\left(\frac{r_d R_s}{r_d + R_s}\right)$$ (1.29)

and if $r_d \gg R_s$,

$$\frac{g_m R_s}{1 + g_m R_s} = \frac{R_s}{(1/g_m) + R_s}$$

This is recognized as the gain of a simple attenuator, as shown in Fig. 1.13. It is seen that $r_s = 1/g_m$. The output resistance by Thévenin's theorem is seen to be $R_s r_s / R_s + r_s$.

The FET is a poor substitute for the transistor in the grounded base condition and accordingly the grounded gate amplifier is seldom used.

The FET is simpler to model than the transistor because its very small gate current has no direct influence on the drain current. The transistor can also use g_m as a design parameter and the approximate gain equations, for the common emitter and emitter follower are the same as the counterparts for the FET. The $g_m = 1/r_e$ is, however, much higher. For $r_e = 5\ \Omega$, $g_m = 200{,}000\ \mu\text{mhos}$, which is about 10 times the value of a comparable FET. The available voltage gain of a transistor is accordingly much higher than that of a FET. But if the input loading is taken into account, the reverse may be true. g_m is not generally used to describe the transistor because it does not convey all of the transistor's characteristics.

The JFET as shown in Fig. 1.11d is fully conducting at 0 V gate–source potential (depletion model). It has a reverse-biased diode as the gate input and accordingly loses its high-input impedance as the gate–source voltage approaches the 0.6-V diode forward bias condition.

1.3.2 The MOSFET

The MOSFET has properties similar to the JFET except for the input which is a capacitor instead of a reverse-biased diode. It comes in

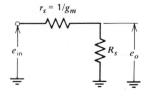

FIGURE 1.13   Equivalent circuit of a source follower.

both depletion, as the JFET, and enhancement types. The enhancement condition is by far the most common. This means that the FET is nonconducting at 0 V gate to source and must reach a threshold before it allows a defined drain current to flow. This is like the transistor where the JFET resembles the vacuum tube. Unlike the transistor, the threshold voltage is not a defined 0.6 V; instead it varies over a large range. The MOSFET turn-on voltage is limited by the breakdown of the gate dielectric.

Since the gate input of a MOSFET is a capacitor, a breakdown causes irreversible damage. Because of its high input impedance permanent damage easily occurs with common static charges, and the device must be handled carefully. Many MOSFETs have a zener-protected input. The zener is set to have a nondestructive breakdown before the dielectric failure, thus protecting the device. The disadvantages are that the zener reduces the normal input resistance and creates a low impedance input when the MOSFET is biased in the cutoff direction, placing the zener diode in its on condition.

The MOSFET is a simple device and as such it is used extensively in large monolithic designs, whereas the JFET has virtually no use in larger arrays. The MOSFET is also constructed on a substrate that is doped in the polarity opposite to the channel. This forms a diode, and the substrate must be biased so that this diode cannot become forward-biased under any operating condition. The substrate also acts as a low-gain gate, so that the bias level has an influence on the MOSFET operation.

1.3.3 Extended Temperature Operation

A very important property of both JFETs and MOSFETs is that they can operate at cryogenic temperatures. The JFET has improved g_m and r_d to about 125 K and then falls off rapidly in the vicinity of liquid nitrogen, which is 77 K. The MOSFET has improved g_m and r_d clear down to liquid helium, which is about 4 K. Many types of radiation detectors require operation at these low temperatures, and the ability to place electronic amplifiers directly in the dewar chamber is vital to that technology. The normal transistor is generally in difficulty at the low end of the military range, which is $-55°C$ or 218 K, and is completely inert before liquid nitrogen temperatures are reached.

At higher temperatures the JFET does not lose its ability to function as rapidly as the MOSFET and it is far better than the normal silicon transistor. At the time of this test, April 1981, the gallium arsenide JFET was just becoming available [2]. This device can operate from liquid helium temperature (4 K) to at least 300°C. Table 1.1 shows the results of some tests that were made on a gallium arsenide JFET and a silicon JFET (the 2N3821).

TABLE 1.1
JFET Operation at High Temperatures

Temperature	I_D	Transconductance	Gate Current
Silicon (2N3821)			
23°C	0.68 mA	1330 μmhos	0.04 μA
200°C	0.68 mA	870 μmhos	0.1 μA
250°C	0.68 mA	870 μmhos	1.4 μA
300°C	0.68 mA	800 μmhos	16.7 μA
Gallium Arsenide			
23°C	1.0 mA	5700 μmhos	0.12 μA
200°C	1.0 mA	4700 μmhos	4.0 μA
250°C	1.0 mA	4700 μmhos	12 μA
300°C	1.0 mA	3600 μmhos	63 μA

It is seen that the GaAs JFET has much higher transconductance than its silicon counterpart. It also has very low capacitance and low-power requirements. This particular GaAs FET operated as a flip-flop at 500 MHz. At present, flip-flops are available that operate at 10 GHz, with much higher speeds projected for the near future.

The gate leakage current of early devices was higher than expected; however, since they were developed for cryogenic use and then tested at elevated temperatures, this is not surprising. Leakage currents depend, among other things, upon the size of the chip, so direct comparisons can be misleading. Today, devices are however far below this value.

JFETs have a specific value of drain current that is approximately independent of temperature, which should be used if the operating temperature range is large. The value of this current differs with the device, but it is of a low level, generally less than 1 mA.

1.3.4 FETs as Switches

A common application of JFETs and MOSFETs is in the construction of analog switches. To pursue this subject it is necessary to point out that both transistors and FETs are inherently symmetrical devices. For example, in a transistor the emitter and collector leads can be interchanged and the device still functions as a transistor. The normal transistor, however, has its characteristics optimized to perform as labeled and does not function as well in the transposed condition. There are some transistors that continue to operate the same in both, which are referred to as symmetrical transistors. The FET is usually symmetrical, but not always, so that care must be taken in some applications. Figure 1.14 is a simplified sketch of how the FET is structured.

The JFET consists of a bar of doped silicon with a spot of oppositely doped silicon which forms a diode and is the gate. The MOSFET has a capacitor formed on the channel for the gate and also has the substrate in the opposite polarity. The gate bias is commonly referred to as the voltage between the gate and source, which can be very misleading.

Figure 1.15 shows an N channel FET acting as an analog switch with an AC-coupled sine wave as an input. The gate bias is the voltage between the gate and the end of the channel that has the largest turn-on polarity. For either a MOS or JFET the N channel device is turned on as the gate-to-channel voltage becomes more positive. When the sine wave is $(+)$, the FET $[(-)$ for P channel] is less turned on than when it is $(-)$, thus presenting an undesirable variable resistance to the signal. If R_L in Fig. 1.15a is replaced by a capacitor, we have a sample-and-hold circuit. Now if a $(-)$ signal is sampled, it appears across the capcitor. When the turn-on pulse is removed, the voltage remaining at the gate is the shutoff voltage. This must be sufficiently more negative than the voltage across the capacitor to keep the FET turned off. It is seen that under this condition the gate–drain voltage is controlling the conduction of the FET.

If a resistor is connected as shown in Fig. 1.15b and a JFET is used, the FET is in its low-resistance state when the switching transistor is turned off. This resistance is independent of the input signal because the gate and source are connected. When the switching transistor is on, the FET is off, and if the transistor is connected in the constant-current mode, the gate follows the input signal. The turnoff voltage is accordingly independent of the input signal. This turnoff voltage must still be sufficient to prevent the capacitive load from turning the FET on. The value of the resistance can be a problem. If it is too low, the switching current distorts the input signal. If it is too high, the switching speed is reduced because of the RC time constant. If an enhancement MOSFET is used, the on–off condition is reversed.

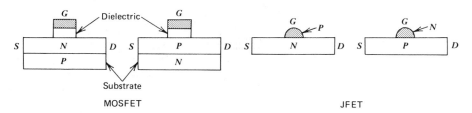

FIGURE 1.14 General FET structure.

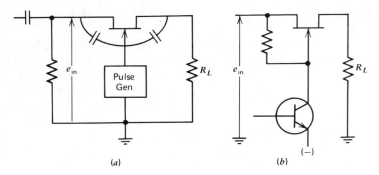

(a)   (b)

FIGURE 1.15 FET switch considerations.

A remaining important set of parameters are the gate–drain and gate–source capacitances. Depending on how the FET is used, one capacitor puts a switching spike in the input signal and the other puts a spike in the output. This can be very serious for low-level signals.

As the details of building a practical switch are examined, it turns out that the type of connection shown in Fig. 1.15b is more suitable for a JFET than the MOSFET. Consequently, most commercially available MOSFET switches have an "on" resistance that depends strongly on the input signal. A very good solution to this undesirable condition is achieved by putting an N channel MOSFET in parallel

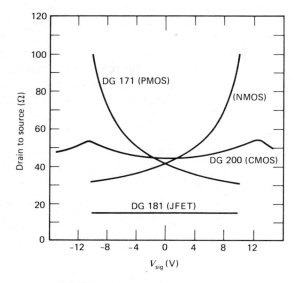

FIGURE 1.16 FET "on" resistance.

with the P channel device. This is a CMOS stage such as is used in the CMOS digital line. Figure 1.16 compares the different techniques. The PMOS and the NMOS have opposite "on" resistance characteristics, and by combining the two a very much improved CMOS switch is obtained.

There are many varieties of complete switches available in a single package. The overall specifications are quite detailed and warrant some study. The design of an analog switch with discrete devices has many subtle problems and should not be undertaken if a suitable commercial product is available.

1.3.5 Comparison of FET and Bipolar Power Transistors

To an extent, the comparison of these devices is shifting as time passes because of steady developments, particularly with the FETs. There are, however, some very basic differences between the FET and bipolar power transistors and that is what concerns us here.

The drive requirements of the bipolar transistor are dominated by a finite β, and in particular, as the transistor is driven into a highly conductive state, the β typically drops to about 10 or even less. The required driving voltage is low, that is, on the order of a volt.

The FET, on the other hand, is strictly a voltage-controlled device; it does, however, have a large input capacitance so the driving source must be able to provide a substantial transition current, although after conduction is established, the drive current is essentially reduced to zero.

For example, the IRF150 has $C_{GS} = 3000$ pF, $C_{DG} = 350$ pF, and $C_{DE} = 1000$ pF.

Referring to the switching power supply in Section 9.11 and the previous use of the IRF150, there was an *effective* gate swing of 5 V in 0.5 μs which resulted in a drain change of 56 V or a gain of $56/4 = 14$. Because of the Miller effect (Appendix I), the effective input capacitance is approximately $3000 + 15 (350) = 8250$ pF. The input current is defined by the relation $I = CE/t$, so that the driving current is $8250 (10)^{-12} 4/0.5 (10)^{-6} = 70$ mA average over the defined 0.5 μs. A comparable transistor would have a saturated $\beta = 10$ and the 4 A collector current of the circuit in Section 9.11 would require 400 mA during the entire on time of the cycle.

The term *effective* gate swing is used because in both types of transistors there is a jump in input current, due to the Miller effect, during the actual transition period. The exact waveform is difficult to estimate and it is best to make a measurement followed by an iterative correction of the driving source if necessary. The bipolar transistor has the same capacitive consideration as the FETs but the values are smaller and as such are dominated by the β requirement.

The intrinsic switching speed of the FET is much higher than that of the corresponding bipolar transistor, the speed limitation being generally controlled by the capacitance. Specific data sheets must be consulted for applications.

The FET does not have a storage delay, which is one of its major advantages over the bipolar transistor. However, all power FETs have a parasitic bipolar transistor in parallel, as shown in Fig. 1.17a. This will often be represented as a diode, as illustrated in Fig. 1.17b. This diode will act to discharge a reverse voltage that can develop with an inductive load and sometimes this is a help. However, as in the case with all diodes, there is a recovery period required before the diode stops conducting, and a fast reversal of the drain voltage can result in a destructive short circuit. In this regard it is best to use the most recent FET design releases, as much has been done in improving the recovery time and minimizing the possibility of damage. The manufacturer's specific data sheets should be checked when FET designs are being considered. References [3] and [4] contain further information on this subject.

Another major advantage of the power FET over its bipolar counterpart is shown in Fig. 1.18. Here the safe operating area (SOA) of a comparable FET and bipolar transistor is shown. The collector–base breakdown voltage of the bipolar transistor is reduced as the collector current is increased. This calls for close control of transient switching conditions and often results in reduced ratings. There is no corresponding limitation for the power FET.

A final advantage of the power FET over the bipolar transistor is its ability to operate in parallel. This is brought about because of the positive temperature coefficient of the on resistance. When transistors

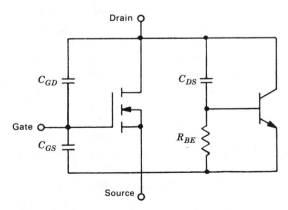

FIGURE 1.17 (*a*) The power MOSFET with its parasitic capacitances and parasitic NPN bipolar transistor.

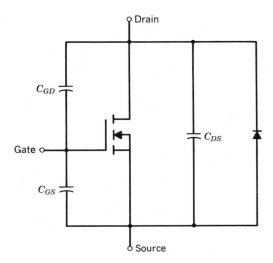

FIGURE 1.17 (*b*) Simplified version showing parasitic diode.

are operated in parallel it is difficult to ensure that all of the transistors will conduct evenly. With the FET the higher temperature caused by "current hogging" raises the on resistance, whereas in the bipolar transistor the higher temperature lowers the resistance, leading to thermal runaway. It is always important, however, to match transistors connected in parallel carefully to guard against a condition that is beyond control.

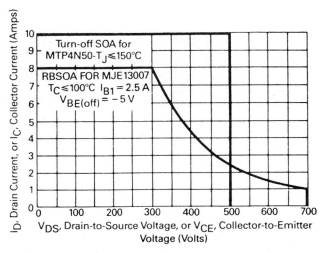

FIGURE 1.18 Comparison of the MOSFET turnoff SOA rating and the RBSOA rating of a bipolar of similar die area.

An important concern with operating FETs in parallel is their tendency to support parasitic oscillations. It is imperative that small resistors (50 to 100 Ω) or ferrite beads be placed in series with each gate. This is also a sound procedure for bipolar transistors, although they are generally not as prone to this form of oscillation.

REFERENCES

[1] R. F. Shea, *Principles of Transistor Circuits*, Wiley, New York, 1955.
[2] R. Zuleeg, J. K. Notthoff, and K. Lehovec, Femto-Joule, High Speed Planar GaAs E-JFET Logic, *IEEE Trans. Electron Devices*, Vol. ED-25, pp. 628–639, 1978.
[3] R. Sevens, Avoiding *dV/dt* Turnon in Power MOSFET's, *Electron. Prod.*, Jan. 15, 1983.
[4] K. Gauen, *Insuring Reliable Performance from Power MOSFET's, Motorola Application Note AN929*, Motorola, Inc., Phoenix, AZ.

GENERAL REFERENCES

R. F. Shea, *Transistor Circuit Engineering*, Wiley, New York, 1957.

K. Gauen, *Paralleling Power MOSFET's in Switching Applications, Motorola Application Note AN918*, Motorola, Inc., Phoenix, AZ.

W. R. Skanadore, *Methods for Utilizing High-Speed Switching Transistors in High Energy Environments*, General Semiconductor Industries, Inc., June 1981.

H. Granberg, RF Power MOSFETs, *Electron. Prod.*, Dec. 12, 1983.

TWO

Discrete Amplifiers

Monolithic and hybrid amplifiers are steadily replacing discrete amplifiers as practical design choices. A knowledge of available products, their advantages and limitations, and their price is necessary to make the correct selection.

The need for discrete amplifiers is very definite, however, and a knowledge of this procedure will be required for a long time to come. The design examples outlined in this chapter should serve as a good guide for most applications.

2.1 WIDEBAND AMPLIFIERS

The first amplifier to be discussed is the video amplifier or wideband amplifier. Actually, the term "video" is relative; its significance is that some high-frequency factors are accounted for.

Figure 2.1 shows a video amplifier that can be used as a building block for almost any set of broadband low-level requirements. The design of this amplifier is described in considerable detail. Much of the information is the same for the amplifiers that follow and therefore is not repeated.

The transistors for the amplifier were selected because of their high f_T and in the case of the 2N2857 because of its low C_{CB} of 0.7 pF. In proceeding with the step-by-step design of the amplifier, some rather arbitrary decisions must be made. Whether these decisions would be as flexible in another design depends on the restrictions applied to that particular amplifier.

2.1.1 Basic Considerations

This amplifier is intended to have a gain roll-off of 3 dB at 50 MHz. The factors that affect the high-frequency response are mainly the

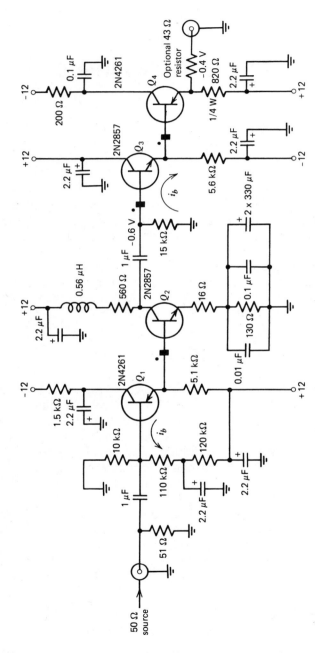

FIGURE 2.1 50 MHz Video amplifier. Resistors are all $\frac{1}{8}$ W unless marked. Asterisks denote Ferroxcube beads 4B.

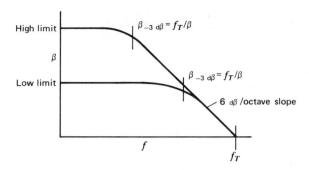

FIGURE 2.2 β vs. frequency.

RC time constants and the β loss. The RC time constants will be determined as the design progresses. The relation between β and frequency is shown in Fig. 2.2. The tolerance for β ranges from about 3 to 1 to as high as 10 to 1 for some transistors. The tolerance on F_T is usually smaller, perhaps 2 to 1. This makes an accurate design somewhat impractical, so that it is important not to use the transistor to its greatest potential if a first-try design is to be successful. β is also a function of current as well as frequency. Consequently, an estimate should be made of the current required in each stage to evaluate β. This is often a trial-and-error process, but we take the liberty of using the final values in an effort to clarify the procedure. Table 2.1 tabulates the design values used in the circuit.

Because the information given on transistors varies considerably, it is necessary to examine the data of the chosen transistor and proceed with good judgment from that point. The 2N4261 data sheet states that at 10 mA, the β at 100 MHz is 20 minimum. The only clue to where $β_{-3d\,B}$ would be is the statement that $h_{FE} = 30/150$, indicating that $β_{-3\,dB}$ is not much above 20. On a linear basis the β at 50 MHz would be 40. A choice of 30 is the somewhat arbitrary judgment. Q_1 has a 2 mA collector current and Q_4 15 mA. A second decision is made that $β_{50\,MHz}$ is 20 for Q_1 and 35 for Q_4. This appears a bit wild, but the fact is that the manufacturer is simply not giving enough information to make a more exact decision and the effort entailed is much greater in making high-frequency measurements than in making corrections on the circuit.

The 2N2857 data sheet does not give a high-frequency β value. From the f_T curve it is seen that $f_T = 1600$ MHz for $I_C = 8$ mA. Accordingly, for Q_2, $β_{50\,MHz} = 1600$ MHz/50 MHz $= 32$.

Q_3 has $I_C = 2$ mA and $f_T = 1200$. In this case $β_{50\,MHz} = 1200$ MHz/50 MHz $= 24$. h_{FE} is given as 50/220, so it is judged that these values are good.

TABLE 2.1
Tabulated Design Parameters

Stage	I_C mA	h_{FE}	I_B mA	r_e Ω	f_T MHz	β_{50MHz}
Q_1 (2N4261)	2	30/150	0.067	15	1500	20
Q_2 (2N2857)	8	50/220	0.16	5.25	1600	32
Q_3 (2N2857)	2	50/220	0.04	15	1200	24
Q_4 (2N4261)	15	30/150	0.50	3.7	3400	35

The ohmic value of the emitter resistance is estimated at 2 Ω. For Q_2, we then have $r_e = 26/I$ mA $+ R$ Ω $= 26/8 + 2 = 5.25$ Ω.

The values for the other transistors are listed in Table 2.1.

The required base currents are estimated by using the manufacturer's minimum value. This is done partly to be conservative and partly because the data sheets can be depended on to be optimistic.

2.1.2 High-Frequency Calculations

The initial task in the design of the gain stage Q_2 is to determine the capacitance at the collector. This is estimated as shown in Table 2.2. From this it can be seen that the load capacitance comes from the output of Q_2 and the input of Q_3. The base–emitter of Q_3 has a low capacitance because of the feedback of R_E in that emitter follower. For example, if the gain were exactly unity, the effective base–emitter capacitance would be zero, regardless of how high the capacity of the junction might be.

The base–collector capacitance of Q_3 is seen as its full value because the collector is bypassed, which makes it an AC ground. It should be specifically pointed out that because there is no collector gain in the emitter follower there is no Miller multiplication of C_{CB}. This, of course, is why the emitter follower is used following the gain stage.

It is seen that over one half of the total capacitance is due to strays, even in a good layout. It should be clear that a little carelessness in this matter greatly degrades the frequency response of the amplifier. Chapter 10 on laboratory procedures should be reviewed before construction is started.

The collector RC time constant of Q_2 controls the frequency response of this amplifier. At 50 MHz the reactance of 5.5 pF equals 560 Ω, which is the value that is selected for the load resistor.

The choice of the current in this stage is governed by several factors, one of which is to place the collector at a potential to allow equal positive and negative voltage swings (approximately $V_{BB}/2$). Another is to optimize β and f_T. Finally, of course, the resulting power dissipation must be considered to ensure that the transistor is operating at a safe temperature.

A current of 8 mA has been selected for this stage. This allows a change of ± 7 mA, producing an output voltage of $14(10)^{-3}(560) = 7.8\ V_{PP}$. Reference to the data sheets for the 2N2857 shows that the maximum f_T occurs at this current and that reasonable performance is maintained at the extremes of 1 and 15 mA.

Since many of the parameters needed for a particular design are not given on the data sheets, more estimates must be made. The 560 Ω selected for load resistor is substantially lower than the anticipated output resistance r_o of the transistor; hence the gain can be given by

$$A_v = \frac{-R_L}{[(R_B + r_b)/\beta_{50\ \text{MHz}}] + R_E + r_e} \tag{1.6}$$

The equation is from the low-frequency model discussed in Chapter 1, which has been modified by using $\beta_{50\ \text{MHz}}$. This is the first-order frequency loss of the transistor, but does not account for all of the loss factors. As the frequency is increased, the circuit gain is smaller than that predicted by the equation. To account for these parameters is a very complex procedure, and it is usually better simply to design for a little extra gain and bandwidth and make the proper adjustments after the circuit has been built.

Once the load resistance is established, it remains to determine the emitter resistance in order to calculate the gain of this stage. The emitter resistance is called total r_e because it is comprised of several terms.

At this point in the design we must make a jump to the input stage to determine its high-frequency output impedance. This is necessary because the output impedance of Q_1 is part of the input impedance of Q_2, which, as previously shown, appears as added emitter impedance of Q_2. It would be well to recognize at this time that the discussion uses *impedance* and the equation below derives *resistance*.

TABLE 2.2
Estimated Capacitance at Collector of Q_2

$C_{CB}\ Q_2$	0.7 pF
$C_{CB}\ Q_3$	0.7 pF
Socket Q_2	0.5 pF
Base–emitter Q_3	0.2 pF
Strays	3.4 pF
Total	5.5 pF

The resistance is an approximation, and as the frequency is increased, the error increases and possibly even results in instability. Again, the completely correct determinations are beyond the practical level of difficulty. The point of significant improper operation is moved as far away as possible by the choice of high-performance transistors and good layout techniques.

The output resistance is Q_1 is given by

$$
\begin{aligned}
r_o &= \frac{R_B + r_b}{\beta_{50\ \text{MHz}}} + r_e \\
&= (25 + 10)/20 + 15 = 16.7\ \Omega
\end{aligned}
\tag{1.16}
$$

$R_B = 25\ \Omega$ because the source is 50 Ω with a 50 Ω termination. r_b is estimated to be 10 Ω. We can now complete the calculation:

$$
\begin{aligned}
\text{Total } r_e &= \frac{r_o Q_1 + r_b Q_2}{\beta_{50\ \text{MHz} Q_2}} + r_e Q_2 \\
&= (16.7 + 10)/32 + 5.25 = 6.08\ \Omega
\end{aligned}
\tag{2.1}
$$

The gain can then be made as high as R_L/total $r_e = 560/6.08 = 92$. However, it is generally not desirable to build an amplifier without any external emitter resistance. There are several reasons for this. The gain depends on parameters that are temperature sensitive to some degree. Distortion is high because the emitter current is changing with the signal and in turn varies the gain. The high gain–bandwidth product enhances the chances of instability and oscillation, and it is usually sensible to allow for extra reserve in case the circuit does not perform as well as expected.

Part of this reserve is the peaking coil that is placed in series with the load resistor. This extends the high-frequency response. Just how much extension occurs and what the exact value of the inductance should be are difficult to judge, since this is a kind of a cleanup operation. The roll-off of the high frequency is affected by secondary effects that have not been taken completely into account, so that this response is not that of a simple RC. A first-order estimate of the inductance is the value needed to resonate the calculated 5.6 pF capacitance at that point for 50 MHz. This would be 1.8 μH. A resistor across the peaking inductance is sometimes used to control the Q. In this example, however, 0.56 μH was required with no damping resistor.

The amplifier stage is designed for a gain of 25, and accordingly the total effective emitter resistance is $R_L/G = 560/25 = 22.4$. This makes R_E, the external emitter resistance, $22.4 - 6.08 \cong 16\ \Omega$. If the internal emitter resistance changes 10%, the gain is $560/(16 + 1.1(6.08)) = 24.7$, a change of 1.2%.

One other very important consideration is the effect of the collector-to-base capacitance C_{CB} of Q_2. The data sheet gives this as 0.7 pF and, adding 0.5 pF for the socket, we have 1.2 pF. Due to the Miller effect (see Appendix I), this capacitance is seen at the base of Q_2 as $(G + 1) C_{CB} = 26(1.2) = 31.2$ pF. The gain would be down 3 dB at 50 MHz with a source resistance of only 100 Ω. This is why the emitter follower, which in this case presented only 16 Ω, is generally used to drive the gain stage.

There is another practical consideration in having an emitter follower as an input stage—ensuring stability. A high or even moderately high gain stage often oscillates or at least is underdamped when a cable or long lead is attached to its input. The 50-Ω termination, in this case, would probably provide stability, but a source termination of the cable would be a bad risk (see Section I.6). This instability is not at all predictable and is often of an intermittent nature, causing difficulty throughout the operational life of the amplifier.

2.1.3 DC Drift Stabilization

The low-frequency response of the amplifier would be difficult to maintain if a blocking capacitor were used between Q_1 and Q_2. This is because the input resistance of Q_2 is low. In addition, the large base current required by the 8-mA collector current would cause additional bias problems.

Without modification there is only $16(8)(10)^{-3} \cong 0.13$ V developed across the emitter resistor of Q_2 to stabilize the temperature-sensitive base–emitter drop of 0.6 V. This does not allow very much degeneration for good DC stability. Part of the problem is solved by making Q_1 a PNP transistor. The temperature coefficients of the emitter-to-base voltage of Q_1 and Q_2 are about the same, approximately 2 mV/°C, but the polarities are opposite so that this variation is largely canceled.

The voltage drop across the base resistor of Q_1 is not compensated, however. To determine the stabilization that this requires it is again necessary to jump ahead to the results of the first-stage design. There it is established that the base current of Q_1 develops 0.67 V across its base resistance. β can be expected to increase about 1%/°C as the temperature rises. Accordingly, a 30°C change in temperature would produce a base voltage change of 30% = 0.67(0.3) = 0.2 V. This represents an increase of 25(0.2) = 5 V at the collector of Q_2. With only 4.48 V across the load resistor of Q_2, 5 V is clearly too large a change.

To correct this condition a second emitter resistor is added in series with the original 16 Ω resistor and then bypassed with a capacitor. The purpose of this resistor is to reduce the DC gain to make the drift acceptable. If this gain is set to 4, the change at the collector of Q_2

is $4(0.2) = 0.8$ V. This is accepted as a reasonable value. Accordingly, we have $R_{E(DC)} = R_L/G_{DC} = 560/4 = 140\ \Omega$. Subtracting 16 Ω and going to a standard value, we have 130 Ω for the added emitter resistor.

The emitter bypass capacitor is set so that the gain of the amplifier is not decreased until the low-frequency cutoff of 15 Hz is reached. At this point the impedance of the capacitor equals the effective r_e of the transistor plus the 16 Ω of unpassed resistance.

The capacitor necessary to bypass this resistance at 15 Hz is 470 μF. 330 μF at 6 V in a D size case is a standard value, and so two of these are used in parallel. These large capacitors, because of their inductance, cannot be depended on to bypass properly at 50 MHz (see Appendix IV); hence a second smaller capacitor is used for higher frequencies. A 0.01-μF capacitor has 20 Ω of reactance at 0.75 MHz and should be adequate for the high-frequency requirements. The 0.01-μF capacitor should be placed close to the emitter resistors, while the larger capacitors fortunately can be placed at a reasonable distance from this congested circuit area. Final testing of the amplifier disclosed that an additional 0.1-μF capacitor was necessary for complete bypassing (see Fig. 2.1).

The voltage requirement of the base of Q_2 is now $8(10)^{-3}(130 + 15) + 0.6 = +1.77$ V. Since the drop across R_L is $8(0.560) = 4.48$ V, there remains $12 - (1.77 + 4.48) = 5.75$ V from collector to base of Q_2. This allows about the same magnitude of positive and negative swings of the signal and is therefore satisfactory. If this were not the case, a change in the choice of the collector current might have been necessary at this stage.

Now that the input bias requirement for Q_2 has been established ($+1.77$ V), we can proceed with the design of the first stage.

2.1.4 The Input Stage

The input stage is an emitter follower for three reasons. It presents a high input impedance, it presents a low output impedance to the second stage, which is absolutely essential for good high-frequency performance, and it serves to stabilize, as previously explained. The first stage in this amplifier is to be AC coupled. Since it is also desirable to have a good low-frequency response, the input resistance must be kept high so that a reasonably sized blocking capacitor can be used. Accordingly, a lower collector current is used in Q_1 than in Q_2, say 2 mA. If 10 kΩ is selected as the base resistor, a 1 μF capacitor gives a low-frequency cutoff at 15 Hz. This is considered acceptable. Table 2.1 gives the base current of Q_1 as 0.067 mA. Accordingly, the base voltage is $0.067(10) = 0.67$ V.

The polarity of this voltage is easily determined if it is remembered that the emitter current is larger than the collector current and consequently for a PNP the current flows as shown in Fig. 2.3a, producing a positive voltage at the base. Figure 2.3b produces the required output voltage. Figure 2.3c shows how this voltage is developed from the existing power supply, and finally Fig. 2.3d divides the resistors so that a filter capacitor can be inserted.

The step from Fig. 2.3b to Fig. 2.3c is made by application of Thévenin's theorem. This defines the two equations:

$$V_{BB} = \frac{R_1 V_{CC}}{(R_1 + R_2)} \tag{2.2}$$

$$R = \frac{R_1 R_2}{(R_1 + R_2)} \tag{2.3}$$

Solving for R_1 and R_2 we have

$$R_1 = \frac{R V_{CC}}{(V_{CC} - V_{BB})} \tag{2.4}$$

$$= \frac{10(12)}{12 - 0.5} \cong 10 \text{ k}\Omega$$

$$R_2 = R_1 \frac{(V_{CC} - V_{BB})}{V_{BB}} \tag{2.5}$$

$$= \frac{10(12 - 0.5)}{0.5} = 230 \text{ k}\Omega$$

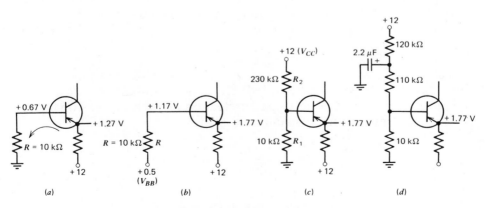

FIGURE 2.3 Steps in biasing Q_1.

This resistor is made up of a 120 and a 110 kΩ resistor. The resulting filter of 120 kΩ/2 and a 2.2 μF capacitor is down 3 dB at 1.4 Hz and drops 6 dB/octave as the frequency rises.

2.1.5 The Ouput Stage

A double emitter follower is used in the output stage to produce a suitably low output resistance. These calculations proceed as follows. Q_3 is buffered from the output so that a small quiescent current can be used; 2 mA should suffice. This produces a base current of $I_E/h_{FE} = 2/50 = 0.04$ mA. With a selected base resistor of 15 kΩ this represents a drop of $0.04(15) = 0.6$ V. We then have

$$R_E = \frac{(12 - 1.2)}{2} \cong 5.6 \text{ k}\Omega$$

$$r_e = \frac{26}{2} + 2 = 15 \text{ }\Omega$$

$$R_B = \frac{R_L Q_2}{\beta_{50 \text{ MHz}}} = \frac{560}{24} = 23.3$$

$$\therefore r_o Q_3 = 15 + 23.3 = 38.3 \text{ }\Omega$$

The output current of the last stage is made large to enable it to drive a low-impedance load. From the data sheets it can be seen that a quiescent current of 15 mA would be a good choice, allowing a maximum swing of ±15 mA. The transistor can furnish more than 15 mA to the load from the negative supply, but can only decrease its current on the positive swing by the 15 mA of steady-state current. After this the positive current is limited by the emitter resistor.

The maximum signal to the base of Q_4 has been determined to be ±3.9 V. Accordingly, the minimum load resistance that can be driven at maximum voltage from the positive supply is defined by the circuit in Fig. 2.4.

With a 50 Ω load a signal of only $±0.015(50) = ±0.75$ V can be developed. However, a special case exists for driving a transmission line that is essentially open-ended. Here the technique of source termination can be used as described in Section I.6 on transmission lines.

The dynamic output resistance of Q_4 is

$$r_o Q_4 = \frac{r_o Q_3 + r_b Q_4}{\beta_{50 \text{ MHz}} Q_4} + r_e Q_4$$

$$= \frac{38.5 + 10}{35} + \left(\frac{26}{15} + 2\right) = 5.1 \text{ }\Omega$$

$R_E = 820 \ \Omega$

$+12$ —W— $+3.9$ V

R_L

$$\frac{R_L}{3.9} = \frac{820}{(12 - 3.9)}$$

$R_L = 395 \ \Omega$

FIGURE 2.4   Drive capability of the output stage.

This would require a 43 Ω source resistor to match the line, and then the full ± 3.9 V would be available at the end of the cable.

Finally, a 200 Ω resistor is placed in the collector to limit the power dissipation of the transistor in case of an accidental overload. A short circuit on the output, even for a very brief period, generally burns out an unprotected emitter follower. The capacitor is used to furnish or store extra current for fast rise times into capacitive loads.

At this time it is well to mention a couple of alternative methods for providing an output stage for an amplifier of this type.

The first involves the use of a complementary emitter follower as shown in Fig. 2.5. This circuit has the important advantage that both positive and negative currents can be supplied to the limit of the respective output transistors. The steady-state current of the output stage has a theoretical limit of zero, although some current is nec-

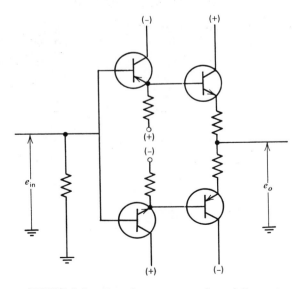

FIGURE 2.5   Complementary emitter follower.

essary to minimize distortion. The resistors in the output emitters are optional, but it is a good idea to provide safety against burnout at a small cost of gain and output impedance.

The input stage is also a complementary emitter follower but with reversed polarities. This results in a temperature-compensated balance of the base–emitter voltages so that there is a theoretical zero output offset voltage.

One more unique feature remains—the input bias current of the PNP and that of the NPN cancel each other. If the match is perfect, the bias current is zero.

To produce a properly operating complementary emitter follower, careful balances of the transistors are necessary. For this reason, and to reduce the number of parts, it is usually better to purchase a single-package device from one of many sources. NSC has a line of three such buffers designated as the LH0002, the LH0033, and the LH0063 in order of increasing power and frequency response.

A second method that has a more limited application is to drive a terminated transmission line directly out of the high-impedance collector as shown in Fig. 2.6. To clarify this connection, Section I.6 on transmission lines should be reviewed at this time. The load resistor can be connected to a supply voltage if desired, but in all cases a quiescent current is required if a bidirectional swing is necessary. The limitations, in this case, are the same as with the single emitter follower.

2.1.6 General Comments

Ferrite beads are necessary with high-frequency transistors of this type to prevent parasitic oscillations. These generally occur in the region of 400–1000 MHz, which is beyond the range of most oscil-

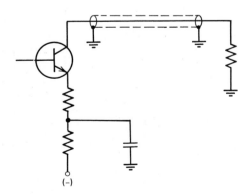

FIGURE 2.6 Collector-driven transmission line.

loscopes. Their presence can be detected by moving a hand close (but not touching) to the circuit. If the circuit is oscillating, one or more of the DC levels change with the movement. Sometimes the oscillation is intermittent or a function of the signal level. The latter case can often be detected by unusual forms of distortion, which are again altered by hand movements. The intermittent case results in inconsistent operation and often renders the circuit useless. The only solution is careful layout and proper use of the ferrite beads. The beads are generally needed when two high-frequency transistors are connected without any resistance between them. Resistors ranging in value from 50 to 100 Ω can be used instead of the beads, if preferred.

Amplifiers of all types must have their power supplies adequately bypassed or decoupled. This is generally more important at high frequencies and more difficult at low frequencies. For low frequencies sometimes the only solution is a small local regulator. For higher frequencies the regulator is of no value, and proper use of resistors, inductors, and capacitors is required. In all cases a good layout is essential.

Bypass capacitors must always be checked for proper size, or at least there should be an awareness based on experience in determining the proper value. Data in this book on the series resonance of capacitors is a good guide. A useful equation is the following:

$$I_A t_S = C_F E_V = Q \qquad (C)$$

This equation is exact, but its application need not be in order to obtain good information. For example, if there is a 0.01 F capacitor from collector to ground of the output stage, it is intended that all of the current in the leading edge of the output pulse comes from this capacitor.

If we have a maximum output of 2 V/50 = 0.04 A for $10(10)^{-9}$ there will be a voltage change of

$$E_V = \frac{0.04(10)(10)^{-9}}{10^{-8}} = 0.04 \text{ V}$$

This is a negligible change for the transistor and in this instance the equation has served a useful purpose.

Figure 2.7 is a photograph of the wideband amplifier discussed in this section. The details of the layout should be carefully studied as a guide to other circuits of this type. The amplifier produced an overall gain of 23 with the high-frequency -3 dB point at 54 MHz. The addition of a 0.5 μH inductor in the collector of Q_2 raised the high-frequency cutoff to 65 MHz with no overshoot. It was observed that there was a 2 dB dip at 12 MHz. This was caused by insufficient

FIGURE 2.7   Completed amplifier.

decoupling of the 130 Ω emitter resistor of Q_2 in the frequency cross-over region. An additional 0.1 μF capacitor solved the problem.

2.2 LOW-NOISE PREAMPLIFIER

The term preamplifier is used here because the low-noise properties of an amplifier need only be considered when the signal is at a low level. When the amplitude is sufficiently large, the noise is no longer a factor and the design proceeds as required by the bandwidth, gain, and power output requirements.

2.2.1 Noise Definitions

To discuss the design of low-noise amplifiers we must first review noise properties and definitions. The basic noise relationship is probably that of the ideal resistor. This is given as

$$E_{n\,\text{rms}} = 7.42(10)^{-12}\sqrt{TBR} \tag{2.6}$$

where T = temperature (K), B = bandwidth, and R = resistance. For room temperature (273 K) this becomes $E_{n\,\text{rms}} = 1.28(10)^{-10}\sqrt{BR}$. As a handy reference: a 1 kΩ resistor has $1.28(10)^{-10}\sqrt{1000} = 4.05$ nV/$\sqrt{\text{Hz}}$ at room temperature.

The noise, evenly spread over the entire spectrum, is called "white noise." It is also the lowest noise that a resistor can have. The excess noise in a resistor can be due to manufacturing carelessness as well as the physical properties of different materials, and is therefore hard to pinpoint. In general, the best material is wire wound, followed by metal film, deposited carbon, and finally the poorest choice—composition carbon. The composition carbon resistor has a $1/f$ characteristic at the low frequencies. This is illustrated in Fig. 2.8. The excess noise is largely due to current passing through the carbon granules and, as seen, is a strong function of this current. There are generally only a few places where low-noise resistors should be used, and after that the usual composition carbon resistor will be all right.

Semiconductor noise is invariably of the nature shown in Fig. 2.9. The lower-frequency noise is called $1/f$, although the slope is not necessarily $1/f$. The upper-frequency slope is also quite variable. The two breakpoints in the graph vary widely for different devices.

2.2.2 The Concept of Noise Voltages and Currents

The methods used to designate noise in a system are varied and often confusing. To this author's mind, the clearest way to present noise information is in the form of an equivalent noise voltage and current. However, in the event that the manufacturer uses another method, the designer must be prepared to interpret the given data and proceed from other references.

Figure 2.10 shows how the noise voltages are applied to an op-amp. In Section 3.1.8 on op-amps it is shown that the input offset voltage could be inserted at either the ($-$) or the ($+$) input, but that it was easier to put at the ($+$) input. The same is true for noise voltages; in fact, the input offset voltage can be considered to be a DC

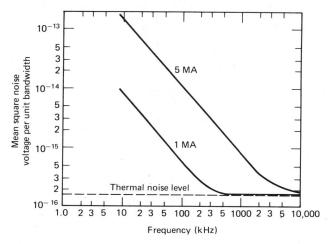

FIGURE 2.8 Noise of a 10 kΩ composition resistor. (Courtesy of H. W. Ott.)

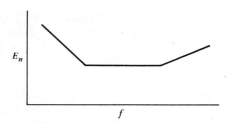

FIGURE 2.9   Typical semiconductor noise.

noise. The input noise current is converted to another input noise voltage as it flows through the impedances that are in its path. The input noise current is treated in the same manner as the bias current, and there is a noise current at each input of the op-amp. These currents are of equal average magnitude, but since they are random in structure, no phase relationship exists. There is no such thing as an input *offset* noise current. Noise voltage is random and, according to the mathematics of such things, must be combined in an rms fashion, that is, as the square root of the sum of the squares.

In addition to the op-amp, the resistors at each input produce their own thermal noise. Even a complex resistive network is generally not too difficult to resolve to a single resistor, which is then the sole resistor noise source for that network. Pure inductors and capacitors have no noise of their own, but form a frequency-dependent impedance that develops a noise voltage with a noise current. They also greatly complicate the calculation of just how much resistor noise gets to the amplifier.

2.2.3 A Sample Noise Calculation

An op-amp is used to demonstrate how various noise sources are combined. The Signetics NE5534A is typical of low-noise devices

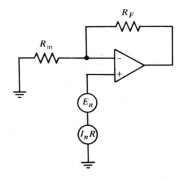

FIGURE 2.10   Noise relations in an op-amp.

available at this time; it is also guaranteed to meet the published specifications. Figure 2.11 defines the noise characteristics.

Figure 2.12 shows the circuit to be used. In the inverting input R_1 and R_F are in parallel, and the effective noise resistance is $2(18)/(2 + 18) = 1.8$ kΩ. If the op-amp voltage offset is a problem, R_2 must be inserted to achieve optimum operation. As can be seen, however, this adds to the total noise.

A spot noise calculation is made at 1 kHz. At this point there is no excess low-frequency noise, and Fig. 2.11 gives the values $E = 4.5$ nV/$\sqrt{\text{Hz}}$ and $I = 0.4$ pA/$\sqrt{\text{Hz}}$.

The separate noise voltages now are

	$(10)^{-9}$ V/$\sqrt{\text{Hz}}$ [from (2-6)]
$R_1 \parallel R_F = 1.28(10)^{-10}\sqrt{(1)(1800)}$	$= 5.43$
R_2	$= 5.72$
$I_n (R_1 \parallel R_F) = 0.4(10)^{-12}(1.8)(10)^3$	$= 0.72$
$I_n(R_2) = 0.4(10)^{-12}(2)(10)^3$	$= 0.8$
E_n direct from data sheet	$= 4.5$

These noise voltages must now be combined as the square root of the sum of the squares:

$$E_{ni} = \sqrt{(5.43)^2 + (5.72)^2 + (0.72)^2 + (0.8)^2 + (4.5)^2}\,((10)^{-9})$$
$$= 9.14 \text{ nV}/\sqrt{\text{Hz}}$$

The bandwidth of the amplifier is defined as down 3 dB at 100 kHz. The roll-off of the network shown in Fig. 2.12 is a normal 6 dB/octave.

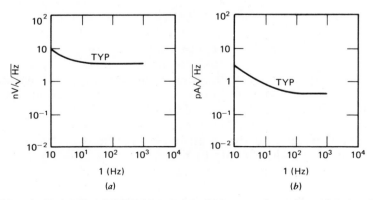

FIGURE 2.11 Noise data NE5534A op-amp: (*a*) input noise voltage density; (*b*) input noise current density. (Courtesy of Signetics.)

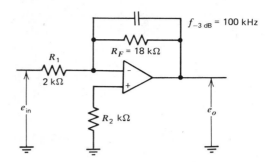

FIGURE 2.12 Op-amp with resistor noise sources.

To account for the noise beyond the $f_{-3\,dB}$ point, the cutoff frequency must be multiplied by a correction factor, which for this case is 1.57. Different types of roll-offs have varying correction factors. The total noise input voltage now becomes: total $E_{ni} = 9.14(10)^{-9}$ $\sqrt{1.57(10)^5} = 3.62\ \mu V$. Since this noise voltage has been shown to be at the noninverting input, $E_{no} = (9 + 1)\,3.67 = 36.7\ \mu V$ rms.

Noise voltage must be read by a true rms meter to be valid. Unfortunately, most observations are made by a scope without an rms meter. Various conversions, all of them bad, have been offered to relate the peak-to-peak observations on the scope to the true rms value. However, if an estimate is needed before the proper equipment arrives, try dividing V_{PP} by five.

2.2.4 Additional Noise Considerations

A number of important details should be attended to at this time. First, the expression $nV/\sqrt{Hz}$ means nV per $\sqrt{Hz}$ or nV for each $\sqrt{Hz}$. It does not mean nV divided by $\sqrt{Hz}$. This was shown in the arithmetic preceding this section.

From Figs. 2.8 and 2.11 it is apparent that noise is a function of frequency. The previous calculation ignored the excess contribution at the low frequencies. For this calculation the approximation was very proper and is so also in most amplifiers. Noise is developed per unit bandwidth. The excess noise of the NE5534A is largely contained in the bandwidth of 0 to 1 kHz. There are, however, 157 1 kHz bands in this amplifier, and so the contribution of the 0 to 1 kHz area is generally not very significant. In the case of special low-frequency amplifiers, however, the excess noise must be considered (see the next section).

The noise of different frequency bands does not necessarily produce the same results in final use. For example, there may be resonating elements that create aggravated disturbance when noise of a reinforcing frequency range is encountered. In television display, high frequencies control picture sharpness that is not always observable at a distance, while low-frequency noise produces large area disturbances that are noticeable at any viewing distance and hence more distracting. The polarity of a noise spike is important in both video and sound systems. For example, a bright spot on a black background is obvious, whereas the black spot on bright background is not. In music a noise spike that increases the sound level is easily detected, while in the reverse condition the sound can actually be cut off for a brief period and remain undetected.

One particular type of low-frequency disturbance is commonly known as "popcorn" noise. This consists of random crashes or spikes, which vary in amplitude from less than 1 μV to several hundred microvolts and last several milliseconds. Their exact cause is not clearly understood but known to be related to surface contamination. These spikes can be very harmful in some cases because they pass through the normal low-frequency cutoff circuits and cause damage at the output.

2.2.5 Noise in the Low-Frequency Region

For this example we combine several noise sources as a function of frequency in Table 2.3. In the second row, these noise voltages are squared, bringing about the term E^2/Hz. This is done to simplify the procedure that follows. E^2/Hz is now plotted in Fig. 2.13 and by preconceived manipulation turns out to be a straight line. It is further assumed that the effective bandwidth is defined by the vertical lines at 10 and 90 Hz.

The area under the curve is (E_n^2/Hz) Hz which is E_n^2. To calculate this, the plot is broken into segments, four in this example. These following values, shown in Table 2.3, are added:

$$(17.8 + 13.4 + 9 + 4.8)(10)^{-12} = 45(10)^{-12}\,\text{V}^2$$

TABLE 2.3
Noise Structure for Sample Problem

Hz	20	40	60	80
$E_n/\sqrt{\text{Hz}}$	$9.4(10)^{-7}$	$8.2(10)^{-7}$	$6.7(10)^{-7}$	$4.9(10)^{-7}$
E_n^2/Hz	$8.9(10)^{-13}$	$6.7(10)^{-13}$	$4.5(10)^{-13}$	$2.4(10)^{-13}$
E_n^2	$17.8(10)^{-12}$	$13.4(10)^{-12}$	$9\ (10)^{-12}$	$4.8(10)^{-12}$

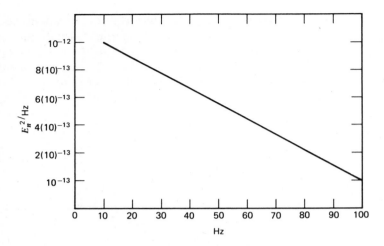

FIGURE 2.13 Typical low-frequency noise.

The noise voltage then is

$$E_{\text{rms}} = \sqrt{45(10)^{-12}} = 6.7 \ \mu\text{V}$$

It is apparent that there is no need to break a straight line into segments. This is just an example of the technique to be used on more complex functions. The number of segments used is up to the designer. However, common sense should be used, since the data tend not to be very accurate and detailed calculations are usually a waste of time.

2.2.6 Low-Noise Devices

The key issue in designing low-noise amplifiers is, of course, the selection of a low-noise device. Unhappily, noise specifications are probably the most inaccurate of all the data furnished by the manufacturer. It is not uncommon for the data sheets to be in error by an order of magnitude, always on the optimistic side, of course. Greater confidence can generally be given to the data if they are stated as guaranteed instead of typical.

In addition to the NE5534A, the μA739 is a good choice for a low-noise op-amp. The μA725 made by Precision Monolithics and Fairchild is another good choice. The BIFET op-amps such as NSC LF156 have a low-noise voltage and a very low-noise current.

The JFET has the lowest noise of all currently available semiconductor amplifiers. A carefully controlled device approaches $1/g_m$ as its equivalent noise resistance. For $g_m = 20{,}000 \ \mu$mhos, $1/g_m = 50$

Ω and $E_n = 0.9$ nV/$\sqrt{\text{Hz}}$. This is in the flat region of the noise spectrum. The noise current is also very much lower than in any bipolar transistor. Teledyne/Crystalonics makes a good line of low-noise JFETs and can be consulted for specific data on its latest devices.

2.2.7 A Sample Low-Noise Amplifier Design with Frequency Shaping

Figure 2.14 shows a low-noise circuit with a JFET in a cascode input stage. This amplifier is intended to amplify the output of a television vidicon tube. The vidicon is essentially a current source with a large, 39 pF output capacitance. For it to be flat to 10 MHz would require that a 400 Ω load resistor be used producing a very small output. Now the gain is proportional to the load resistor, but the noise is proportional to the square root of the load resistor. To obtain a maximum signal-to-noise ratio, the load resistance is made large and the resulting loss of high-frequency response is restored by peaking the amplifier. The load here is a 500 kΩ metal film resistor, with about 10 pF added circuit capacitance. This produces a high-frequency roll-off of 6.5 kHz.

The amplifier has a frequency response that rises 6 dB/octave from approximately 5 kHz to 10 MHz. There are two stages of peaking following the input stage. The first has a 3.9 kΩ emitter resistor shunted by 91 Ω in series with 6800 pF = 3.9 kΩ at 5 kHz. From that frequency on, the total emitter resistance drops at 6 dB/octave, which will make the gain rise at 6 dB/octave. This continues until 6800 pF = 91 Ω which is at 225 kHz. At this point the next gain stage takes over, with 130 pF = 5.6 kΩ at 225 kHz. The rise continues until 130 pF = 130 Ω at 9.5 MHz. It can be seen that the noise spectrum of the input stage is amplified much more at the high frequencies and therefore the signal–noise ratio is much greater at the low frequencies. This is done because the human eye, in looking at a television screen, is much more sensitive to low-frequency noise than to high-frequency noise. The voltage gain of the amplifier below 5 kHz is 1.9, but this is a bit misleading, since the gain of the amplifier at 10 MHz is 10^7/(5000) = 2000 times as great as the low-frequency gain.

A cascode input stage is used to eliminate the Miller feedback from the load resistor. This occurs because the input resistance at the emitter of the load transistor is very low, resulting in a small voltage gain for the JFET. The voltage gain of the complete first stage, however, is the same as a JFET with a high drain resistance, that is, gain = $g_m R_L$. For this JFET the $g_m = 15,000$ μmhos and the gain = $15,000(10)^{-6}1500 = 22.5$. High transconductance results in high gain and low noise but requires a large drain current. In this case $I_D = 13$ mA, and the drop across the 1.5 kΩ load resistor is 20 V.

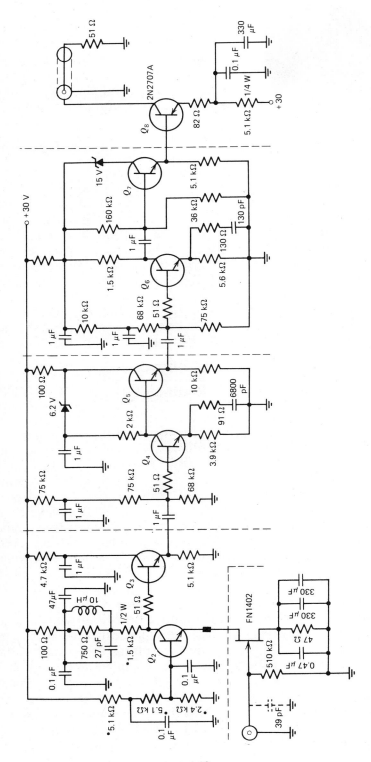

FIGURE 2.14 Low-noise peaking amplifier. All transistors 2N2857, except Q_1 and Q_8. All resistors ⅛ W carbon unless marked. Dots indicate metal film resistor. Bandwidth = 11 Hz → 10 MHz.

The base of Q_2 is biased at 5.8 V. This sets the collector of Q_2 at 10 V, which is but adequate.

The bypassed base of a high-frequency cascode stage can be very troublesome if the job is not done correctly, resulting in instability. Short leads, a good ground plane, and selective shielding are absolutely essential.

The remainder of the amplifier, except for the emitter peaking, is very much as described for the video amplifier. There is a peaking coil to boost the high end of the frequency response, and emitter followers are used to isolate the gain stages.

2.3 TUNED CLASS A AMPLIFIERS

Inductively tuned, or LC resonant circuits, as they are commonly called, are useful over a wide range of frequencies, but do have high and low limits. On the low-frequency side, where the inductors become large and expensive, the active RC circuits take over extremely well. This border is not clearly defined, but it is in the range of 100 kHz. These amplifiers are discussed in Chapter 7 on filters.

The high-frequency limit occurs when the coil inductances become short pieces of straight wire and the required capacitance starts to approach the irreducible level of the strays in a well laid-out circuit. This is again not an exact number, but is in the range of 400 MHz. After this, resonant cavities must be used, which is a subject not covered in this book.

Tuned RF amplifiers are in many ways less demanding than the broadband amplifier. Although stray capacitance is always undesirable and should be kept to a minimum, it can usually be absorbed in the tuned circuit without much loss of performance. The gain of the tuned circuit, for the same frequency, can be made much higher, and it has less noise than its broadband counterpart because of the reduced bandwidth and less distortion due to filtering.

2.3.1 Design Specifications

A frequency of 10 MHz is selected for the example. This frequency is used because it is high enough to demonstrate some high-frequency considerations and low enough for the transistor not to have reached the power roll-off point.

The starting specifications of the amplifier we are about to design are as follows:

Input $R = 50 \ \Omega$

Output to drive a 50 Ω terminated coaxial line

Output level as high as is reasonable with the transistors selected and class A operation

Gain as high as possible for two stages and consistent with good stability

Bandwith 4 MHz$_3$ (Q = 2.5)

At first glance it may seem that these specifications are more or less unbounded. This, however, is not true, for the key to the design is a request for high all-around performance. It is easy to overspecify one parameter and then find that every other property may have to be badly degraded to meet this one requirement. Once a high-performance amplifier has been built, it is generally possible to make reasonable trade-offs in performance without undue difficulty.

Whenever a design is being conceived, it is important to identify the most compromising areas early and solve these first. In this case it is the power stage. For easy reference, the completed design is shown in Fig. 2.15.

2.3.2 Output Stage Thermal Conditions

We limit ourselves in this design to a single class A output stage. In a TO-5 case size, a suitable transistor is the 2N3866A.

In the data sheets it is seen that a 60 mA current would peak the f_T at 800 MHz and allow a ±60 mA swing. The power dissipation with no signal is 60(12) = 720 mW. The data sheets state that this transistor can dissipate 5 W if the case is held at 25°C. Since the maximum allowable junction temperature is 200°C, this gives a junction-to-case thermal resistance of 175/5 = 35°C/W. The thermal resistance of a TO-39 case to still air is about 150°C/W (see Table 2.4). The thermal resistance from junction to air is then 150 + 35 = 185°C/W. The junction temperature is T = 0.72(185) + 25 = 158°C.

An estimate must now be made for the dissipation at maximum power output, and this requires some background discussion. Figure 2.16 shows a tuned circuit with a resistive load. The load may be coupled to the collector by various means, but at resonance it can be represented as shown. Although we are considering a linear circuit, for maximum power the transistor goes from full-off to full-on. In the on condition the voltage at the collector is zero. When the transistor is off, the magnetic field in the inductor collapses and a voltage of opposite polarity is induced. This adds to the supply, resulting in a maximum collector voltage of two times the supply voltage. This voltage is sinusoidal, and since there is no AC voltage across the power supply in these limiting conditions, the signal voltage across the load must be equal to the signal voltage across the transistor.

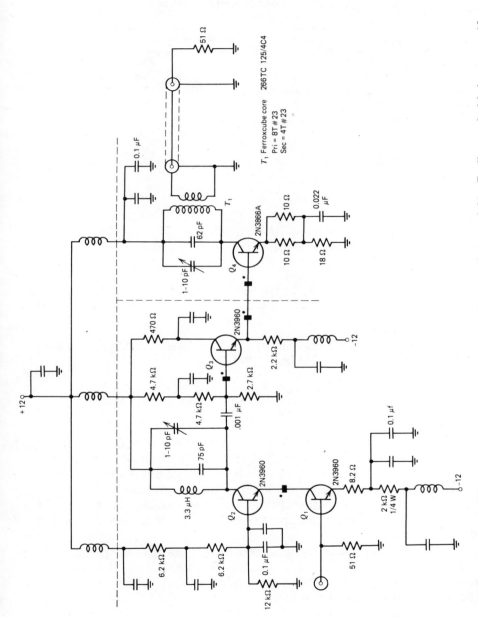

FIGURE 2.15 10 MHz class A tuned amplifier. All unmarked capacitors are 0.01 μF; all unmarked inductors are 10 μH. All resistors are ⅛ W unless marked. Asterisks denote Ferroxcube ferrite beads 4B.

TABLE 2.4
Case-to-Ambient Thermal Resistance for Typical
Transistor Cases

Case	θ_{CA} (°C/W)
TO-3	30
TO-5	150
TO-8	75
TO-18	300
TO-36	25
TO-39	150
TO-46	300
TO-60	70
TO-66	60

Accordingly, the power in the load resistor is $(E_{\text{rms}})^2/R_L$. This is equal to $(E_P/\sqrt{2})^2/R_L$. When a scope is used to measure voltage, E_{PP} is the handiest form. From this

$$P = \frac{(E_{PP}/2\sqrt{2})^2}{R_L} = \frac{(E_{PP})^2}{8R_L} \tag{2.7}$$

In this amplifier we are going to produce 60 mA change with a 12 V change, hence $R_L = 12/0.06 = 200\ \Omega$ and

$$P = \frac{(24)^2}{8(200)} = 0.36\ \text{W}$$

This result can be more or less intuitively understood by referring to Fig. 2.16b. Here it is seen that the current increase during the positive lobe is equal and symmetrical to the current decrease during the negative lobe. As the signal level is varied, there is no change in the DC current drawn by the circuit, hence no change in total power. When the signal is increased, part of the transistor power dissipation is tranferred to the load.

The discussion can be generalized to say that the maximum efficiency of an inductively coupled class A amplifier is 50% and that maximum transistor dissipation occurs at no load, which is twice the transistor dissipation of full load.

In this case there is no need for a heat sink at room temperature. However, to establish the procedure let us assume that the power dissipation is 1.5 W. In free air this would create a destructive junction temperature of $1.5(185) + 25 = 302°C$. With an infinite heat sink the junction temperature would be $1.5(35) + 25 = 77.5°C$.

Many types of heat sinks are available to control the operating temperature of a transistor. For example, International Electronics Research Corporation (IERC) manufactures a model, TX0506, that would be suitable for this application. Figure 2.17 gives the thermal characteristics of this device. The unit incorporates a *BeO* washer, which is an excellent insulator, and has a thermal conductivity equivalent to that of aluminum. Heat sinks must be used with care in RF circuits because they increase radiation and add capacitance. The capacitance in this case is 2.6 pF.

As is generally the case, no specific thermal information for the application at hand is given, but we use the rating of 60°C/W for the 4 × 4 epoxy board given in Fig. 2.17 as a conservative value. This results in a junction temperature of

$$T_j = 1.5(35 + 60) + 25 = 167.5°C$$

2.3.3 Output Stage Gain

Once the output load resistor has been determined, the gain calculations are the same as those in the video amplifier design. For this transistor the β at 10 MHz has not decreased substantially, so that the low-frequency design equations can be used.

The emitter resistance is established as

$$r_e = \frac{26}{i} + K = \frac{26}{60} + 1.5(\text{est.}) \cong 2\Omega$$

Therefore, the maximum possible gain is

$$G = \frac{R_L}{r_e} = \frac{200}{2} = 100$$

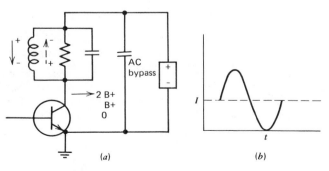

FIGURE 2.16   Loaded tuned circuit.

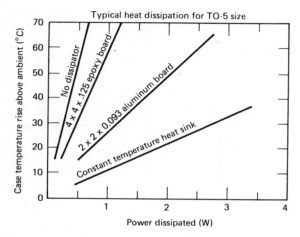

FIGURE 2.17   Thermal characteristics of TX0506. (Courtesy of IERC.)

To increase the stability of the amplifier, we reduce the gain rather arbitrarily to 30. A 5 Ω emitter resistor produces a gain of 28. In addition, a bypassed resistor is added for DC stability. The midstage also uses an NPN transistor, so that there is an overall voltage shift from the two emitter–base junctions of 4.4 mV/°C. Since the DC voltage gain of Q_4 is essentially zero, the only concern is the shift in the DC current. If we allow 10%, this is 6 mA. The total voltage change for 30°C is 30(4.4) = 132 mV. Therefore, R_E = 132/6 = 22 Ω, of which 5 Ω is unbypassed and the remaining 18 Ω is bypassed. The bypass capacitor must be substantially less than 7 Ω at 10 MHz. 0.022 μF is 0.7 Ω and should be satisfactory.

The 23 Ω have a DC drop of 0.06(23) = 1.38 V. Adding the 0.6 V of the emitter–base junction, we have an input DC bias requirement of E_{in} = 1.38 + 0.6 $\cong$ 2 V.

2.3.4 *RC* Output Coupling

The desired output load is 50 Ω. This requires a 4 to 1 transformation to produce 200 Ω at the collector of the output transistor. A transformer is shown (Fig. 2.15), but there are a variety of other methods that can be used.

Figure 2.18 shows how a capacitor can be used to couple to the load. This technique is discussed in greater detail in Section 8.5. Further details on transformer coupling are contained in Chapter 5.

To proceed with the design of the output stage it is necessary to determine the effect of the transistor output impedance under the specified operating conditions. Unfortunately, virtually all of the pa-

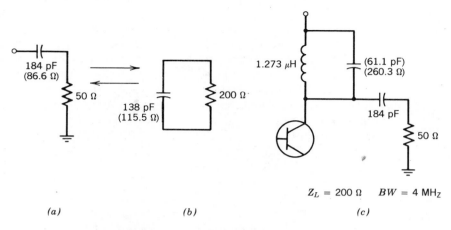

FIGURE 2.18   Capacitive coupling (10 MHz).

rameters of the transistor depend upon the voltage and current, both of which have a large dynamic range in this application.

One reason for picking the 2N3866 transistor is that it is well documented. A detailed study of the data sheets (Motorola) is well worth the effort.

As a reasonable compromise, a set of values of 1000 Ω for the dynamic output resistance and 2.5 pF for the capacitance appears to be good choices. The output resistance is defined by a test circuit in the data manual which has a 50 Ω source resistance and whose emitter resistance is bypassed. The circuit being designed is driven by an emitter follower whose resistance is considerably lower than 50 Ω and that has a 5 Ω external emitter resistor.

Figure 1.5 shows that the output resistance in this circuit is higher than that specified in the data sheets. The exact numerical increase is difficult to determine from the data and is best determined by measurement. However, a first approximation would be to consider the output resistance high enough to be ignored. The final results should be close enough to the calculated values so that only minor adjustments would be necessary. In this case, as in many other designs, rigorous design procedures are more an exercise in mathematics (and many time futility) than a practical procedure.

2.3.5 Transformer Output Coupling

A transformer offers an alternate means of coupling. The design and construction of the transformer are an additional step, but with a tightly coupled transformer, resistive load variations do not detune the output stage.

Because the secondary of this transformer is untuned, it is necessary to have the coupling of the primary and secondary windings as close to unity as possible. This requires a high-permeability core. Here again, a collection of manufacturers' data sheets is essential for design. Good information on powdered iron and ferrite cores can be obtained from Micrometal and Ferroxcube, respectively. In this frequency range the powdered iron has a permeability of 9 with a temperature coefficient of 30 ppm/°C. The ferrite has a permability of 125 with a temperature coefficient of 1300 ppm/°C (0.13%/°C). A 25°C increase in temperature would change the inductance by 3.25% and the frequency by 1.8% or 180 kHz. In view of the low Q of the output stage, this is a very reasonable value.

An initial selection of a 266TC125/4C4 ferrite core is made. This cores has an O.D. of 0.375 in., which is much larger than required for the power level. It is a convenient size for hand winding, however, and, more importantly, it is available.

The selection of the value of inductance to be used involves some trade-offs. Section 8.1 on parallel resonant circuits should be reviewed at this time.

The inductance of the selected core is given as 55 mH/1000 turns. 3.3 µH is chosen as the primary inductance and, since L is proportional to N^2, the turns are determined by

$$\left(\frac{N}{1000}\right)^2 = \frac{3.3(10)^{-6}}{5.5(10)^{-2}}$$

where $N^2 = 60$ and $N \cong 8$.

The impedance transformation is approximately 4 to 1 and varies as the square of the turns ratio. The four secondary turns are wound over the primary for close coupling. The turns are held in place by an application of Q-Dope, a low-loss glue made for this purpose.

2.3.6 The Input Stage

This input stage is a cascode amplifier. It is really a common emitter amplifier that drives a common base stage. This connection serves the same purpose as the emitter follower–common emitter combination used in the output, but offers some design variations. As with the low-noise amplifier, the voltage gain of Q_1 is very small because its collector load is the emitter resistance of Q_2. Therefore, there is no Miller capacitance multiplication to affect the input impedance. The gain of Q_2 is high, but the current due to the Miller effect flows through the base capacitor of Q_2 and no harm is done. Since the cascode connection has a common base output stage, the output resistance is about β times higher than a common emitter connection.

The transistor cascode amplifier may be thought of as sort of a "tetrode" transistor where the second base acts to increase the output resistance of the collector and to isolate it from the signal base. At this time no such transistors are available, although there are a number of dual-gate FETs that do work in this manner (for example, the Motorola MFE3008). The normal gain equations for the common emitter stage apply if the values of C_{CB} and r_P are changed. The base of Q_2 is biased at a DC level that is sufficient to provide the required operating potential for Q_1. The base of Q_2 must be carefully bypassed (short leads and a low-impedance capacitor). The bias network must be very well decoupled and adequate shielding provided or the circuit will oscillate. In addition, it is a good idea to put a ferrite bead or a 50 to 100 Ω resistor in the emitter line of Q_2 (the upper stage). This is because high-frequency transistors often develop a negative resistance input which leads to oscillation.

The input stage is biased at the emitter to avoid a coupling capacitor at the input of the amplifier. The desired 6 mA of current is obtained by a 2 kΩ resistor and the -12 V supply. Since the emitter has the same voltage gain as the input, very careful decoupling is required in this network.

The h_{FE} of Q_2 is 70, and with the collector current at 6 mA, a base current of $6/70 = 0.09$ mA is required. The current through the Q_2 bias chain is conservatively set at 0.5 mA.

6 V seems like a good choice for the base of Q_2. Since the signal level at the tank circuit is very small, this allows about the same voltage across each of the transistors. 6 mA would give an effective r_e of

$$\frac{R_B + r_b}{\beta} + \frac{26}{i} + K = \frac{50 + 10}{70} + \frac{26}{6} + 2 = 7.2 \ \Omega$$

The inductor in the collector is set at 3.3 μH. The resonating capacitor is 75 pF, which includes a 1 to 10 pF trimmer capacitor for tuning. Since the circuit Q has been defined as 10, we have

$$R_L = QX_L = 10(2\pi fL) = 10(207) = 2070 \ \Omega$$

The maximum possible gain is now

$$G = \frac{2070}{7.2} - 287$$

For stabilization we add another 8.2 Ω externally. The first-stage gain now becomes

$$G = \frac{2070}{15.4} = 134$$

The overall gain of the amplifier is

$$G = (134)(28)(0.5) = 1876$$

2.3.7 Midstage Design

The input and output stage of this amplifier must be isolated by an emitter follower. Were this not done, the resulting amplifier would bear no resemblance to the calculations that have been made.

The midstage will be RC coupled to the first stage, with the $R = 2070$ and the C of such a value as to offer negligible reactance at 10 MHz. This allows proper loading of the input stage so that the desired $Q = 10$ is achieved. The input bias required for Q_4 was shown to be 2 V. Adding 0.6 V for Q_3, we have 2.6 V at the base of Q_3. Figure 2.15 shows that a resistor chain from $+ 12$ is used to produce the bias. The current through the bias network is 2.6 V/2.7 kΩ = 1.0 mA. This is large enough so that the base current of Q_3 can be ignored. The equivalent parallel resistance of the divider is approximately the required 2070 Ω.

Q_3 is of the same polarity as Q_4. Therefore, whatever normal biasing current Q_4 may need is adequately furnished from the emitter of Q_3. However, the capacitive load presented by the Miller effect requires an AC component. The Miller capacitance is

$$C_{CB}(G + 1) = 4(28 + 1) = 116 \text{ pF}$$

which is 135 Ω at 10 MHz. The peak signal at the base of Q_4 is 12 V/28 = 0.43 V. This requires a current of 0.43/135 = 3.2 mA. To be safe, the emitter resistor of Q_3 should be able to furnish this current. Accordingly, a quiescent current of 5 mA is set for Q_3.

2.3.8 Decoupling

A 0.01 μF capacitor that has a reactance of 1.5 Ω at 10 MHz is a good choice for the general bypass function. This capacitor should have leads that are as short as possible. In some cases a 0.1 μF is placed in parallel for added insurance. These leads must be equally short. The series portions of the decoupling networks are not too critical, so that some relief for the packaging problem can be obtained. The inductive decouplers are 27 μH with a minimum self-resonance of 20 MHz; this is about 1.7 kΩ of X_L at 10 MHz. The RF chokes chosen here are toroidal and as such produce a very small exterior

FIGURE 2.19 The completed amplifier.

magnetic field. The axial RF chokes have the advantage of a higher DC current rating, higher resonant frequency, and lower cost. However, if their exterior fields are not properly contained, they can cause unstable gain variations or oscillation.

2.3.9 Test Results

The schematic of the final amplifier is shown in Fig. 2.15 and a photograph of the completed circuit in Fig. 2.19. The gain with the LC coupling was 2000 and with the transformer 2500. The Q in both cases was 13.

Two Ferroxcube 3B beads were inserted, as shown, between the emitter of Q_3 and the base of Q_4 to minimize interaction between the two stages. Later the beads were replaced by a 47 Ω resistor, and in the case of the transformer output the gain dropped to 1750 and the Q was reduced from 13 to 10.8. This indicates that the beads were not completely successful in eliminating all of the positive feedback. The maximum output with the beads was the expected 12 V_{PP}, but with considerable distortion. 8 V_{PP} was a clean output, and the tests were run at 5 V_{PP} out. The resistors dropped the maximum output to 10 V_{PP}.

The measured Q of the unloaded output transformer was 136, and no deviation from unity coupling could be observed.

To tune the low Q output stage, it is first necessary to detune the input stage. This was done by placing a 100 Ω resistor across the tank in Q_2. The output stage was then tuned by changing the tuning capacitor in that stage.

GENERAL REFERENCES

H. W. Ott, *Noise Reduction Techniques in Electronic Systems*, Wiley, New York, 1976.

J. K. Hardy, *High Frequency Circuit Design*, Reston, Reston, VA, 1979.

H. L. Krauss, C. W. Bostian, and F. H. Raab, *Solid State Radio Engineering*, Wiley, New York, 1980.

D. DeMaw, *Practical RF Design Manual*, Prentice-Hall, Englewood Cliffs, NJ, 1982.

THREE

Monolithic and Hybrid Analog Devices

This chapter covers the operational amplifier and a few of the more important classes of linear circuits. Chapter 9 on miscellaneous circuits contains additional information.

The monolithic and hybrid devices described here represent a giant expansion over the techniques described in Chapter 2 for discrete devices. Circuit design with transistors and the required passive elements should seldom be considered unless a suitable solution with these integrated circuits does not exist.

This obviously requires a thorough knowledge of the available monolithic and hybrid devices, their characteristics, and their cost. The monolithic structures are invariably lower priced than the hybrids and should be considered first.

The operational amplifier (op-amp), by far the most widely used analog integrated circuit, is discussed in the first part of this chapter.

3.1 THE OPERATIONAL AMPLIFIER

An op-amp is used primarily as a mechanism for connecting discrete elements in a straightforward manner to perform a required function.

The principal characteristics of the op-amp operation are gain and the ability to invert.

The properties of the op-amp, just as those of the transistor, are most easily understood if the ideal case is considered first. The ideal operational amplifier is assumed to have

1. Infinite gain
2. Infinite input resistance
3. Zero output resistance
4. Unlimited bandwidth

We first proceed with these assumptions to explain the various modes of operation and then take the effect of practical limitations into account.

3.1.1 Construction

The op-amp has a differential amplifier as its input stage, as shown in Fig. 3.1. Q_3 acts as a constant current source, so that the sum of the currents through Q_1 and Q_2 remains constant, and when E_{in} is at ground the currents are equal. If E_{in} is made $(+)$, the current through Q_1 increases and consequently the current through Q_2 must decrease by the same amount. It can be seen that applied voltages on Q_1 and Q_2 produce output voltages of opposite polarity.

The remaining gain in the op-amp is shown simply as $(-A)$. There may or may not be additional differential stages, but the output is single-ended. This is because there is only one connection from the output to the input in normal use.

In Fig. 3.1 the input at Q_1 is the inverting $(-)$ input and the input at Q_2 is the noninverting input $(+)$. Now a simple connection to the op-amp can be made, as illustrated in Fig. 3.2a.

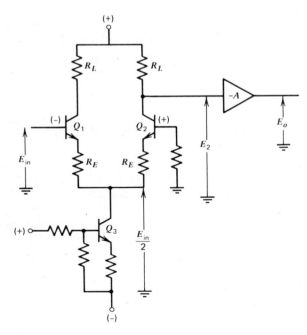

FIGURE 3.1   Op-amp input state. $G = $ (gain of preamp) $(-A)$.

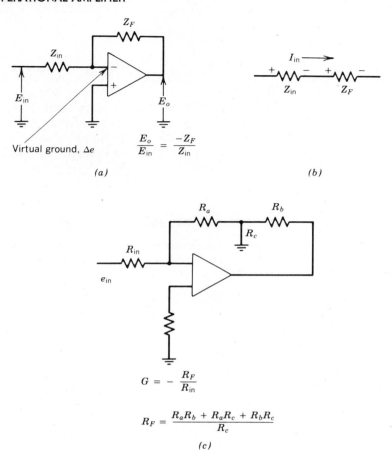

$$\frac{E_o}{E_{in}} = \frac{-Z_F}{Z_{in}}$$

(a)

(b)

$$G = -\frac{R_F}{R_{in}}$$

$$R_F = \frac{R_a R_b + R_a R_c + R_b R_c}{R_c}$$

(c)

FIGURE 3.2   Inverting amplifier.

3.1.2 Basic Operation

This amplifier is stable because the output is out of phase with the input. (A feedback amplifier can become unstable only when the output acts to increase or reinforce the input.)

The ($+$) input is at ground and, since the gain of the amplifier is assumed to be infinite, there can be no voltage between the ($+$) input and the ($-$) input. The ($-$) input is therefore called a virtual ground. Because of this, the current through Z_{in} is E_{in}/Z_{in}. Since the input resistance is infinite, the current through Z_F must be the same as that through Z_{in}, and the voltage across $Z_F = Z_F(E_{in}/Z_{in})$. Again, because of the virtual ground the voltage across Z_F is the output voltage, and we have

$$E_o = -E_{in}\left(\frac{Z_F}{Z_{in}}\right) \tag{3.1}$$

Figure 3.2*b* verifies that for a resistor network the output is out of phase with the input. When nonresistive networks are used, the phase relationships are modified and the network must be analyzed to see if the system is stable. This is true for the ideal amplifier and becomes more restrictive when practical limitations are imposed.

Figure 3.2*c* is an interesting variation of the inverting amplifier. It is useful for very high gains when the feedback resistor would normally have an undesirably large value.

3.1.3 Some Fundamental Connections

Using the type of reasoning just demonstrated, more useful connections to the op-amp can be determined. Figure 3.3 shows a signal applied to the (+) input. Because the gain is infinite, the voltage at the (−) input is equal to E_{in} (this is called the common-mode voltage),

$$\therefore I_{in} = \frac{E_{in}}{Z_{in}}$$

and the voltage across $Z_F = (E_o - E_{in})/I_{in} = (E_o - E_{in})Z_{in}/E_{in}$, from which

$$E_o = E_{in}(1 + Z_F/Z_{in}) \tag{3.2}$$

It can be seen that if $Z_{in} \gg Z_F$, $E_o = E_{in}$ and we have the voltage follower shown in Fig. 3.4*a*.

In Fig. 3.4*b* the current through R is E_{in}/R, which is independent of E_o. Therefore, the C is being charged by a current source and the voltage across it is directly proportional to the time the voltage is applied. The op-amp has accordingly converted the RC circuit to a true integrator.

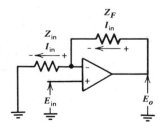

FIGURE 3.3   Noninverting amplifier [$E_o/E_{in} = 1 + (Z_F/Z_{in})$].

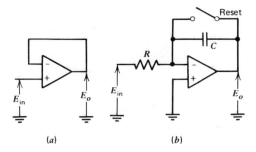

FIGURE 3.4 Two common connections: (*a*) voltage follower. $E_o/E_{in} = +1$; (*b*) integrator.

If the input is a DC voltage, the expression for the gain can be derived from the relation. Q (the charge on a capacitor) $= CE = It$.

Taking into account the inverting action of the op-amp, we have

$$E_o = \frac{It}{C} = \frac{-E_{in}t}{RC} \tag{3.3}$$

The general expression would be

$$E = -\frac{1}{RC} \int E_{in}\, dt \tag{3.4}$$

For a sine wave this becomes

$$E_o = \frac{E_{in}}{\omega RC} \cos \omega t$$

The reset switch is shown because a nonideal op-amp drifts and a reset is often necessary to remove the voltage that builds up across the capacitor.

Figure 3.5 is an expanded version of Fig. 3.2. Consider first the signals E_1, E_2, and E_3, with $E_4 = 0$. They all have their respective resistors meeting at the virtual ground of the inverting input. This means that these input signals are completely independent of each other and that they all add algebraically in accordance with their specific gain ratios.

The resistors R_{4a} and R_{4b} only serve to make $E_4 = E'_4 R_{4b}/(R_{4b} + R_{4a})$, as any unloaded resistor chain would do. The net result is that E_4 is applied to the $(+)$ terminal.

The gain of E_4 is $1 + R_F/R_{in}$(total) where R_{in}(total) is all the input resistors to the $(-)$ terminal in parallel. E_4 has a positive gain, whereas E_1, E_2, and E_3 have negative gains.

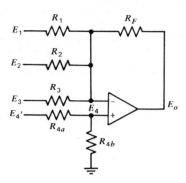

FIGURE 3.5 Multiple inputs.

The op-amp is such a versatile device that almost any type of function can be developed by its application (at least with the use of the ideal op-amp that has been considered thus far).

There are many sources of op-amp circuits for log functions, multipliers, dividers, comparators, constant current generators, peak detectors, etc. Unfortunately, much of this information is from earlier sources and as specialization advances, dedicated op-amp-type chips become available that can do the job far better than wired connections to a discrete op-amp. Laser trimming, natural monolithic balance, and other techniques provide a far superior product.

To select the right device, one must study the manuals and know the products that are available for a specific design. These are many applications of op-amps, both specialized and ordinary, scattered throughout this book. Specifically, attention is called to Section 3.5 on analog computers. These applications as well as the others are referenced in the index.

3.1.4 Frequency Considerations

At this point we depart from our ideal amplifier and admit that there is a finite frequency response. Nevertheless, we hedge with the expression "ideal finite frequency response." Figure 3.6 shows the frequency response of an amplifier that has only one RC roll-off. The frequency response is also shown as a straight-line approximation, sometimes called a Bode plot. The response is shown as flat until the $f_{-3\,dB}$ point is reached and then it falls off at a constant 6 dB/octave rate. This is a very desirable roll-off characteristic, as it minimizes the possibility of oscillation and allows more accurate calculations when oscillations occur. Such a frequency response is deliberately produced by making one stage with a much lower frequency response than the others. Unfortunately, this type of response does not give maximum

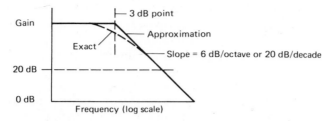

FIGURE 3.6 Ideal finite frequency response.

performance. In general, op-amps that need no compensation at unity gain have this characteristic.

3.1.5 Stability Considerations

To determine the stability of the amplifier we must know the feedback ratio β. This is the fraction of the output signal fed back to the input.

If we disregard the op-amp of Fig. 3.2a and apply a signal at E_o, there would be a voltage of $(E_o)Z_{in}/(Z_{in} + Z_F)$ at the $(-)$ input of the amplifier:

$$\frac{Z_{in}}{Z_{in} + Z_F} = \beta \quad \text{and} \quad \frac{Z_{in} + Z_F}{Z_{in}} = \frac{1}{\beta}$$

where $1/\beta$ is recognized as the noninverting gain.

The stability is determined by examining the intersection between the amplifier open-loop response and the $1/\beta$ response. For example, if $Z_{in} = 1$ kΩ and $Z_F = 9$ kΩ, then $1/\beta = (1 + 9)/1 = $ a ratio of 10, or 20 dB. β has a phase characteristic as well as an amplitude response, and both measurements are necessary for an absolute determination of stability.

To avoid oscillation it is necessary to have less than 180° phase shift, through the amplifier and the feedback network, at unity gain. If the phase shift is just short of 180°, violent ringing occurs with signal changes. The difference between 180° and the actual phase at unity gain is called phase margin. As this value is increased, the ringing is reduced and the system stability increased.

The gain and phase characteristics can be difficult and tedious to calculate and measure. Fortunately, approximations can be made under certain conditions that greatly simplify the problem. In the type of circuit defined as a minimum phase network, there is a consistent and useful relationship between the amplitude and phase response. This means that the stability can be determined by the amplitude response alone. Bode [1] derives the analytical definitions for these networks, but his work unfortunately is beyond the scope of this book. The following discussion, however, gives some insight into the definitions.

Networks such as delay lines and canceling circuits are not of the minimum-phase type. For example, a lumped-parameter LC delay line or a transmission cable has a propagation time that is a constant and an amplitude that is not attenuated. This means that as the input frequency is changed the output amplitude is constant but the phase is changing. The propagation delay of a transistor is also of this nature, but the response is usually controlled by the passive elements in the circuit. However, in very high-frequency circuits this could account for unpredicted results.

A canceling or nulling circuit generally has a theoretical infinity associated with its gain circuit. A parallel LC tuned circuit, for example, always has zero-degree phase shift at resonance, but the amplitude depends on the circuit Q and the rules are changed. The twin-T, which is an RC circuit, and other types of bridges are also of this class. Complex filters, such as those described in Chapter 7, have differing gain and phase relations. At times it is necessary to compute or measure the gain and phase characteristics of these networks separately to be sure of their relationship. In some cases a network is a nonminimum phase network only over a certain frequency range.

Consider the resonant circuit in Fig. 3.7. At resonance it is not a minimum-phase circuit. However, at frequencies substantially higher than resonance it is simply a capacitor and at lower frequencies it becomes an inductor. R_C and C_S are added to remind the reader that an inductor can seldom be used without taking into account the resistance and stray capacitance.

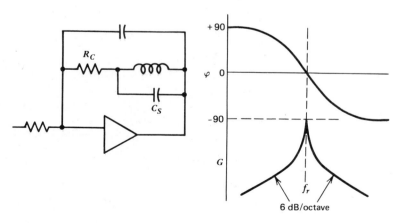

FIGURE 3.7   Resonance characteristics.

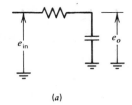

(a)

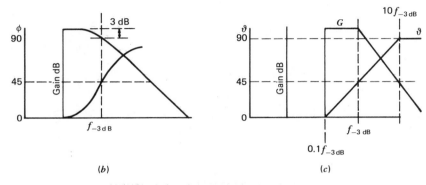

(b)   (c)

FIGURE 3.8   Gain and phase relations.

Fortunately, most networks used with operational amplifiers are noncanceling RCs and are of the minimum-phase type. Figure 3.8a shows a simple RC network and Fig. 3.8b shows its amplitude and phase response; Fig. 3.8c is the straight-line approximation. At $f_{-3\,\text{dB}}$ the slope abruptly goes from 0 to -20 dB/decade. The phase is closely approximated by a slope of 45°/decade from $0.1f_{-3\,\text{dB}}$ to $10f_{-3\,\text{dB}}$ and passing through 45° at $f_{-3\,\text{dB}}$. To illustrate these statements, a design example is shown in Fig. 3.9. This is a circuit whose output is the derivative of the input; put another way, if the input represents position of a signal, the output is its velocity.

β was defined at the beginning of Section 3.1.5 as the feedback ratio. To evaluate β for this amplifier we again refer to the information in Appendix I on decibels and complex algebra.

With this in mind we can proceed as follows:

$$\beta = \frac{Z_{\text{in}}}{Z_{\text{in}} + Z_F}$$

where Z_{in} = input impedance and Z_F = feedback impedance.

We disregard R_1 at this point and explain its purpose later. Then

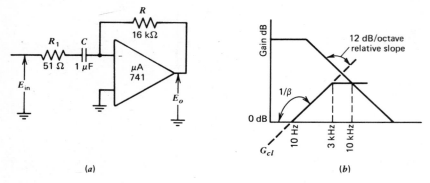

FIGURE 3.9 The differentiating circuit.

$$\beta = \frac{-jX_C}{R - jX_C}$$

From this we derive

$$\beta = \frac{X_C}{\sqrt{R^2 + X_C^2}} \angle \varphi$$

or the absolute value of $1/\beta$ is

$$\left| \frac{1}{\beta} \right| = \frac{\sqrt{R^2 + X_C^2}}{X_C}$$

and φ is the phase angle.

Let us set $X_C = R$ at 10 Hz. Now, because X_C is increasing as the frequency decreases, $1/\beta$ reduces to a constant,

$$\frac{1}{\beta} = \frac{\sqrt{X_C^2}}{X_C} = 1 \text{ or } 0 \text{ dB}$$

at frequencies below 10 Hz. At frequencies above 10 Hz,

$$\frac{1}{\beta} = \frac{\sqrt{R^2}}{X_C} = \frac{R}{X_C}$$

In this region, the value of $1/\beta$ is directly proportional to the frequency. This is expressed as a slope of $+6$ dB/octave ($+20$ dB/decade). Figure 3.9b shows the plot of these equations together with the open-loop gain response of an op-amp with a -6 dB/octave slope.

It is seen that the intersection of a $+6$ dB/octave slope and a -6 dB/octave slope produces a relative slope of 12 dB/octave, and the circuit oscillates. The insertion of R_1 corrects this situation. At some frequency prior to the intersection, R_1 is made equal to X_C. This produces a change in slope from $+6$ to 0 dB/octave. The relative slope between the two lines is now a safe 6 dB/octave. In Fig. 3.9b this breakpoint is shown at 3 kHz, and at this frequency $X_C = 51\ \Omega$.

Remember that the breakpoint is an approximation. If it is too close to the amplifier open-loop response, undesirable ringing and overshoots occur; if too far away, the frequency range over which the op-amp is properly taking the derivative is unnecessarily reduced.

It is desirable to apply a typical input signal with various values of R_1 and look at the output response. When R_1 is too small, ringing is evident and the value should be increased.

Often the amplifier response may be falling at a rate greater than 6 dB/octave, in which case a capacitor in parallel with the feedback resistor may help. The size of this capacitor should be such that $X_C = R$ in the region of the intersection. Again, testing is of great value.

Figure 3.9b also shows, as a dotted line, where the closed-loop gain departs from $1/\beta$. For emphasis it is stated again that the $1/\beta$ response is used to determine the stability and not the inverting closed-loop gain. In many approximations and for certain parts of the frequency spectrum they are the same, which often leads to errors due to carelessness.

When the amplitude response is used to predict stability, it is essential to keep in mind that the phase does not change instantly when a corner approximation is reached. Figure 3.8c shows that the straight-line phase approximation of a 6 dB/octave change in slope is 45°/decade. In other words, at 0.1 of the corner frequency the phase begins an effective change, at the corner frequency the change is 45°, and it takes another decade of frequency change to approach the full 90° closely.

As shown in Figs. 3.2 and 3.3, the gain of an op-amp is controlled by Z_{in} and Z_F. Within the bounds of the minimum-phase network definition there is no limit on the complexity of these impedances. The active filters described in Chapter 7 and Appendix III are good examples of this.

However, as the complexity of the impedances increases so does the difficulty in determining the resultant stability of the circuit. Great care must be taken. Resonant, canceling, and delay properties have a way of creating errors in the straight-line amplitude response. Also, when there are multiple components, the straight-line asymptotic conditions may never develop, making this type of analysis very confusing.

Additional information on stability requirements and calculations is given in Section 9.6.

Aside from the calculations, it is easy and desirable to check the amplifier for stability after it has been built. The test is most apparent if the amplifier is intended to have a flat response. A square wave applied to the input produces a slightly rounded square wave on the output if the amplifier has a satisfactory margin of stability. As the stability margin decreases, the output square wave develops larger overshoots, followed by increasing lengths of ringing that, in the limit, develop into a full, sustained oscillation. If the intended amplifier response is not flat, the underdamped condition is still there, but is modified and sometimes harder to evaluate. The frequency of the square wave is not critical, but it is most useful in the range of about $\frac{1}{5}$ of the $1/\beta$ and op-amp gain intersection point.

Computer analysis, on the other hand, is natural for this type of design, since advanced software programs can develop the response directly from the schematic diagram.

It must be remembered that it is the *phase* at the intersection of the amplifier open-loop response and the $1/\beta$ function that determines the stability. The amplitude plot, when applicable and used correctly, is an easier method of approximating the phase condition.

3.1.6 Other High-Frequency Considerations

Higher performance op-amps generally start their roll-off at 6 dB/octave and then break into a steeper slope before unity gain is reached.

At low gains it is generally necessary to achieve stability by placing a capacitor in parallel with the feedback resistor or by placing a capacitor to ground from a pin provided for the purpose. This results in a lower high-frequency response for the low-gain applications.

A parameter that becomes important in high-performance amplifiers is the input capacitance, which is generally on the order of a few picofarads. This capacitance, which is shown in Fig. 3.10, causes the $1/\beta$ response to have a corner where $R_{in}//R_F = X_{Cin}$ followed by a $+6$ dB/octave slope. As previously shown in Fig. 3.9, this leads to instability. If a capacitor is placed in parallel with R_F to make the feedback RC time constant equal the input RC time constant, $1/\beta$ has a flat frequency response and the problem is corrected. This does, however, degrade the frequency response. For maximum high-frequency response, R_{in} is made as low as possible.

In practice the capacitor across R_F may be a little larger to compensate for the op-amp gain characteristic. Obviously, stray wiring capacitance increases the input capacitance; care must be taken to produce a good layout.

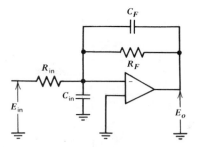

FIGURE 3.10 Input capacitance compensation.

Several other characteristics of an op-amp have to do with its high-frequency performance.

The first of these is slew rate. This condition occurs when a steep wavefront is applied to the input of the op-amp and the feedback signal cannot match the rise time of the input signal. The amplifier is now simply going as fast as it can in the right direction to catch up with the signal. This is an overload condition, and the internal parameters of the op-amp are substantially different from what they were in the linear mode. Two amplifiers with the same linear gain–bandwidth product can, and very often do, have vastly different slew rates. A sine wave input becomes a triangular output under slew conditions. To estimate slew requirements, it is good to know that the steepest slope of a sine wave (0 and 180°) is π times as large as the average slope (a line drawn from peak to peak).

When an amplifier comes out of a slew condition there is a recovery period, generally of a ringing nature. Called settling time, it is defined as the time required to come within a given error band after a specified input has been applied. For example, the HA2525 has a typical settling time of 250 ns, for an error of ± 10 mV of final value. This is specified for a voltage follower connection with a load of 2 kΩ and 50 pF and an applied signal of -5 to $+5$ V. Settling time depends greatly on the use of the op-amp, and the manufacturer's data cannot be reliably transposed to a different operating condition.

Another common way of relating to the slew characteristics is by specifying full power bandwidth. The HA2525 states this as 2 MHz for ± 10 V_{out}. This turns out to be (20 V/(0.25) μs) = 80 V/μs. This is less than the stated slew rate of 120 V/μs, so as to limit the distortion.

If the closed-loop gain is high, the $1/\beta$ curve intersects the open-loop gain response at a lower frequency and the bandwidth is smaller.

A somewhat more subtle loss of bandwidth comes about when multiple inputs are used. This is illustrated in Fig. 3.11a. Let us say that $R_1 = R_F$ for a single input. $1/\beta$ is then $(R + R)/R = 2$, which

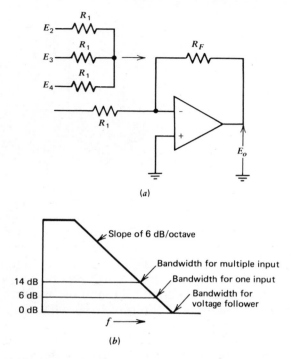

(a)

(b)

FIGURE 3.11   Reduction of bandwidth by multiple inputs.

is a bandwidth reduction of 6 dB (for a 6 dB/octave slope). Now, if three more identical inputs are added, $1/\beta = (R + R/4)/R/4 = 5$, which is a bandwidth loss of 14 dB.

Figure 3.11b illustrates that a 6 dB/octave slope is a unity slope and that is why a 6 dB loss of gain is a 6 dB loss of bandwidth. The voltage follower (gain = +1) has a $1/\beta = 1$ or 0 dB and its bandwidth is the full f_T. It is seen then that an op-amp with a true 6 dB/octave slope, connected for a gain of +1, has twice the bandwidth than when connected for a gain of −1.

Fully compensated low-performance op-amps such as the μA741 have this characteristic. High-performance op-amps such as the HA2525 do not, and consequently the bandwidth advantage of the voltage follower is somewhat diminished by the extra compensation required.

3.1.7 Accuracy

The ideal operational amplifier assumed infinite open-loop gain and input impedance. Accordingly, the closed-loop relations were exact as developed. If the gain is recognized to have a finite value A and the input impedance is still maintained as infinite, a useful expression for the closed-loop gain can be developed. Referring to Fig. 3.2, we see that for the inverting amplifier a difference voltage Δ_e is defined at the virtual ground. To clarify the derivation it is best to define E_o as carrying its own sign. On this basis we can write the expression

$$I_{\text{in}} = \frac{E_o + E_{\text{in}}}{Z_{\text{in}} + Z_F}$$

from which

$$\Delta_e = E_{\text{in}} - I_{\text{in}}Z_{\text{in}} = E_{\text{in}} - \left(\frac{E_o + E_{\text{in}}}{Z_{\text{in}} + Z_F}\right) Z_{\text{in}}$$

Since by definition $\Delta_e = E_o/A$, (A = open-loop gain), we have the expression

$$\frac{E_o}{A} = E_{\text{in}} - \left(\frac{E_o + E_{\text{in}}}{Z_{\text{in}} + Z_F}\right) Z_{\text{in}}$$

which, after some manipulation, becomes

$$\frac{E_o}{E_{\text{in}}} = \frac{-Z_F/Z_{\text{in}}}{1 + 1/A\beta} = \frac{-Z_F}{Z_{\text{in}}} \left(\frac{A}{A + (1 + Z_F/Z_{\text{in}})}\right) \qquad (3.5)$$

Here E_o is now defined as inverted by the negative sign in the equation. In a similar manner it can be shown that for the noninverting amplifier we have the expression

$$\frac{E_o}{E_{\text{in}}} = \frac{1 + Z_F/Z_{\text{in}}}{1 + 1/A\beta} = \left(1 + \frac{Z_F}{Z_{\text{in}}}\right) \left(\frac{A}{A + (1 + Z_F/Z_{\text{in}})}\right) \qquad (3.6)$$

It must be recognized that all of the variables in these equations can be complex numbers. However, in the region where both the amplifier open-loop response and the amplifier closed-loop response are flat, the calculation is straightforward, as shown below for a μA741 amplifier and a noninverting connection.

Open-Loop Gain	Closed-Loop Gain ($A = \infty$)	Correction Factor for Actual Gain	-3 dB Bandwidth
100 dB $= 10^5$	1	0.99999	1 MHz
	10	0.9999	100 kHz
	10^2	0.999	10 kHz
	10^3	0.990	1 kHz
	10^4	0.9091	100 Hz
	10^5	0.5	10 Hz

3.1.8 Limitations of the Input Stage

The ideal op-amp assumed infinite input impedance. When this restriction is lifted, two other limitations must also be recognized. These are the input currents and the offset voltage. The input resistance generally is not much of a restriction on the inverting input. An exception to this is the transimpedance amplifier. Here the signal is a current source, and a FET input stage must be employed. Usually, a high input resistance is needed when the ($+$) input is used to measure the voltage across a capacitor or other high-impedance source. Examples of this are sample-and-hold circuits and peak detectors.

The input current comes from two sources. The first is the bias current necessary because of a finite β in the input transistor stage. The second is the collector-to-base leakage current. For silicon transistors this is very small at room temperature, being on the order of a few nanoamperes for low-level transistors. This value, however, doubles about every 10°C, so that at high temperatures it becomes a factor to consider. In op-amps the manufacturers attempt to make the currents to both the ($+$) and the ($-$) inputs equal. The inequality is called the input offset current. To take advantage of this balance the resistance seen from each input terminal must be the same. This is illustrated by the inverting amplifier in Fig. 3.12a. Obviously, R can be adjusted for a complete cancellation of the input currents at a given set of operating conditions.

The input offset voltage V_{IOS} is the difference between the base–emitter voltage drops of the two input stages. For the μA741, not one of the better devices, this is 3 mV maximum, with a maximum temperature coefficient of 15 μV/°C. Considering that a single transistor has an emitter-to-base voltage of 600 mV, with a temperature coefficient of 2.2 mV/°C, this is a rather remarkable balance. V_{IOS} acts as if it were in series with either one of the inputs. It is, however, generally placed at the ($+$) input for ease of computation. That this is true can be demonstrated from Fig. 3.12b. If V_{IOS} is placed at the ($-$) terminal, we have

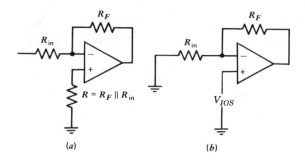

FIGURE 3.12   Input offset voltage.

$$\left(V_{IOS} - \frac{E_o R_{in}}{R_{in} + R_F} \right) A = E_o$$

from which

$$\frac{E_o}{V_{IOS}} = \frac{1}{1/A + R_{in}/(R_{in} + R_F)} \cong \frac{R_F + R_{in}}{R_{in}}$$

This is recognized as the noninverting gain.

Another input restriction is the common mode voltage. A common mode voltage develops when an input signal is placed on the noninverting input of the amplifier. As previously explained, the high gain of the op-amp forces almost the same voltage on the inverting input. There is a limit to the magnitude of this voltage relative to the power supply.

When a common voltage is applied to both inputs, as shown in Fig. 3.13, that voltage is reduced at the output by the common mode rejection ratio CMRR. This relationship is given as

$$V_o = - \frac{R_2}{R_1} \left(e_s + \frac{e_{cm}}{\text{CMRR}} \right) \tag{3.7}$$

The CMRR becomes smaller as the frequency increases, so this must be taken into account as the frequency enters this region.

The amplifier in Fig. 3.13 also takes the difference of the two input signals. The accuracy of this depends more on the accuracy of the inverting and noninverting resistor ratios than it does on the op-amp. Sometimes it is better to invert one of the signals with another op-amp and add them.

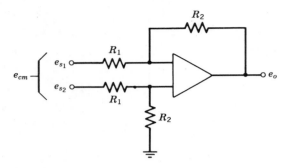

FIGURE 3.13   Differential amplifier with CMR.

A third, and perhaps best, method is to use an "instrumentation amplifier," which consists of three separate op-amps with laser-trimmed resistors in one package. The gain is set by a single external resistor or by selecting taps from the package.

An additional advantage of this circuit is that each input signal goes to the inverting high impedance input of one of the internal op-amps. This device is especially useful for measuring the output of bridge circuits and other off-ground signal sources. A problem with the instrumentation amplifier is often a limited frequency response.

3.1.9 Output Impedance and Error Correction

The open-loop output impedance of an op-amp is relatively high. For the μA741 it is about 75 Ω. In the closed-loop version, however, it is greatly reduced as shown by the equation

$$Z_{CL} = \frac{Z_{OL}}{A\beta - 1}$$

or, if $A\beta \gg 1$,

$$Z_{CL} = \frac{Z_{OL}}{A\beta} = \frac{Z_{OL}(\text{gain } CL)}{A} \tag{3.8}$$

Here again, $1/\beta$ = closed-loop gain in the noninverting amplifier and is generally close to the closed-loop gain in the inverting connection.

For example, if there is a 40 dB (100 times) difference between the open-loop gain A and $1/\beta$, the μA741 has $75/100 = 0.75\ \Omega$ output resistance.

However, for a large capacitive load, the amplifier is limiting, and a corrective signal cannot properly develop. The low output resis-

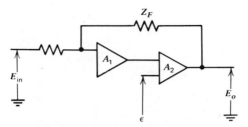

FIGURE 3.14 Error correction.

tance now reverts back to the open-loop value and the charging time constant is lengthened accordingly. If the output stage needs more drive capability, a buffer such as the NSC LH0002 or LH0033 can be connected to the output stage. For most applications, the frequency response of these devices is sufficiently high for them to be placed within the feedback loop without causing instability. There are also numerous power op-amps with extended ratings in various combinations of current, voltage, and power.

The finite output impedance can be considered in a more general sense as a distortion and as being equivalent to the insertion of an error signal. This is so because it causes the output signal to be different from the input.

Figure 3.14 illustrates this point. Here the open-loop gain is defined as $A_1 A_2$ and the error voltage ϵ is inserted at the input of A_2. The output voltage is now expressed as

$$E_o = \frac{(E_{in} + \epsilon/A_1)}{(1 + 1/A_1 A_2 \beta)} \text{ (gain } CL) \tag{3.9}$$

It is seen that any distortion error or noise entering after the input is divided by the gain between that point and the input.

3.2 COMPARATORS

A comparator detects which of two input signals is larger. This device is structured very much like an op-amp. It is not a good idea to use an op-amp as a comparator, however, since it is not optimized for this function. An op-amp can be used as a model to explain the operations of the comparator. Figure 3.15 shows the connections.

The comparator normally operates without feedback and is usually at a (+) or (−) limit. This is in contrast to the op-amp which operates in the linear region and is not supposed to go into a limit. The com-

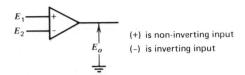

E_1
E_2
E_o

(+) is non-inverting input
(−) is inverting input

FIGURE 3.15 The Comparator. (+) is noninverting input; (−) is inverting input.

parator is designed to prevent its transistors from going into hard saturation, so that a limit can be pulled out very rapidly. This is the principal reason why an op-amp should not be used as a comparator. On the other hand, the comparator is optimized for maximum slewing speed and is not necessarily very stable in the linear region. This can sometimes be a problem, as discussed later.

In the usual form of operation a reference is put on one input and a variable voltage on the other. The output is normally at one limit or the other, depending on which input is greater. The LM111, for example, has a gain of 200,000. An output swing of 10 V would therefore require an input differential to 50 μV.

To see how the output responds to the input, let us assume that the two inputs are equal and the output is at its midpoint. If the (+) input goes more (+), the output goes (+); if it goes more (−), the output goes more (−). It does not matter at what voltage (called common mode voltage) or at what polarity the inputs were balanced; it is the difference between the voltages that is amplified. Obviously, saying that the (+) input went more (+) is equivalent to the (−) input going more (−), getting inverted, and coming out with the same (+) going output.

If the incoming waveform changes very slowly, the comparator is in the linear transition stage for a longer time. An oscillating condition could then occur. Another problem is that the input signal may have noise or jitter, causing the output to be unstable. To prevent this, positive feedback is sometimes used, as shown in Fig. 3.16, where

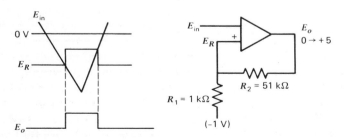

FIGURE 3.16 Comparator with hysteresis. When $E = 0$ V, $E_R = (51/52)(-1) = -0.98$ V. When $E = +5$ V, $E_R = -1 + [(5 + 1)/(R_1 + R_2)]R_1 = -0.88$ V.

E_{in}, E_R, and E_o are plotted. Initially, the difference between E_{in} and E_R is $(+)$. This is applied at the $(-)$ input, so that E_o is low, which we call zero volts. When E_{in} drops below E_R, E_o becomes high. Because of the positive feedback, E_R becomes more $(+)$, ensuring that E_o remains in its high condition. When E_{in} starts going positive, it crosses E_R at a slightly more positive voltage. Accordingly, the $\downarrow$ and $\uparrow$ comparison points are not equal. This may or may not be acceptable in a given system. The numerical calculation is shown for more clarity.

The important characteristics of a comparator is

1. Gain
2. Slewing speed or response time
3. Input offset voltage
4. Input bias and offset currents
5. Output characteristics

Gain determines the sensitivity of the device. The response time is determined by offsetting the comparator with a given voltage, usually 100 mV, and then overdriving that bias by a given number of millivolts. The input offset voltage and the bias currents affect the accuracy of the comparison. They can both be set to zero. After that the temperature and random stability of the circuit and power supplies determine the final accuracy. The output characteristics vary with different comparators. The LM111 has an open collector rated at 50 V maximum with the ability to sink 50 mA of current, so that it can drive small relays and lamps directly. The LM111 data sheets characterize that device in detail and show some good applications.

3.3 SAMPLE AND HOLD

These devices operate exactly as the name implies. A basic system is shown in Fig. 3.17. The signal input is buffered and then goes to a FET switch. When the gate signal is on, the FET turns on and charges the capacitor. When the gate signal is off, the sampled voltage remains on the capacitor for a length of time determined by the size of the capacitor and the leakage current. The figure of merit for the S/H depends on low leakage currents, low "on" resistance for the FET, and the speed of the FET switch and buffers. For a given S/H the capacitor is the trade-off parameter. A large capacitor holds the charge for a long time but requires a greater sample period.

Harris, Analog Devices, and Burr Brown are among the many companies producing a variety of S/H packages. The trade-off is generally increased power consumption for higher speed.

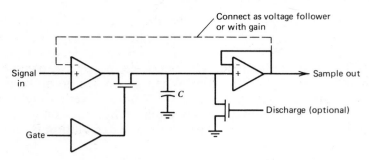

FIGURE 3.17   Harris sample and hold (HA2425).

The Harris family consists of the HA2425, HA5320, and the HA5330 with acquisiton times to 0.01% of 5 μs, 1 μs, and 0.4 μs, respectively. These are convenient devices since everything is contained in one 14-pin DIP (dual in-line package) except the capacitor. Figure 3.17 shows the construction.

These circuits are very flexible because the S/H is part of an overall op-amp. It is shown in the data sheet connected as a voltage follower, which is its highest speed condition. It can, however, be used with the conventional feedback and input resistor if desired. The output buffer is an internally connected voltage follower that gives good accuracy in the hold mode when the overall feedback is disconnected by the open switch. The overall feedback loop puts the input buffer into a "hard-on" condition so that maximum voltage is applied to the conducting FET. This condition lasts until $(E_{in} - E_o)$ × open-loop gain of the input buffer becomes less than 10 V. The open-loos gain is a function of frequency, so that, as the sample time is reduced, the open-loop gain falls.

3.4 VOLTAGE REGULATORS AND POWER SUPPLIES

Voltage regulators and power supplies must be added to the ever-increasing list of "don't do it yourself without good reason" devices. Many companies make a great variety of these components, and it is important to review the current literature before filling a given need. The older regulators required many passive parts to complement the integrated circuit. These systems, although flexible, are generally not worth the trouble. If a fixed standard voltage is required, the regulator, except for two capacitors, is a self-contained three-terminal device. A capacitor on the input and output is recommended on all regulators. The capacitor on the output of the regulator is used to lower the output impedance at the higher frequencies, and the man-

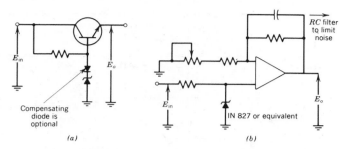

FIGURE 3.18   Simple voltage regulators.

ufacturer generally shows a plot of output impedance versus frequency with and without a recommended capacitor. This does not
eliminate local bypassing for the higher frequencies, however, because the inductance of the line from regulator to load increases the
impedance. Also, the local capacitor is required to contain the high-
frequency energy so that unwanted feedback does not occur. The
input capacitor is used because the lead inductance of a long line
sometimes causes the regulator to be unstable.

The use of an external pass transistor for larger currents is generally
shown on the manufacturer's data sheet. This should be avoided,
however, since high-current regulators in a single three-terminal package are available. Lambda has a good selection of these devices.

There are, of course, times when there is good reason to develop
your own power source. An example is when a very economical voltage reduction is required with some modest regulating properties.
Figure 3.18a show a transistor whose base is clamped by a zener.

A compensating diode can be added if desired, but the temperature
coefficient of the zener must be considered. Figure 3.19 shows some
of the important properties of zener diodes.

A resistor can be used in place of the zener diode if the initial supply
is regulated or if the application is less demanding.

Figure 3.18b provides a precision voltage reference. The degree of
precision depends upon the quality of the op-amp and the reference
zener. An important feature of this voltage source is that the magnitude is adjustable. The zener is chosen only for its stability.

Another good reason to develop your own power source is when
a special transformer is required to couple the AC line to the DC
power source efficiently. After the transformer has been built and the
necessary filtering system installed, an available regulator package is
usually the most suitable way to go.

Finally, a switching regulator design has been included in Section
9.11; it contains so many important and interesting features that it
fits well within the intent of Chapter 9.

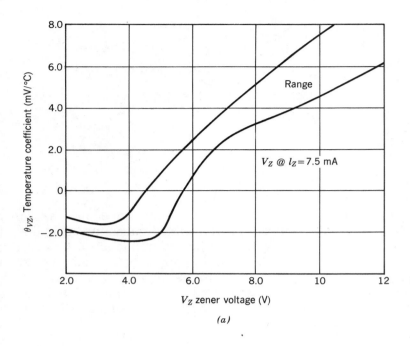

(a)

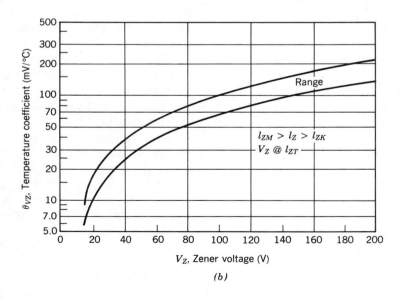

(b)

FIGURE 3.19 Zener characteristics: 1N5221 through 1N5281 series.

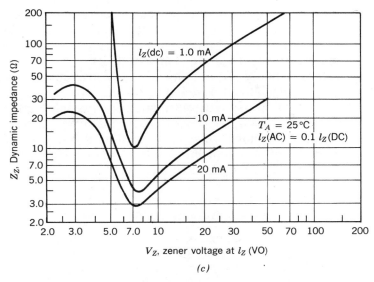

V_Z, zener voltage at I_Z (VO)

(c)

FIGURE 3.19 (*Continued*)

3.5 ANALOG COMPUTERS

The earliest computers were of mechanical construction and very limited in application. However, as the electronics industry developed, electronic computers, both analog and digital, gradually became more capable and soon dominated the computer field. In the beginning, the digital computers were huge and expensive machines and the analog computers were neat, simple systems with somewhat limited accuracy.

The choice between analog or digital computation had to be looked at carefully. As the transistor development produced integrated circuits of increasing capability, the digital computer emerged a clear winner. However, the development of the semiconductor industry that led to the digital computer also produced techniques for very advanced and accurate analog processing. Although it is certainly true that the analog computer will never seriously compete with the digital computer on a general basis, there are areas where the analog computer is clearly a better choice. Understanding these components and their applications is essential for any engineer involved with computation techniques.

The principal application of analog computers is for fast real-time processing of analog signals. Despite the fact that modern digital computers operate at very high clock speeds, the techniques of multiple instructions and looping results in actual operating bandwidths that are usually less than that of the analog counterparts.

Analog computers are not general-purpose instruments that can in any way compete with their digital counterparts for laboratory use. They are effective for special-purpose applications in which space, power, and operating bandwidth are at a premium.

Analog systems usually require considerably less design time and very little, if any, specialized design equipment.

The following section lists current analog processing components and briefly describes their properties and capabilities. Since such products are constantly improved, this list will not represent the best choices for very long; it should, however, remain a guide and basis for comparison for some length of time.

A: Function Generators
AD639 Analog Devices

This is a very flexible device and it comes in a 16-pin DIP. The current drain is 7.5 mA from $+15$ V and 4.0 mA from -5 V.

With this device all the standard trigonometric functions can be generated (sin, cos, tan, cosec, sec, cot, arcsin, arccos, arctan, etc.). Accuracy, speed, and distortion vary with the application; for example, the sine function has a specified error of $\pm0.2\%$, a distortion level of -74 dB, and a bandwidth of 1.5 MHz.

The different functions are produced primarily by pin connections. There is an occasional resistor, but no trim pots are required for accuracy or balance. One limitation is that the functions are not continuous; this may restrict some applications.

B: Multipliers/Dividers
AD539[2] Analog Devices

A very fast dual channel multiplier/divider, it also comes in a 16-pin DIP. It has two identical signal channels Y_1 and Y_2 with a common X input providing linear control of gain. The signal channels have a -3 dB of 60 MHz with a current output and 25 MHz when used with a high-speed op-amp such as the LH0032. The control channel (X input), however, has a -3 dB of 5 MHz and this, of course, limits the speed as a two-variable multiplier. Although the signal inputs are bipolar, the control input is limited to positive voltages only, so the result is a two-quadrant multiplier.

The power consumption is 135 mW with ±5 V supplies. Accuracy and distortion are functions of the control voltage becoming better for higher voltages, which is typical of log multipliers. $\pm\frac{1}{4}$ dB accuracy and 0.15% distortion are stated for a control voltage of 0.1 V. This distortion value is very questionable in practice, however, as nonideal compensation produces ringing and overshoot which have very high levels of distortion. No trim pots are required.

AD534 ANALOG DEVICES

This is a full four-quadrant multiplier. It is a slower than the AD539 being specified at -3 dB for 1 MHz at small signals, a slew rate of 20 V/μs and a settling time of 2 μs for a 20 V step to 1%. It comes in a 14-pin DIP and consumes 300 mW from ± 15 V supplies. The output error ranges from $\pm 1.5\%$ to $\pm 0.5\%$ depending upon the grade selection.

AD429 ANALOG DEVICES

This modular device comes in a package 1.5 × 1.5 × 0.62 in. high. It is included because it is of a reasonable size and offers a worthwhile increase in performance over the monolithic devices. It is a four-quadrant multiplier with an $f_{-3\,dB}$ of 10 MHz. A nonlinearity of 0.5% is specified with 0.2% by the use of three optional trim pots. It can also be used as a divider, a square rooter, and to produce some trig-onometric functions.

A good example of the use of a multiplier is that of a high-speed wattmeter. In this application the multiplier is used in conjunction with a standard laboratory test instrument. A multiplier such as the AD429, which gives a 10 MHz response in both channels, or a AD539, which has a 25 MHz response in one channel and a 5 MHz response in the second channel, are good choices.

The voltage is applied to one channel and the output of a current probe to the other. An excellent selection for the current probe is the Tektronix A6302 together with the AM503 probe amplifier which has a frequency response of DC to 50 MHz.

The AD539 multiplier is a good choice for inductive circuits, a common application, because the current wave form is always much slower than the voltage change, and also in most cases the current does not reverse. There are some important exceptions such as the parasitic diode in power FETs (see Section 1.3.5). In these cases, it may be necessary to take two measurements, one for each direction of the current, or possibly to use a four-quadrant multiplier such as the AD429 or the XR-2208.

With this type of multiplier, direct high-speed power measurements can be made, avoiding laborious multiplication of the individual current and voltage waveforms.

C: LOG/ANTILOG
755 P/N AND 759 P/N ANALOG DEVICES

These are modular devices. The 755 is 1.5 × 1.5 × 0.4 in. and features a high accuracy of $\pm 0.5\%$ to $\pm 1\%$ and a bandwidth of 80 Hz to 100 kHz depending upon the level of the input signal. The 759 is 1.25 ×

1.25 × 0.4 in. and has a small signal bandwidth of 250 Hz to 200 kHz with an accuracy of ±1% to ±5%.

The log function is dependent on the emitter–base current-to-voltage characteristic of a transistor. This impedance increases as the current decreases and consequently the frequency response is lowered.

There are six decades of current input from 1 nA to 1 mA and four decades of voltage input from 1 mV to 10 V.

Although these modules are considerably larger than a 16-pin DIP there is only one optional pot required for operation and this can often offer better packaging considerations than the dip with passive components.

If high-speed operation is required, the XR-7000 by Exar should be considered. This device comes in a 40-pin DIP and has seven logging elements, each with a range of 12 dB and an $f_{-3\,dB}$ of 30 MHz, capable of an overall range of 84 dB. The problem is that each stage requires a high-speed op-amp, and, of course, the overall frequency loss is the sum of the losses per stage, so depending upon the logging range required, the overall frequency range can be substantially reduced.

REFERENCES

[1] H. W. Bode, *Network Analysis and Feedback Amplifier Design*, Van Nostrand, New York, 1945.

GENERAL REFERENCES

Kitchin and Wheeler, Voltage—Controlled Amplifier Handles 50 MHz Frequencies, *Electron. Prod.*, Jan. 15, 1985.

D. H. Sheingold, *Nonlinear Circuits Handbook*, Analog Devices, Inc., Norwood, MA, 1976.

R. G. Irvine, *Operational Amplifier, Characteristics and Applications*, Prentice-Hall, Englewood Cliffs, NJ, 1981.

P. Horowitz and W. Hill, *The Art of Electronics*, Cambridge University Press, Cambridge, UK, 1981.

J. G. Graeme, *Applications of Operational Amplifiers, Third Generation Techniques*, McGraw-Hill, New York, 1976.

Y. J. Wong and W. E. Ott, *Function Circuits, Design and Applications*, McGraw-Hill, New York, 1976.

J. G. Graeme, G. E. Tobey, and L. P. Huelsman, *Operational Amplifiers, Design and Applications*, McGraw-Hill, New York, 1971.

M. G. Rekoff, *Analog Computer Programming*, Charles E. Merrill, Columbus, OH, 1967.

Nonlinear Circuits Handbook, Analog Devices, Inc., Norwood, MA, 1976.

FOUR

Digital Design

Digital design can be divided into two general areas. The first is the creation and production of direct hardware from available building blocks. The second is the computer software or programming aspects, which may or may not involve the design of hardware items.

The second area employs techniques that are quite different from those of conventional hardware design and also require a substantial investment in special test equipment for efficient development and debugging. The quantity of information needed is worthy of a separate book and is not covered here.

Many aspects of computer technology, however, are very important in conventional hardware design. Among these are the programmable read-only memories referred to as PROMs and the read-write memories called RAMs (random-access memories). The word firmware is commonly used for these applications.

The design of digital circuits differs greatly from the design of analog circuits, being more like a systems design on a small scale. For the large part it consists of connecting standard building blocks without the use of modifying passive components. This is very evident in the construction of these circuits, which often take on an even pattern as if put together by a bricklayer. Many circuits do, of course, contain both analog and digital parts, and the construction of these systems is a combination of the two techniques.

4.1 FUNDAMENTALS

Digital design is based on the simple concept of yes or no, true or false, high or low, and so on. Electronically, the basic circuit is the NAND gate. A simple version is shown in Fig. 4.1.

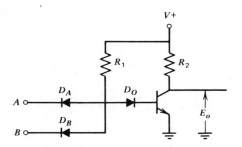

FIGURE 4.1 Simple NAND gate.

If both A and B are open or tied to a $(+)$ voltage, a current flows from R_1 through the base–emitter junction of the transistor, which is turned "hard-on" or put into the so-called saturation mode. E_o is then near ground potential, and its output is called a "0" or "low." If either A or B or both are grounded, the current through R_1 is diverted to that ground. This provides a voltage drop of one diode at the anode of D_o. However, a voltage equal to two diode drops, that of D_o and the transistor, is required to turn the transistor on. With the transistor off, E_o approaches the $V+$ level and is called a "1" or "high."

It will be noticed that an inversion is involved in this circuit. That is, if the inputs are low, the output is high, and vice versa. To make the circuit noninverting would require an extra stage. This is why digital circuitry is based on inverting logic. The word NAND is a contraction of the phrase "INVERTING AND."

With each logic element there is a "truth table" that explains how the unit works. These tables are generally in positive logic. This means that the function is described for input signals that are 1's. Negative logic is when the function is described in terms of input zeros. The use of negative logic is often confusing and is not used in this text. The truth table for the two-input NAND gate is shown in Table 4.1.

This table states that if both A and B are "1" (or Hi), the output is a "0" (or Lo). It is sometimes easier for the beginner to think in terms of an AND gate followed by an inverter. The logic of an AND gate states that if both A and B are Hi, the output is Hi. In hardware, an AND gate is really a NAND gate followed by an inverter.

If we look again at the truth table, it also says if A or B are 0 the output is a 1. In other words, the NAND circuit does a NAND function with respect to 1's at the input and a NOR function with respect to 0's at the input. If the two inputs are tied together, the NAND circuit becomes an inverter. Figure 4.2 shows three common symbols. The small circle at the output means inverting, so that if the circles

TABLE 4.1
Truth Tables

NAND			NOR			EX-NOR		
A	B	Out	A	B	Out	A	B	Out
0	0	1	0	0	1	0	0	1
0	1	1	0	1	0	0	1	0
1	0	1	1	0	0	1	0	0
1	1	0	1	1	0	1	1	1

are removed the three symbols become AND, OR, and EXCLUSIVE OR, respectively.

The truth tables for the NOR and EXCLUSIVE NOR are also shown in Table 4.1. The NOR truth tables states that if A or B are a 1, the output is a 0. The EXCLUSIVE NOR is the same thing except that the condition where both A and B are 1's produces a 1. Figure 4.3 shows how a NOR circuit can be build out of NAND circuits.

It is seen that if A or B is a 1, one or more of the inputs to the NAND gate are a 0. From the truth table of the NAND gate, we know that this produces a 1 at its output. Inverting the 1 produces a 0, and we have a NOR gate. This is a very poor way to make a NOR gate, and not the manner in which they are made. The purpose of the example was to demonstrate a simple use of the NAND gate and the process by which more complex building blocks can be evolved.

An important difference should be noted at this time between digital and analog components. There is very little need for the circuit designer to know how a digital function is accomplished. If the job is well done, important properties such as propagation delay, power consumption, number of leads, and the need for supporting modules will be favorable. If the performance specifications of the device are adequate, attempting to study the technique is generally a waste of time. The reason for this is that a digital device is exact. It is yes or no. This does not mean that it necessarily produces a correct result, but it does produce a defined one. The analog world is full of relative

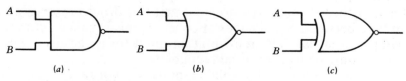

FIGURE 4.2 Same standard gates: (*a*) NAND; (*b*) NOR; (*c*) EXCLUSIVE NOR.

Digital design

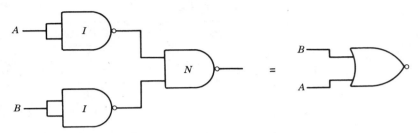

FIGURE 4.3   Construction of a NOR gate. I = inverter; N = NAND.

numbers, trade-offs, and approximations, all of which depend heavily
on the basic semiconductor properties. These properties are both var-
iant and different from unit to unit. The designer of the digital blocks
faces the same problems, but once the digital unit has been properly
designed and built, the circuit designer is largely relieved of these
considerations.

When digital circuits are operated near their maximum speeds they
approach a failure mode that is largely analog in nature and all the
troubles and uncertainties of the analog circuit accompany it.

High-frequency performance is specified in different ways. One
common expression is "maximum toggle frequency." This means
that the output is going between the logic Hi and Lo states at its fastest
possible rate but without the duty cycle or rise and fall times defined.
It does not mean that the device can operate properly at that speed.
Just how fast the device can operate depends on an analog type of
analysis of the system.

The speed limitations of a digital circuit show up in four different
forms: propagation delay, setup time, rise time, and fall time.

Propagation delay is basically the time between a signal edge's
entering a device and leaving the device. When a number of digital
devices are connected in series, their propagation delays add up.
When a similar set of digital devices are operating in parallel, the sum
of their propagation delays, because of the tolerances, is not necessarily the same. This problem is sometimes referred to as "skew."
It is, of course, essential in digital circuits that signal edges occur in
a known order.

It is a further absolute requirement that this order preserve a minimum time between signal edges of concern; this is called setup time.
Put simply, a signal must remain at an input for a certain minimum
amount of time or it will not be recognized.

The rise and fall times limit the response by not reaching the next
logic level in time to be recognized. The rise and fall times can be

somewhat controlled through good layout to reduce capacitance and inductance, by limiting the number of stages that are driven, and by occasional use of a pull-up resistor in the output circuits.

To summarize, the problems with digital circuits increase rapidly as the toggle frequencies are approached. Much difficulty is avoided if the operating frequencies are limited to one half of the minimum toggle value and if the setup times are increased by a factor of two or three over the manufacturer's stated minimum values.

4.2 FAMILY GROUPS

The major family groups of logic components in use today are T^2L, MOS, and ECL. There has also been much recent progress in GaAs, so this merits a separate section as well.

4.2.1 T^2L

The basic logic techniques had a changing format during the development of digital logic. These earlier forms are history at this time and play no significant part in today's circuits. As this book is being written, the most popular form for small- and medium-scale integration is the T^2L. This is a bipolar system and means transistor–transistor logic.

Although this form of logic has been greatly improved in the past few years, various forms of CMOS (complementary MOS) logic are catching up and may well be the dominant process in the next few years.

The T^2L technique underwent a major breakthrough when it added Schottky diodes to keep the transistor out of saturation (see Section 4.5). This has led to the S (for Schottky) and LS (for low-power Schottky) series to be added to the standard and L (for low-power) series.

There have been quite a few separate numbering systems for logic elements in the past and there remain differences at this date. However, the Texas Instruments (TI) designations of SN54/74 have become the predominant numbering system and are often referred to, generally without the manufacturer's name.

4.2.2 MOS

A metal oxide semiconductor (MOS) is an FET with a capacitive input, as contrasted with a JFET which has a diode input (see Section 1.3). Logic families have been constructed from PMOS, NMOS, CMOS, HCMOS, and ACMOS.

The original CMOS products operated from $+5$ to $+15$ V; the performance ranged from poor at the former to reasonable at the latter. The MOS logic basically trips at the midpoint of ground and the supply voltage. Thus, they feature a high noise immunity, particularly at $+10$ or $+15$ V, and are very useful in noisy environments. However, some of the MOS products have T^2L-compatible inputs and the noise immunity is thus reduced.

The small- and medium-scale logic families are built almost exclusively of CMOS. As the name suggests, there is an N channel and P channel output FET and the drive capability is symmetrical. This is different than the T^2L logic where the sink output greatly exceeds the source output.

There are three other major differences between CMOS and T^2L. First, CMOS has much lower standby power drain but has a dynamic current drain that is directly proportional to the frequency. At some specific high frequency, the CMOS device generally reaches and then exceeds the power consumption of its T^2L counterpart. The second difference is that the CMOS device has a very high input resistance which virtually eliminates fan-out problems and opens the door to many new applications. Third, and to its disadvantage, CMOS parts are more susceptible to static damage and hence must be handled more carefully.

Unlike the T^2L circuits that can operate with an input open, although not recommended, it is *imperative* that all unused MOS inputs be terminated. The unterminated input wanders about from high to low, often stopping in the middle where it draws a very large current. As an example, a digital system of 35 assorted HCMOS ICs drew 2.2 mA when the clocking was disabled. When 13 buffers gates were added without input terminations the current consumption rose to 90 mA. In addition, these circuits often oscillate and are very sensitive to pickup.

Figure 4.4 shows how the supply current changes as the input voltage is moved through the transition zone. This would predict less current than the example stated above, but it should be remembered that all ICs are not the same and that Fig. 4.4 is stated as typical of RCA's QMOS devices.

In addition to the static change of supply current with input voltage, there is also a dynamic current based on the charging and discharging of the internal capacitance of the CMOS chip. The switching time of the HCMOS family is intended to be no slower than about 60 ns. Figure 4.5 shows that as the transition time increases above that point, the effective input capacitance also increases. This is a mathematical way of defining the extra power lost because too much time is spent in the transition area. Equation 4.1 defines the power dissipation of a CMOS gate.

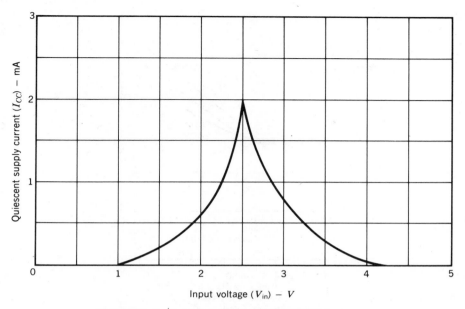

FIGURE 4.4 I_{CC} versus V_{in} for QMOS HC types.

$$P_{\text{total}} = (C_L + C_{PD})V_{CC}^2 f + I_{CC}V_{CC} \qquad (4.1)$$

C_L is the load capacitance and C_{PD} is the effective input capacitance as shown in Fig. 4.5a, whereas I_{CC} is the quiescent leakage current of the device. The frequency term in the equation really relates to the number of transitions per second. When the input transitions are not cyclic, an average rate per second must be determined.

It is evident that the power-saving feature of the CMOS family is diminished as the input frequency increases. Figure 4.5b shows a comparison between a gate of the T²L LS series and that of some comparable CMOS devices. The power consumption is about the same above 10 MHz.

The HCMOS family is a high-speed version of the earlier CMOS device and has been followed by an improved version, sometimes called ACMOS (advanced CMOS). The HCMOS is about equal in speed to the T²L LS series, whereas the ACMOS is about twice as fast and has four times the drive capability. The operating range of these newer CMOS devices is 2–6 V, being optimized for 5 V.

The output of a CMOS logic element closely approaches ground to V+ and when used with a +5 V supply, is more than adequate to drive a T²L device. The output of the T²L device, however, has a more limited swing and cannot safely drive a 5 V MOS logic element.

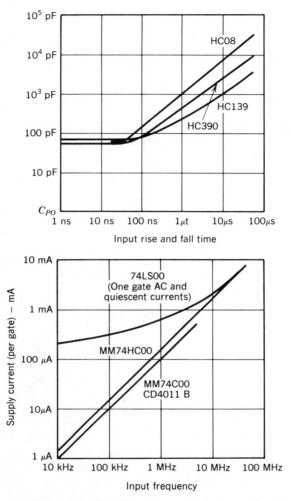

FIGURE 4.5 (*a*) Comparison of typical C_{PD} for MM54HC/MM74HC08, MM54HC/MM74HC139 MM54HC/MM74HC390 as a function of input rise and fall time. $t_{\text{rise}} = t_{\text{fall}}$, $V_{CC} = 5$ V, $T_A = 25°$C. (*b*) Supply current versus input frequency for equivalent NAND gates.

The open-collector T^{2}L can be used to drive a 5 V MOS receiver, as its high state is very close to $+5$ V. A pull-up resistor on a totem-pole output stage is often another way to drive the MOS element. Normal values of pull-up resistors produce slower rise times than totem-pole outputs, so care should be taken in this regard.

The SN74HC (MMHC for NSC) series has a subseries labeled HCT. These are the same as the HC series with T^{2}L-compatible inputs and should be used only for necessary interfacing conditions. Al-

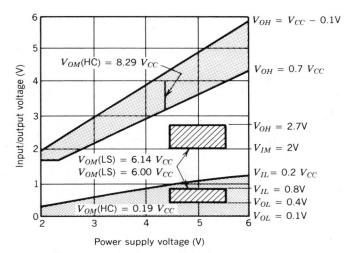

FIGURE 4.6 Worst-case input and output voltages over operating supply range for HC and LS logic.

though this is better than using pull-up resistors for the T^2L outputs, there is a loss of noise immunity with this class of devices.

Figure 4.6 shows a comparison of the worst-case operating range and noise guardband of the HCMOS family versus the LST^2L devices. The shaded areas indicate the noise margin, that is, the difference between the input and output logic levels.

For example, at $+5$ V, in the low state the LST^2L has a guardband of 0.4 V, while the HCMOS guardband is 0.9 V. In the high level state, the LST^2L guardband is 0.7 V and that of the MOS 1.4 V.

A great number of these devices are designated as the TI (Texas Instruments) SN series and are functional and pin replacements for the order T^2L devices.

This logic family has so many good properties that no new design should be undertaken without checking its suitability.

4.2.3 ECL

The last of the logic families to be discussed is called emitter-coupled logic, or ECL for short. This differs from the other forms of logic in that the transistors are operated in a linear mode and not allowed to go into saturation. ECL is therefore a very fast logic form. It also consumes the most power. ECL devices operate from a -5.2 V power supply; a logic low is -1.8 V and a logic high is -0.9 V. The output stages are open-ended emitter followers, which are externally terminated with a 51 resistor to a -2 V supply. This clutters up the circuit a bit, and the -2 V supply because of its low voltage must have a low efficiency. The basic ECL gate is the OR/NOR as contrasted to the NAND gate for T^2L. Figure 4.7 shows how this gate is constructed.

Q_2 and Q_3 constitute a differential amplifier with Q_6 operating as a current source. There are two internal power supplies, V_{CS} and V_{BB}, built into the chip that set up the correct bias condition. The inputs have resistors that go to the V_{EE} supply so that an unused input is a low. Because of the constant current source there is no variation in the supply current as the input signals are changed. This is a major advantage and is in direct contrast to T^2L, which produces large current spikes, often to the detriment of the entire system.

Since this is a symmetrical circuit, it is easy to furnish both the function and its complement. It is seen that if input A or input B is made a high, the collector of Q_2 goes low and that of Q_3 goes high. Hence the NOR/OR function. Q_5 and Q_4 buffer these signals so that a 50 Ω line can be driven.

Several manufacturers make ECL lines. Fairchild has the 10K, 95K, and 100 K series. The 10K and 95K families exhibit about a 2 ns propagation delay, the 95K having additional temperature compensation. The 100K is the fastest line with about a 1 ns delay.

The T^2L and some of the MOS circuits are at least reasonably compatible with each other. ECL circuits are not compatible with other forms of logic and must use special interface chips.

ECL has maintained its position as a logic element because of its high speed. However, part selection is limited and generally expensive and, because terminating resistors must be used, circuit-board

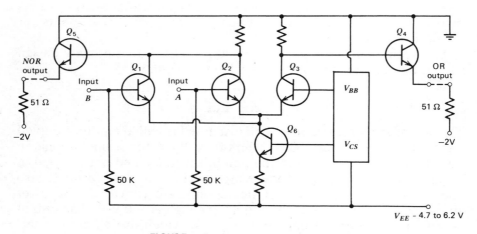

FIGURE 4.7. ECL NOR/OR gate.

layout is awkward. This logic family should be avoided unless there is no other choice.

With the rapid development of the GaAs logic line, it would appear that the ECL's future is very limited.

4.2.4 Gallium Arsenide

Gallium arsenide and its related compounds have some very superior characteristics, specifically, low power, very high frequency, wide temperature operation, and both cryogenic and elevated ranges. The availability of this material has been delayed because of fabrication difficulties, but it is well on its way to establishing a stronghold in both the logic and analog fields.

4.3 A FEW BASIC CIRCUITS

This section describes some of the more common simple-gate connections. Generally, the simple gates are used for simple tasks. When there are too many discrete gates in a system, a review is usually in order to see if another way could be used to simplify the circuit.

A better choice of MSI blocks and possible use of what is called PLA for programmed logic arrays may be helpful. The problem with PLAs is that a special mask must be made at a very substantial cost; this becomes practical only for large-volume production.

There are also electrically programmable and erasable gate arrays available. These are still quite primitive but may hold promise for the future.

The circuits included in this section are only a few of many possibilities. They serve as exercises in thinking as well as a reference section.

4.3.1 The Latch (Memory and Debouncer)

Figure 4.8a shows a NAND latch and Fig. 4.8b shows the NOR version. For the circuit of Fig. 4.8 to act as a latch, a signal can be applied only to one input at a time. If a low is applied to A of Fig. 4.8a, its output goes high and the other output goes low.

The signal input to A can now return to a high, and the circuit remains unchanged. A low to the input of B flips the circuit back to its original condition. If simultaneous lows are put on the input, both outputs go high. This, however, is not a latched condition. As soon as one of the input lows goes high, the circuit performs its normal function. These devices are sometimes called S–R latches, which means set–reset with an active low input.

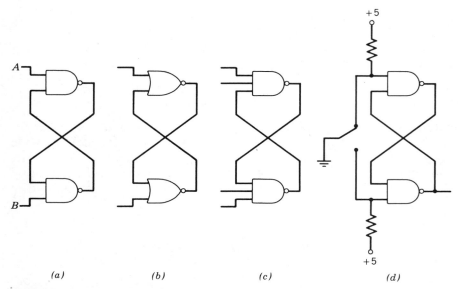

FIGURE 4.8 (a)–(c) The LATCH (memory and debouncer); (d) = debouncer.

Multiple versions of this latch are available. For example, the SN74279 is a quad version in a 16-pin DIP (dual in-line package). The NOR version acts in the same manner but responds to high inputs.

Figure 4.8c shows a latch with a third input. If the third inputs are high, the operation is the same as in Fig. 4.8a. If one of the third leads are low, the signal lead to that gate no longer controls the latch function and the circuit has an added control.

Although the latch is generally used as a memory element, another application is for a switch debouncer, as shown in Fig. 4.8d. The output is set on the first change from a high to a low on the input and is accordingly "debounced."

A drawback is that the "debounced" output voltage must be compatible with the switching function. As an option, CMOS can be used for up to $+15$ V and open-collector devices are available for up to $+30$ V.

Another technique involves the MC14490, a device manufactured by Motorola, which contains six debouncers in one chip.

Hall effect mechanical switches directly produce bounceless transitions and are fine if electronic circuits are not convenient.

4.3.2 An Electronic Toggle Switch

Another useful connection is what might be called an electronic toggle switch; however, it is usually called a multiplexer or a data selector.

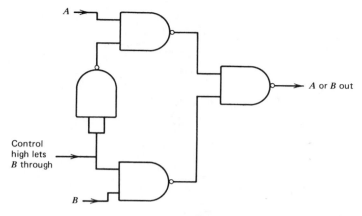

FIGURE 4.9 Data selector.

Figure 4.9 shows how this function can be performed by a single two-input quad NAND gate.

If the control line is high, the B NAND gate passes the inverted B, or $\bar{B}$ as it is called. The high on the control line is inverted and becomes a low on one of the A NAND gate inputs. This forces the output of the A NAND gate to be high regardless of the state of A. This high is applied to one of the inputs of the output gate, and $\bar{B}$, which is on the other input, passes through as B. If the control line is low, A passes through in the same manner. Many multiple selectors are available, such as the SN74150, which has 16 data inputs with four binary-coded control lines packaged in a 24-pin DIP. The SN74151A has eight input lines controlled by three binary-coded lines in a 16-pin DIP.

4.3.3 A Word Recognizer

It is often necessary to recognize a set of parallel binary lines with a given value. For example, suppose that it is desired to recognize the word 100111101. The three lows are connected to INVERTERS so that the word becomes all highs. A multiple input NAND gate produces a low on its output when this occurs. This is illustrated in Fig. 4.10a. An unused input can serve as a disable control. For example, in a NAND gate, a low on any input produces a high on the output, and the word recognizer is disabled. If there are more lines than inputs, the system shown in Fig. 4.10b can be used. A NOR circuit can also be used as a word recognizer; in this case, the INVERTERS are used to produce all lows, which is recognized by the NOR gate with a high on its output. The choice of a NAND or a NOR gate is usually

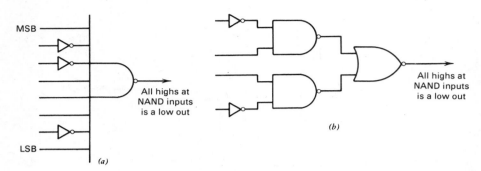

MSB

All highs at
NAND inputs
is a low out

LSB

(a)

All highs at
NAND inputs
is a low out

(b)

FIGURE 4.10   Word recognizer.

made to minimize the number of inverters. All excess inputs must be tied to a high in the NAND circuit and grounded in the NOR versions.

If the word to be recognized is in a serial form, a serial in–parallel out shift register is used to make the serial-to-parallel conversion. The process then is the same as that described previously.

4.3.4 Pulse Generator and Delay Circuits

Pulse generators and delay circuits are combined because they are often used together and share some techniques of operation. Figure 4.11 shows a delay circuit, a variation of which is commonly called a "glitch" remover.

Some justification of this circuit is warranted at this time because it uses a technique properly scorned in bipolar logic circuits.

Bipolar logic has an input current which in most situations *cannot* be ignored. When driven by a similar gate in the low state, it has only a 0.4 V guardband against interferences (see Fig. 4.4). The driving gate is of low impedance to minimize noise pickup. When a resistor is placed in the input line this threshold is reduced by the *IR* drop and the line impedance is raised. The normally low noise immunity becomes worse.

MOS logic, on the other hand, has an input current which in most cases *can* be ignored, and it has a similar threshold of 0.9 V.

A resistor in the input logic line still poses a hazard and should be used with care, as the input impedance has been raised and it is therefore more susceptible to pickup. As indicated in Fig. 4.11a, the lead to the input pin should be as short as possible and the ground lead of the capacitor, also short, should be attached as closely to chip ground pin as possible. (See Chapter 10 for techniques of adding passive parts to digital circuits.) In addition, the impedance of the filter should be kept as low as possible. That is a low *R* and a high *C*.

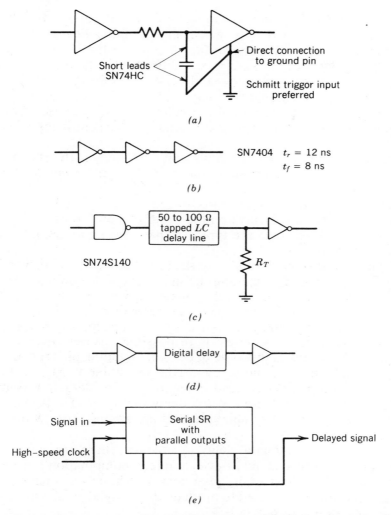

FIGURE 4.11 Pulse delay circuits: (*a*) pulse delay and "glitch-remover"; (*b*) use of propagation delay; (*c*) tapped passive delay line; (*d*) digital delays in dual in-line packages (DIP); (*e*) shift register delay circuit.

If only small delays are needed (<200 ns), most any available gate will usually do; if longer delays are required, a device with a Schmitt trigger input to avoid oscillation is necessary. Much depends upon the layout and placement of parts. In any case, the circuit should always be checked for stability margin by increasing the capacitor by 2–5 times to test for any possible oscillation. Interference tests, such as a drill motor in close proximity, are always good checks for any circuit.

This circuit with a small time constant is, of course, the familiar glitch eliminator, used only when all else fails. Perhaps some re-spectability has finally come to the skeleton in the closet.

If the above precautions are sensibly observed, MOS Logic ele-ments give the designer a new and very useful design tool.

Figure 4.11a is suitable for long or short delays of reasonable sta-bility. There is a shortening of the delayed pulse because of the dif-ference between the charge and discharge characteristics of an *RC* circuit.

Figure 4.11b is for short delays only. As shown, the rise and fall delays are not equal but tend to balance out as the number of stages is increased.

Figure 4.11c requires a high-powered line driver but is useful in some circumstances. Delays on the order of 5 to 300 ns with 10 taps in a 14-pin DIP package are typical. There are many manufacturers to choose from.

Figure 4.11d is very similar to 4.11c except that the driver is in-cluded in this package, making the delay line T^2L-compatible.

Figure 4.11e employs a shift register driven by what is called a "high-speed clock." In many digital systems there is a primary crystal oscillator, say, 16 MHz. If the pulse is derived from a divider, perhaps 1 MHz, then there is a series of 16 possible discrete delays. There are many variations of this type of device, including pin taps, digitally programmable delays, and screw-driver adjustable versions. As with Fig. 4.11c, these devices also consume a considerable amount of power, as contrasted with the *RC* delay of Fig. 4.11a. Again, there are many suppliers. Data delay devices are among those with a good selection.

In addition to the digital delay techniques, there are many others involving clocking systems. For example, a combination of shift reg-ister and counters can easily give delays of hours or longer. ROMs and RAMs can also be used to produce the delayed pulse after certain processing steps are taken.

Figure 4.12 contains some pulse generator circuits, variously called monostables or "one shots."

Figure 4.12a shows an output NAND gate having two paths to the inputs. With a rising signal input, the NAND gate has two Hi's, so the output drops low. At a time of about 0.8 *RC*, the delayed and inverted input reaches the second input and the output goes high. There is no action on the falling edge of the input.

Figure 4.12b uses a NOR gate in the output with an inverse action as displayed.

Figure 4.12c has an EX-OR as the output and the unique feature of producing a pulse on both the leading and trailing edges of an input pulse. (See EX-NOR truth table, Table 4.1.)

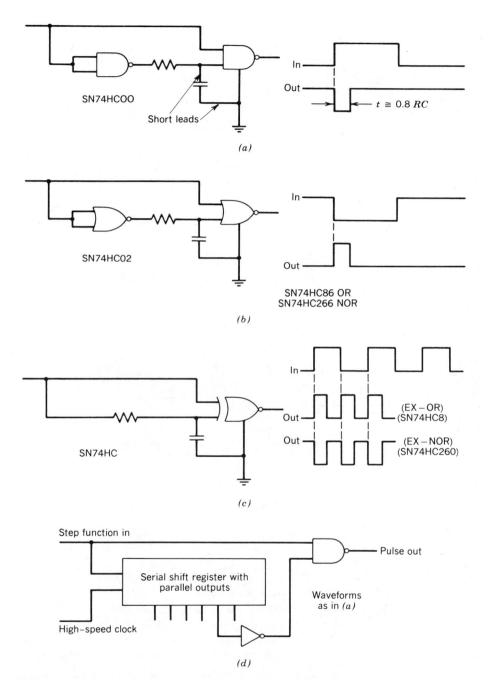

FIGURE 4.12 Pulse generator circuits (*a, b, c,* and *f* for CMOS circuits only): (*d*) shift register pulse generator; (*e*) nested pair E_oA within E_oB; (*f*) pulse stretcher. (*Figure continues on p. 106.*)

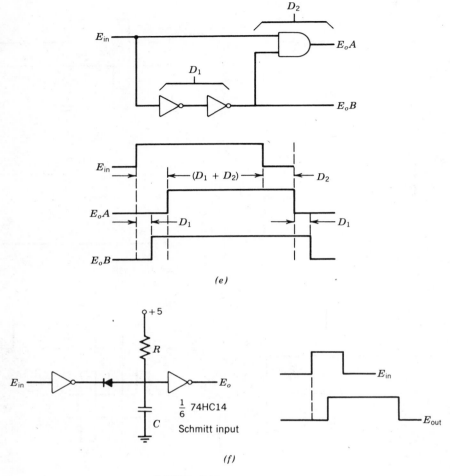

FIGURE 4.12   (*Continued*)

Figure 4.12*d* uses a shift register to produce a pulse much in the same manner as the delay circuit of Fig. 4.11*e*.

Figure 4.12*e* produces a nested pair, that is, one pulse wholly contained within the other. This arrangement is necessary in certain specific clocking and timing arrangements. If CMOS is used, *RC* delay circuits can be put in various spots to increase the delays when required.

Figure 4.12*f* is a circuit that is often very useful. It generates an output of increased width over the input, a pulse stretcher. The gates should be CMOS and the output stage should have a Schmitt trigger input, in particular for longer pulses where oscillations would otherwise occur with a low dV/dt.

The circuit shown in Fig. 4.13 is a passive circuit and produces a "sync" spike for each edge of an incoming pulse train. This is sometimes handy for solving awkward synchronizing problems between laboratory pulse generators. No component values have been specified because of the wide range of applications. (If a box of old pulse transformers is handy, it is not difficult to adapt to most situations.) This circuit mounted between two BNC connectors on a piece of copper-clad board becomes a useful laboratory tool.

Figure 4.14 shows two pulse generators connected together to produce a delayed pulse generator. This circuit contains the same number of parts as the standard monostables, for example, μA9602 and

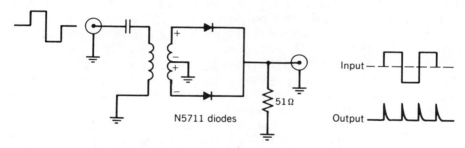

FIGURE 4.13 Sync. doubling circuit.

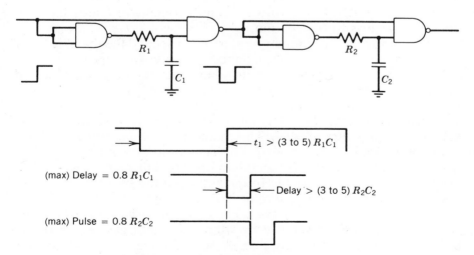

FIGURE 4.14 Delayed pulse generator.

SN74221. They have a higher noise immunity because they are not edge-triggered. This virtually eliminates the common problem of having long duration pulses fired by "glitches" that cannot be found on slow-sweeping oscilloscopes. Furthermore, the timing range is greater, both on short and long durations. There are, however, penalties in flexibility. Complementary triggers and outputs are not available and will require extra inverters if this is a requirement. Also, as shown in Fig. 4.14, there is a setup time necessary that requires that the delay be greater than the output pulsewidth. If these conditions are not met, the output form gradually "shrinks" to the input form. There is no output failure.

4.3.5 Clock Circuits

Most digital systems utilize a clock. This makes the clock generator (square wave oscillator) a very useful circuit. Figure 4.15 shows a collection of circuits for this purpose.

The most direct oscillator is simply a ring connection of an odd number of INVERTERS, as shown in Fig. 4.15a. This is a very inaccurate oscillator because the propagation delay is a function of both operating voltage and temperature. To control the frequency, RC networks are added, as shown in Figs. 4.15b and 4.15c. This also improves the accuracy as the frequency becomes more dependent on the passive components. Figures 4.15b and 4.15c also show that if the input is a gate with two leads, one of the leads can be used to turn the oscillator on and off

Figure 4.15b is an especially useful circuit. It is very simple, taking advantage of the high input impedance of the MOS circuit. A 744HC132, a NAND gate with a Schmitt trigger, provides the necessary hysteresis for oscillation.

If a departure from symmetry is desired, a second feedback resistor can be added in series with a Schottky diode (for speed and low voltage drop). This produces an imbalance between the charging and discharging time constants. The polarity of the imbalance is set by the direction of the diode.

A test circuit with $R = 10$ K and $C = 390$ pF was oscillated at 285 kHz with a symmetry of 44/56. The change in frequency over a voltage range of 4.5–5.5 V was about 3.5%. Temperature variation over the operating range was not detectable on a scope displaying five or six cycles. The maximum usable frequency is on the order of 20 MHz.

A unique feature of this circuit is that it runs very well without a power supply. This is because there is a protective diode between each input and the power line by which the input gating power can be transmitted to the supply line. A 50 Ω source not only operates the oscillator but can drive a good-sized load as well.

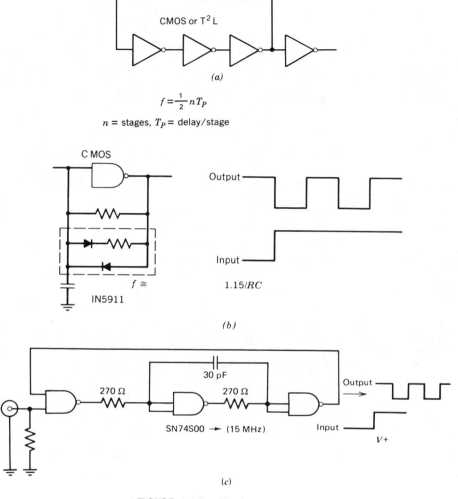

$$f = \frac{1}{2} n T_P$$

n = stages, T_P = delay/stage

$f \cong$ 1.15/RC

FIGURE 4.15   Clock generators.

Figure 4.8a certainly has nothing to offer over the previous circuit but it is included because it is a bipolar T²L and can possibly be formed from spare chips in a bipolar circuit.

A test circuit at 2.5 MHz produced a frequency variation of 17% over a voltage range of 4.8–5.2 V.

Crystal oscillators are a very important class of clock generators and are often designed without due regard to the possible complications. For this reason, an excellent article by *National Semiconductor*, AN-340, is reproduced in the following section [1].

4.3.6 HCMOS Crystal Oscillators

With the high speed HCMOS circuits, it is possible to build systems with clock rates of greater than 30 MHz. The familiar gate oscillator circuits used at low frequencies work well at higher frequencies and either *LC* or crystal resonators may be used, depending on the stability required. Above 20 MHz, it becomes expensive to fabricate fundamental mode crystals, so overtone modes are used.

BASIC OSCILLATOR THEORY

The equivalent circuit of a quartz crystal and its reactance characteristics with frequency are shown in Fig. 4.16. F_R is called the resonant frequency and is where L_1 and C_1 are in series resonance and the crystal looks like a small resistor $R1$. The frequency F_A is the antiresonant frequency and is the point where L_1-C_1 look inductive and resonate with C_0 to form the parallel resonant frequency F_A. F_R and F_A are usually less than 0.1% apart. In specifying crystals, the frequency F_R is the oscillation frequency to the crystal in a series mode circuit, and F_R is the parallel resonant frequency. In a parallel mode circuit, the oscillation frequency will be slightly below F_A where the inductive component of the L_1-C_1 arm resonates with C_0 and the external circuit capacitance. The exact frequency is often corrected by the crystal manufacture to a specified load capacitance, usually 20 or 32 pF.

The Pierce oscillator is one of the more popular circuits, and is the foundation for almost all single gate oscillators in use today. In this circuit (Fig. 4.17), the signal from the input to the output of the amplifier is phase shifted 180°. The crystal appears as a large inductor since it is operating in the parallel mode, and in conjunction with C_A

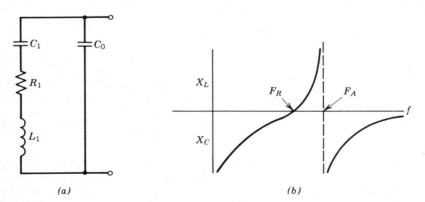

(a)   (b)

FIGURE 4.16 (*a*) Crystal equivalent circuit and (*b*) reactance of crystal resonator.

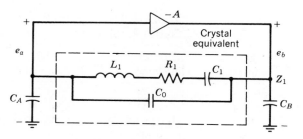

FIGURE 4.17 Pierce oscillator.

and C_B, forms a pi network that provides an additional 180° of phase shift from output to the input. C_A in series with C_B plus any additional stray capacitance form the load capacitance for the crystal. In this circuit, C_A is usually made about the same value as C_B, and the total value of both capacitors in series is the load capacitance of the crystal which is generally chosen to be 32 pF, making the value of each capacitor 64 pF. The approximation equations of the load impedance Z_1 presented to the output of the crystal oscillator's amplifier by the crystal network is

$$Z_L = \frac{X_C^2}{R_L}$$

Where $X_C = -j/\omega C_B$ and R_L is the series resistance of the crystal as shown in Table 4.2. Also $\omega = 2\pi f$ where f is the frequency of oscillation.

The ratio of the crystal network's input voltage to its output voltage is given by

$$\frac{\theta_A}{\theta_B} = \frac{\omega C_B}{\omega C_A} = \frac{C_B}{C_A}$$

C_A and C_B are chosen such that their series combination capacitance equals the load capacitance specified by the manufacturer, that is, 20 pF or 32 pF as mentioned. In order to oscillate the phase shift at the desired frequency around the oscillator loop must be 360° and the gain of the oscillator loop must be greater or equal to one, or

$$(A_A)(A_F) \geq 1$$

Where A_A is amplifier gain and A_F is crystal network voltage gain of the crystal π network: θ_A/θ_B. Thus not only should the series com-

TABLE 4.2
Typical Crystal Parameters

Parameter	32 kHz Fundamental	200 kHz Fundamental	2 MHz Fundamental	30 MHz Overtone
R_1	200 kΩ	2 kΩ	100 Ω	20 Ω
L_1	7000 H	27 H	529 mH	11 mH
C_1	0.003 pF	0.024 pF	0.012 pF	0.0026 pF
C_0	1.7 pF	9 pF	4 pF	6 pF
Q	100 K	10 K	54 K	100 K

bination of C_B and C_A be chosen. The ratio of the two can be set to adjust the loop gain of the oscillator.

For example if a 2 MHz oscillator is required, then $R_L = 100\ \Omega$ (Table 4.2). If $0_A/0_B = 1$ and the crystal requires a 32 pF load so $C_B = 64$ pF and then C_A becomes 64 pF also. The load presented by the crystal network is $Z = (\frac{1}{2}\pi(2\ \text{MHz})\ (64\ \text{pF})^2)/100 = 16$ kΩ.

THE CMOS GATE OSCILLATOR

A CMOS gate sufficiently approaches the ideal amplifier shown above that it can be used in almost the same circuit. A review of manufacturers data sheets will reveal there are two types of inverting CMOS gates:

1. **Unbuffered:** gates composed of a single inverting stage. Voltage gain in the hundreds.
2. **Buffered:** gates composed of three inverting stages in series. Voltage gains are greater than ten thousand.

CMOS gates must be designed to drive relatively large loads and must supply a fairly large amount of current. In a single gate structure that is biased in its linear region so both devices are on, supply current will be high. Buffered gates are designed with the first and second gates to be much smaller than the output gate and will dissipate little power. Since the gain is so high, even a small signal will drive the output high or low and little power is dissipated. In this manner, unbuffered gates will dissipate more power than buffered gates.

Both buffered and unbuffered gates may be used as crystal oscillators, with only slight design changes in the circuits.

In the circuit in Fig. 4.18, R_F serves to bias the gate in its linear region, ensuring oscillation, while R_2 provides an impedance to add some additional phase shift in conjunction with C_B. It also serves to prevent spurious high frequency oscillations and isolates the output

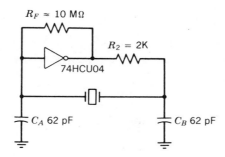

FIGURE 4.18   Typical gate oscillator.

of the gate from the crystal network so a clean square wave can be obtained from the output of the gate. Its value is chosen to be roughly equal to the capacitive reactance of C_B at the frequency of oscillation, or the value of load impedance Z_L calculated above. In this case, there will be a two to one loss in voltage from the output of the gate to the input of the crystal network due to the voltage divider effect of R_2 and Z_L. If C_A and C_B are chosen equal, the voltage at the input to the gate will be the same as that at the input to the crystal network or one half of the voltage at the output of the gate. In this case, the gate must have a voltage gain of two or greater to oscillate. Except at very high frequencies, all CMOS gates have voltage gains well in excess of 10 and satisfactory operation should result.

Theory and experiment show that unbuffered gates are more stable as oscillators by as much as five to one. However, unbuffered gates draw more operating power if used in the same circuit as a buffered gate. Power consumption can be minimized by increasing feedback which forces the gate to operate for less time in its linear region.

When designing with buffered gates, the value of R_2 or C_B may be increased by a factor of 10 or more. This will increase the voltage loss around the feedback loop which is desirable since the gain of the gate is considerably higher than that of an unbuffered gate.

C_A and C_B form the load capacitance for the crystal. Many crystals are cut for either 20 to 32 pF load capacitance. This is the capacitance that will cause the crystal to oscillate at its nominal frequency. Varying this capacitance will vary the frequency of oscillation. Generally, designers work with crystal manufacturers to select the best value of load capacitance for their application, unless an off the shelf crystal is selected.

HIGH-FREQUENCY EFFECTS

The phase shift through the gate may be estimated by considering its delay time:

$$\text{phase shift} = \text{frequency} \times \text{time delay} \times 360°$$

The "typical gate oscillator" works well at lower frequencies where phase shift through the gate is not excessive. However, about 4 MHz, where 10 ns of time delay represents 14.4° of excess phase shift, R_2 should be changed to a small capacitor to avoid the additional phase shift of R_2. The value of this capacitor is approximately $1/\omega C$ where $\omega = 2\pi f$, but not less than about 20 pF (Fig. 4.19).

IMPROVING OSCILLATOR STABILITY

The CMOS gate makes a mediocre oscillator when compared to a transistor or FET. (Note: A logic level crystal oscillator is driven too hard for maximum stability and should not be used in high-precision applications.) It draws more power and is generally less stable. However, extra gates are often available and are often pressed into service as oscillators. If improved stability is required, especially from buffered gate oscillators, an approach shown in Fig. 4.20 can be used.

In this circuit, C_A and C_B are made large to swamp out the effects

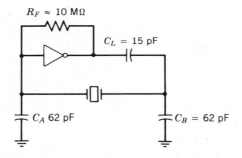

FIGURE 4.19   Gate oscillator for higher frequencies.

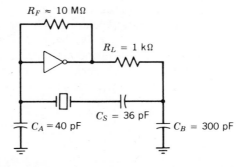

FIGURE 4.20   Gate oscillator with improved stability.

of temperature and supply voltage change on the gate input and output impedances. A small capacitor in series with the crystal acts as the crystal load and further isolates the crystal from the rest of the circuit.

Overtone Crystal Oscillators

At frequencies above 20 MHz, it becomes increasingly difficult to cut or work with crystal blanks and so generally a crystal is used in its overtone mode. Also, fundamental mode crystals above this frequency have less stability and greater aging rates. All crystals will exhibit the same reactance vs. frequency characteristics at odd overtone frequencies that they do at the fundamental frequency. However, the overtone resonances are not exact multiples of the fundamental, so an overtone crystal must be specified as such.

In the design of an overtone crystal oscillator, it is very important to suppress the fundamental mode, or the circuit will try to oscillate there, or worse, at both the fundamental and the overtone with little predictability as to which. Basically, this requires that the crystal feedback network has more gain at the overtone frequency than the fundamental. This is usually done with a frequency selective network such as a tuned circuit.

The circuit in Fig. 4.21 operates in the parallel mode just as the Pierce oscillator above. The resonant circuit L_A–C_B is an effective short at the fundamental frequency, and is tuned somewhat below the deferred crystal overtone frequency. Also, C_L is chosen to suppress operation in the fundamental mode.

The coil L_A may be tuned to produce maximum output and will affect the oscillation frequency slightly. The crystal should be specified so that proper frequency is obtained at maximum output level from the gate.

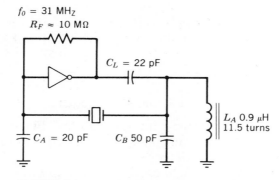

FIGURE 4.21   Parallel mode overtone circuit.

Some Practical Design Tips

In the above circuits, some generalizations can be made regarding the selection of component values.

R_F: Sets the bias point, should be as large as practical.

$R1$: Isolates the crystal network from the gate output and provides excess phaseshift decreasing the probability of spurious oscillation at high frequencies. Value should be approximately equal to input impedance of the crystal network or reactance of C_B at the oscillator frequency. Increasing value will decrease the amount of feedback and improve stability.

C_B: Part of load for crystal network. Often chosen to be twice the value of the crystal load capacitance. Increasing value will increase feedback.

C_A: Part of crystal load network. Often chosen to be twice the value of the crystal load capacitance. Increasing value will increase feedback.

C_L: Used in place of $R1$ in high-frequency applications. Reactance should be approximately equal to crystal network input impedance.

Oscillator design is an imperfect art at best. Combinations of theoretical and experimental design techniques should be used.

1. Do not design for an excessive amount of gain around the feedback loop. Excessive gain will lead to instability and may result in the oscillator not being crystal controlled.

2. Be sure to worst case the design. A resistor may be added in series with the crystal to simulate worst-case crystals. The circuit should not oscillate on any frequency with the crystal out of the circuit.

3. A quick check of oscillator performance is to measure the frequency stability with supply voltage variations. For HCMOS gates, a change of supply voltage from 2.5 to 6 V should result in less than 10 ppm change in frequency. Circuit value changes should be evaluated for improvements in stability.

4.3.7 EX-OR Applications

As a final example of simple-gate applications, Fig. 4.22 shows the EX-OR as (a) a logically controlled inverter, (b) a digital phase detector, and (c) an identity detector.

The truth table in Fig. 4.22a can be derived directly from the truth table for the EX-NOR in Table 4.1.

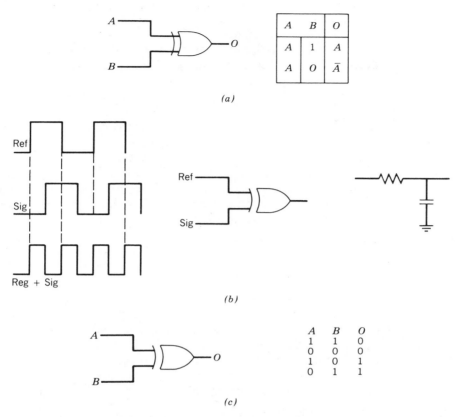

A	B	O
A	1	A
A	0	Ā

(a)

(b)

A	B	O
1	1	0
0	0	0
1	0	1
0	1	1

(c)

FIGURE 4.22   EX-OR applications: (*a*) logic-controlled inverter; (*b*) phase detector; (*c*) identity detector.

In a like manner, the output of the phase detector in Fig. 4.22*b* is also established by the EX-NOR truth table. It is seen that this detector develops a 100% duty cycle for 180° phase displacement and zero output for the in-phase condition. The *RC* time constant is shown as an option if an analog signal output is desired.

4.3.8 Combinational and Sequential Logic Considerations

In the early days of digital hardware, there were only simple gates and flip-flops. When even moderately complex control systems were developed, the organization of the logic became cumbersome and difficult. Under these conditions, Boolean Algebra, assisted by Karnaugh maps and Veitch diagrams, was very helpful in restoring order. Today's great abundance of special-purpose components and extensive use of synchronized logic has greatly reduced the problems associated with combinational logic.

In the past, asynchronous logic was more common and often led to some very difficult sequential timing problems. As the speed of the semiconductors increased and more complex parts became available, synchronous logic became more popular, eliminating many of the earlier problems.

Sequential logic, will, of course, always be a problem, as the operational speed approaches that of the operating devices. In addition, many of the more complex circuits have very specific setup, settling, and duration times, so that timing considerations will always be with us. There are no hard and fast rules of procedure except perhaps to be very careful. Many times, computer studies are necessary to consider all of the complex requirements and the effect of their tolerances.

4.4 BASIC BUILDING BLOCKS

In the previous section, the basic gates and a few of their simple connections were covered in some detail, and these applications are here to stay. However, the demands on today's digital logic hardware systems far outstrip the capabilities of these basic gates. This section describes small subsystems available as discrete packages. Although these functions are constructed from the basic gates, the hardware designer is spared this task.

The list of these building blocks is long, and there are many variations of each kind. Only a limited description can be given, with some applications shown here and others in Chapter 9.

It is up to the designer to "learn his trade" by constant review and application of these devices as they are listed and described in the manufacturer's data manuals.

4.4.1 Flip-Flops

In the early days of digital electronics, flip-flops were the basic building block. They were used in great quantities to make counters, memories, and much miscellaneous logic. The design of synchronous counters from flip-flops can be tricky, but now counters of all kinds are available and the average circuit designer seldom needs to design them. The two kinds of flip-flops used the most are the $J–K$ and the D.

The $J–K$ flip-flop (f/f) has two control lines, J and K, which allow four logical operations. The block diagram and the truth table are shown in Fig. 4.23. $J–K$ flip-flops are actuated by a clock edge to do

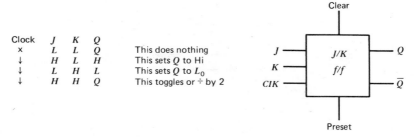

Clock	J	K	Q	
x	L	L	Q	This does nothing
↓	H	L	H	This sets Q to Hi
↓	L	H	L	This sets Q to L_0
↓	H	H	Q	This toggles or ÷ by 2

FIGURE 4.23 Truth table of a J–K flip-flop (f/f).

the function defined by the J and K inputs. The figure shows a negative edge transition such as that used on the SN7473. Others, for example, the SN74109, operate on the positive edge. This device has two principal applications. The first is as part of some overall logic operation. The results of this logic operation are placed on the J–K lines, and the clock then makes Q a high or a low in accordance with the truth tables.

This mode of operation is used widely in the construction of synchronous counters and various types of memories. The second and more common application is as a divide-by-2 counter. The f/f is often used following counters to produce a square wave. For example, if a counter is used to divide a given frequency by 100, the output has a duty cycle of 1 to 99 (or sometimes less). Aside from being hard to see on an oscilloscope, this may not be a satisfactory waveform. The usual way is to program the counter to divide by 50 and then use the f/f to divide by two, which produces an exactly symmetrical wave. Most oscillators do not produce a symmetrical waveform. Again, this problem is easily solved by designing the oscillator for twice the frequency and following it with an f/f.

Two J–K f/fs can be connected as shown in Fig. 4.24 to get a synchronous divide by four or by three, and since f/fs often come two to a package, this is commonly done. To divide by more than four requires additional logic and a counter to generally more suitable [2]. The J–K f/f is available with many modifications for logical flexibility. There are asynchronous clear and preset inputs, which set Q to a low and high, respectively. These inputs override the clock. Then the J and K inputs are combined with various other gates to provide different logical combinations. On these devices, the individual truth tables must be studied to determine their usefulness.

The D f/f is sometimes referred to as a latch or memory element. It has one input called D, and when the device is clocked, whatever is at D goes to Q. It is also a one-stage shift register, as indicated by Fig. 4.25a.

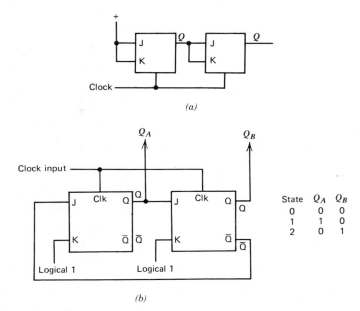

(a)

(b)

FIGURE 4.24   *J–K* f/f dividers: (*a*) ÷ 4; (*b*) ÷ 3.

If there is a high on the input *D* it is closed to *Q* on the rising edge of the clock. However, because of the delay time the input signal does not get to *D* of the second stage in time to be clocked. The signal must wait for the next rising edge and consequently is advanced one stage per clock pulse. This is a very useful device and is widely used.

Figure 4.25*b* shows that an asynchronous signal change of state is transferred from the *D* input to the *Q* output on the rising edge of the clock.

Figure 4.25*c* uses a *D* f/f connected to provide a symmetrical divide by 3 [3]. A glitch, appearing at the output of IC, creates a divide by $1\frac{1}{2}$ signal that is subsequently doubled to achieve a divide by 3 circuit. Although not in phase with the input, the output is a symmetrical signal.

Finally, Fig. 4.25*d* employs 3 *D* f/fs to develop a symmetrical divide-by-5 circuit [4]. The input is asymmetrical.

The asymmetry that the circuit can handle is limited only by the minimum pulsewidth, which is determined by the propagation delay time of FF_3 and the data setup time required by FF_1. The manufacturer's maximum specifications of 45 ns and 20 ns, respectively, for these time intervals yield a minimum clock input pulsewidth t_ω of 65 ns for reliable operation.

Pulsewidths between 30 and 65 ns can be accommodated by replacement of the 7404 inverter with an open-collector buffer such as

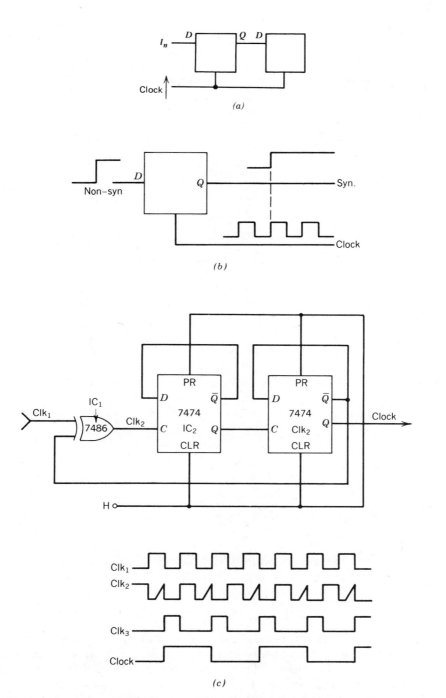

FIGURE 4.25 *D* f/f connections: (*a*) shift register; (*b*) pulse synchronizer. (*Figure continues on p. 122.*)

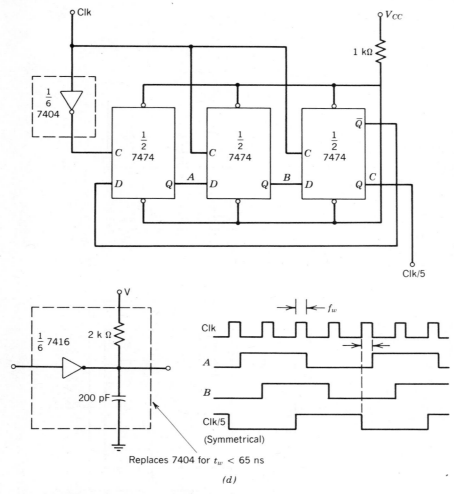

FIGURE 4.25 (*Continued*) (*c*) symmetrical ÷ 3; (*d*) symmetrical ÷ 5.

the 7416. The *RC* time constant of the collector load reduces the slope of the positive-going clock input pulsewidth.

4.4.2 Counters and Dividers

Counters are a very important part of digital circuits and come in many different forms and logic controls. Examples are the SN74LS168 and 169 series. These and similar counters are available in all the major logic forms. Figure 4.26 shows a typical counter.

Most counters have 4-bit outputs plus an end of count (EOC) signal. The counter can be binary with an output of 0–15 (16 states) or binary coded decimal with an output of 0–9 (10 states). The decimal counter has an internal word recognizer that resets the counter when the output reaches 1001; the binary counter changes naturally from 1111 to 0000.

Most counters are synchronous, that is, all of the outputs appear simultaneously, which is important for most logic systems. Asynchronous counters are usually of value only when the EOC is used.

Many counters feature convenient up and down controls. The counters can normally be cascaded and some provision is made for a "carry" on the up count and a "borrow" on the down count. There is normally an enable line as well to gate the counter with some other source of logic so that the counter becomes an active part of the control system in addition to performing its basic functions.

The typical counter features four preset or data inputs and a load control line. This enables the counter to be preset to a given value. If the EOC line is connected back to the load line, the count cycle is then reduced. In the down count mode, the reduced count will equal the preset value.

A word of caution is necessary here. The load control may be synchronized to the clock as in the SN74LS169, or it may be asynchronous as in the SN74LS193. With synchronized loading, the timing and logic of the counter must be carefully determined, but the result is always predictable. With asynchronous loading, the EOC pulse disappears as the count is changed and in some cases the load function leaves the counter with an incorrect value. Sometimes a delay circuit is used between the EOC and load control to avoid this problem. This lengthens the duration of the EOC pulse so that it may be available for other functions.

A counter is automatically a divider. Its function depends upon how it is used. There are many counter connections in the literature

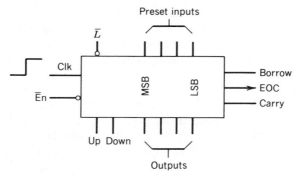

FIGURE 4.26 Typical counter.

for special-purpose conditions and these should be available to the designer when needed. For the discussion here, the presettable cascadable counter with the option of a divide by 2, 3, or 4 and a flip-flop connection at the EOC should solve most problems.

Shift registers, RAMs, and ROMs, can also be used as special-purpose counters and dividers; this is discussed later in this chapter.

4.4.3 Registers

Registers are temporary memories or files, of which are a vast selection. A large number of registers have been developed along with the μ processor to satisfy the special needs of that instrument.

Although this text does not address computer design directly, many computer components have solid application in other areas and these capabilities cannot be ignored.

Elementary forms of a register are the latch and the D f/f. The D f/f, as shown in Fig. 4.22, can be connected as a serial shift register or placed in a parallel mode to receive all of the bits of a given digital word.

An early design, and very flexible, is the SN74194 shift register. This device can be loaded in parallel or serial and will upon command shift in either direction.

Section 4.6 shows how a shift register, the SN74HC595, is used to shift a serial bit stream and then to transfer the contents to a set of parallel outputs, thereby providing a serial to parallel conversion.

Shift registers can also be used to provide delays and monostable pulses. This is a more reliable technique than using RCs and is generally more appropriate to a digital format. This is particularly true for wire wrap boards. Typical circuits are shown in Figs. 4.11 and 4.12.

4.4.4 RAMs and ROMs

Random access memories (RAMs) and read only memories (ROMs) are, of course, memory elements. RAMs are used primarily in computer circuits where large quantities of data are moved around in the process of computations. It is not the usual hardware element for real-time processing.

On the other hand, ROMs, find a great deal of use in real-time hardware design. They are essentially look-up tables on storage areas for a repetitive process that must take place upon command. ROMs, when properly used, can replace a great quantity of conventional digital hardware. Section 9.12 contains an example of just such an application.

Programmable ROMs, designated PROMs, are the most common form of ROMs for hardware design, since special-purpose mask programmed ROMs have a very high initial cost and mistakes cannot be corrected.

Read only memories that are used for real-time processing often operate at high speed and do not require much storage capacity. Consequently, bipolar fusible links are a good choice. For slower-speed applications, an erasable PROM (EPROM) provides greater flexibility and in these cases is the usual choice.

A common problem with ROMs is that their outputs are generally nonsynchronous, and this can cause timing problems. Worse yet, they frequently produce "glitches" at internal switching times which can create improper circuit operation. This often forces the use of *RC* filters in the output lines, and, since we are talking about bipolar logic, it is an unhappy compromise.

Most ROMs have tri-state capability, which sometimes solves the problem; this, however, requires a separate clocking operation.

Another more common solution to the glitch problem is to use an external latch, which also requires a second clocking operation. Section 9.12 deals with this technique. It would seem that glitch-free latches would be included in the ROM package, but since ROMs are basically a computer component, as such they are read at definite periods between address changes. The argument is given that the proper latch would increase the throughput time. This is an unfortunate decision for hardware applications.

Many ROMs have built-in standard programs, notably trigonometric functions. A fast multiplier can be produced as a look-up table, which is particularly useful if the multiplication is over a limited range. This is a big aid in real-time digital processing. Le Croy, Inc., for example, has such a product on the market: their model 2372 multiplies two 6-bit inputs in 60 μs.

For long or complex PROM programs, there are many automatic programmers available that can be driven directly by a μ processor (μP). A calculating loop with the appropriate algorithim is set up in the μP and the PROM directly programmed.

Although, as previously stated, RAMs are not usually used in hardware designs, the task of interfacing them is a common occurrence. In addition, large RAMs are generally composed of smaller RAMs and the proper interconnections can sometimes be challenging. As a guide and example, Fig. 4.27 is the basis of the following discussion.

The basic RAM building block for this array is the Harris HM6516. This relatively new synchronous CMOS device comes in an 11 bit $\times$ 8 channel format; although not as compact as competing NMOS technologies, it features very low power consumption.

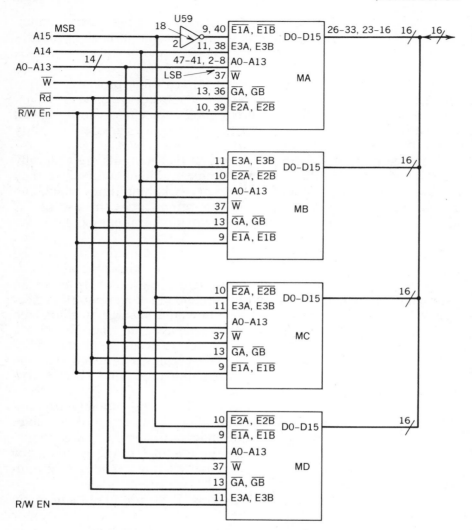

FIGURE 4.27 Connections for a 16 bit × 16 channel RAM.

This RAM comes in a standard 24-pin DIP. The required 16-bit address is $2^{16}/2^{11} = 2^5 = 32$ times as large as an 11-bit address, and since 16 channels are needed, 64 packages are required. This is a very large number of connections, but fortunately Harris also has a modular package containing 16 of the basis chips on a 48-pin 2.66 × 1.8 in. module called the HM92570. This permits a practical number of connections on a reasonably sized board.

It is observed that the mdoular construction has resulted in a 14-bit address which is still 2 bits short of the required 16. That, of course,

TABLE 4.3
RAM Truth Table

A15	A14	Module Enabled
L	L	D
L	H	C
H	L	B
H	H	A

is why 4 modules are required. The incoming address lines A15 and A14 are now used as module selectors.

Three sets of enable inputs $\overline{E1A}/E1B$, $\overline{E2A}/\overline{E2B}$, and $\overline{E3A}/\overline{E3B}$ are used in the address decoding. The two MSBs of the address are connected to these enable inputs so that only one specific 14 bit RAM module is addressed at a given time. This code is given in Table 4.3.

It is now seen that there remains an enable input on each module. Three are active low and are connected to a control line $\overline{R/W}$ En while the active high enable is connected to R/W En. In addition, all the $\overline{W}$ inputs of the four modules are connected to the $\overline{W}$ control line and all of the $\overline{GA}$, $\overline{GB}$, which are active low tri-state enable controls for the data lines, are connected to the Read ($\overline{Rd}$) control line.

Because this is a synchronous RAM, selected for its low power consumption, a price is paid in clocking complications. Detailed Read and Write timing cycles are provided by the manufacturer to control the relations between valid data, R/W En controls, and the respective $\overline{Rd}$ and $\overline{W}$ commands. This adds considerably to board complexity.

A further requirement is the need to transmit and receive data on the same μP bus lines so that bidirectional transceivers must be used; because the hardware is also producing data and addresses, an interlocked system of tri-state controls must also be established.

There are many complete RAM board assemblies available, if one that will efficiently do the job can be located, it is the way to go. However, when the needs of a particular μP with a specific bus system and unique data systems are combined, a custom design is sometimes the only choice.

4.4.5 D/A and A/D Converters

The D/A and the A/D, as they are called, are the connecting links between the digital and analog worlds. They have been around for some time in various forms, but only recently have the low-cost monolithic units become readily available. These are complete in and out devices, requiring only an external power supply and the addition of a clock line for the A/D. There are optional logic inputs and outputs that each manufacturer places on his product, and guidelines for their proper operation must be obtained from the data sheets.

In the past, when only a portion of the total function was supplied in a package, some knowledge of the partial operations was necessary to complete the overall function. This is now largely a requirement of the past.

Sections 9.2 and 9.3 discuss some applications of these devices.

4.5 DISCRETE DIGITAL DESIGN

Discrete digital design should be undertaken only after a careful search has shown that no commercial products are available for this task. The need for discrete design generally comes from interface requirements, and here we are really talking about buffers and level shifters. It seldom makes any sense to perform logic functions with discrete elements.

A switching transistor is optimized and characterized differently than its analog counterpart. Figure 4.25a shows a square wave input and the output of a switching transistor. The output pulse has four errors: an initial delay, rise and fall times that are specified between the 10 and 90% levels, and the storage delay. These parameters are very critically related to the test fixtures and the signals applied. The manufacturer usually specifies the method of test. It is seen that the input pulse goes both above and below 0 V. This is because a transistor in saturation accumulates a charge in the base region. If this charge is not pulled out by a reverse bias, the saturation time is greatly extended. T^{2}L logic elements have no negative supply for performing this function, but their small saturation delays are possible because a design trade-off can be made between high-speed performance and collector voltage breakdown. This is illustrated by the comparison of the two transistors in Fig. 4.28c. If a reverse supply is not available, an RC network can be used as shown in Fig. 4.29. When the turn-on pulse goes back to ground, the capacitor retains a charge so as to reverse bias the transistor. It is important that the input signal source be of low impedance so that the RC time constant allows a fast discharge of the base region.

A very important method of reducing the saturation delay is the use of a Schottky diode across the base-to-collector junction, as shown in Fig. 4.29. A transistor goes into saturation when the base–collector junction becomes forward biased. The Schottky diode has a turn-on voltage of about 0.4 V and thereby clamps the base–collector junction at a voltage lower than the 0.5 to 0.6 V it requires to put the transistor into saturation. To avoid confusion, it is pointed

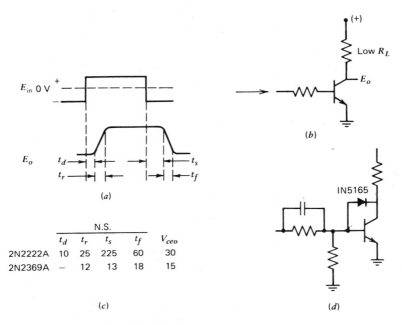

FIGURE 4.28 Pulse transmission.

out here that although it takes about 0.6 V to forward bias the base–collector junction, the collector-to-emitter drop is generally considerably lower, 0.1 to 0.3 V being typical.

The Schottky clamp can be improved by incorporating a pin diode, as shown in Fig. 4.29. A pin diode is a device that is normally used as an RF attenuator, its forward resistance being a linear function of the DC current through the unit. In this case, the pin diode D_2 controls the base current of the transistor in such a way as to make the Schottky diode D_1 more effective [2]. The RC time constant of Fig. 4.28d can also be added to increase the overall effectiveness of the diodes. The circuit of Fig. 4.29 decreased the delay time of the unaided transistor circuit from 11 to 2 ns.

Another method of designing a discrete digital stage is to use the ECL technique. This takes more components and power but provides maximum speed. Level shifting circuitry is probably necessary to produce the signal swings that a specific requirement dictates.

Field effect transistors have no saturation delay but a relatively high "on" resistance, which often makes them less desirable as logic switches. The DMOS, VMOS, and the HEXFET devices described in Chapter 2, however, are very fast, have relatively low "on" resistance, and may be suitable for some applications.

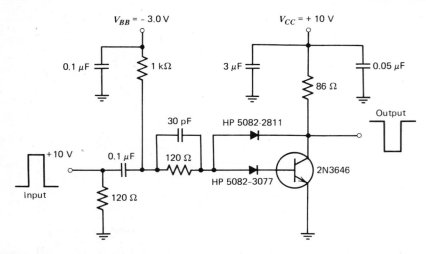

FIGURE 4.29 Nonsaturating transistor switch using *RC* drive and diode-controlled feedback. (From Ref. [2]; courtesy of Hewlett-Packard.)

4.6 COMPUTER TO HARDWARE INTERFACING

The overall interfacing relationships of a computer contain many considerations and procedures not directly related to a hardware processing or control system. The techniques of direct hardware communication to the computer have an emphasis of their own.

4.6.1 Line Driving and Receiving

Two types of construction are considered here. One is the case where the computer and hardware are in the same rack and plug into common bus lines of the "mother-board"; the other is where there is some distance between the computer and the hardware with the connections made by a ribbon cable. We are also considering that communication is based on a pulse of perhaps no less the 0.5 μs. This is not to say that the basic computer clock cannot be much faster. As the communication pulsewidths become shorter, the technques of line driving become more critical and cannot be managed reliably with the methods described here.

In the first case, there are few restrictions and almost any type of logic element can be used to drive the equally random choice of logic elements on the other board. The command lines are generally transmitted as Lo's because T²L elements have much better driving capabilities in this mode. However, since CMOS products have equal drive capabilities in both polarities, this will probably change. For example, the Fairchild FACT series has a ±24 mA drive capability.

In the second case, where ribbon cables are used, and depending upon the length of the cable, more restrictions apply. If the lengths are very long and the pulses very short, coaxial cables must be used. This is a considerable complication. It is difficult to attach absolute numbers to these boundaries, so careful engineering judgment and observation are essential.

Transmission by ribbon cable generally requires the alternate lines to be grounds and this procedure should only be abandoned for short lines and then with the greatest of care. There are also twisted pair flat cable constructions, but these require differential drivers and receivers to be properly effective.

If there are excessive pulse distortions, source termination will generally solve the problem (see Section I.6). Special line drivers may be used; in the past, transistors with load resistors on the receiving end have been used. These resistors, available in multiple arrangements mounted in standard dual in-line packages, are very handy. This combination obviously draws a great deal of power. The high-speed CMOS is the equipment of choice. In particular, the Fairchild FACT family, as previously mentioned, or the equivalent logic of other manufacturers is an excellent choice.

If special receivers are required, there are two basic choices for single-line transmissions. First, there are the Schmitt trigger gates and inverters, which are very helpful in noisy environments. Secondly, there are the exclusive OR/NOR gates, which have no added noise immunity but can change the polarity on the incoming pulse. These can also be used, of course, on the transmit side to change the polarity of the pulse at that point. A Hi on the nonreceiving input of the EX-OR will invert the incoming pulse; a low on this input is the noninverting mode.

An item of convenience should be mentioned. To minimize confusion between the μP programmer and the hardware designer, it is very desirable to avoid polarity inversions and, in particular, if there is an inversion to maintain the inversion for all lines. For example, if the hardware requires a 0110 code, the programmer should be able to enter a 0110 and not a 1001. Disregarding this procedure invariably leads to errors and confusion.

4.6.2 Data and Address Bus Lines

The title of this section has the word computer rather than μP because a computer can have any conceivable combination of functions on its lines and is not as restricted as the basic μP. The bus structure can range from one set of lines that handles in and out data and in and out addresses to a separate set of lines to handle in data, out data, in addresses, and out addresses. Furthermore, there are again any possible combination of commands, flags, interrupts, poling, acknowledges, etc., lines.

The hardware engineer must have good communication with the computer programmer so that the specific set of conditions at hand are well defined. Once this is settled there is a certain class of hardware and controls that are available to the hardware engineer.

4.6.3 Tools for the Hardware Designer

In a hardware/computer system, the function of each must be carefully balanced and equated. This requires clear thinking and good judgment.

In a very basic sense the hardware deals with obtaining the data, doing some processing, and then communicating this information to the computer. In this function, the hardware is connected to the bus lines of the computer that are also in common with many other devices. The basic tools for this interface are tri-state-controlled logic elements that perform the functions of bidirectional control, isolation, serial to parallel conversion, and temporary storage as well as the timing logic necessary to make these devices function properly. Figure 4.30 shows how some typical parts would be connected.

This demonstration design problem has a signal processor whose data output is in serial form and is either too slow or unpredictable in its occurrence so that a RAM must be used to store the information. At a given time, the computer reads this RAM and stores the contents in its own memory for further processing and computation. Provision is also made for the computer to write into this RAM and then read out the known information as a confidence check.

The computer and the RAM are purposely left undefined in order to keep the discussion general. The example is meant to show interfacing techniques and considerations.

The $\overline{\text{SP}}$/Comp (signal processor/computer) line is low during signal processing and high when the computer addresses the RAM. SP/$\overline{\text{Comp}}$ is the complement. These lines control the tri-state or high-impedance status of the interfacing chips.

This computer has 16 data lines that are bidirectional and a total of 22 outgoing address lines; of the latter, 16 are directed to the RAM and 6 to select operations. This means that a total of 64 operations can be selected.

The RAM with a 16-line address ($2^{16} = 65,536$ locations) and 16 lines of data has a total of $2^{16} \times 2^4 = 2^{20}$ or approximately $1.048(10)^6$ stored bits of information.

Serial data transmission is often the method of choice when opto-isolators are used with low-power CMOS circuits because of the relatively large amount of power these devices consume. This brings

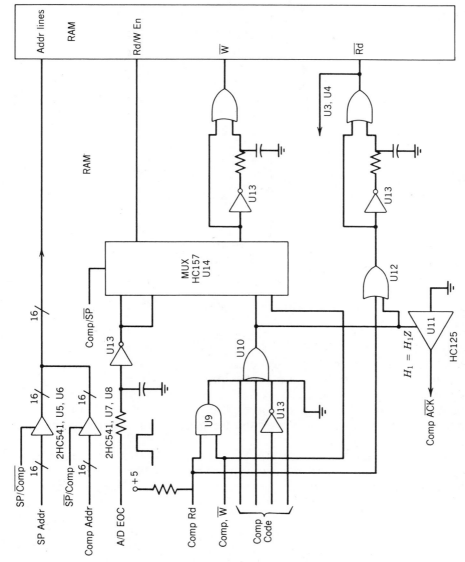

FIGURE 4.30 Computer and hardware interface schematic. (*Figure continues on p. 134.*)

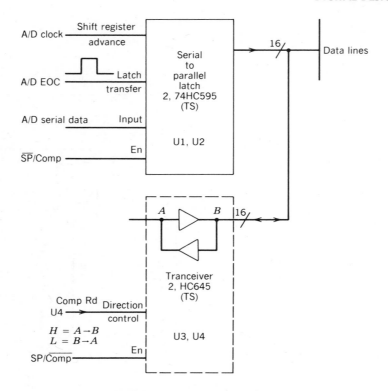

FIGURE 4.30 *(Continued)*

about the necessity of serial to parallel (S/P) conversion. The SN74HC595 is a serial to 8-bit converter latch so two of the units are required in this application. Three inputs from the A/D are shown going directly to the S/P converter. This is probably an oversimplification because there are timing requirements and possible inversions necessary in most cases. This must be worked out when the specific A/D is defined.

It will be noted that both the S/P converter and the computer transceiver are connected to the same data lines of the RAM. To avoid having two outputs active at the same time, the enable lines $\overline{SP}$/Comp and SP/$\overline{Comp}$ are complementary.

When the analog to digital end of conversion (A/D EOC) occurs, the accumulated 16 bits of data are latched by U1 and U2 and applied to the RAM. The A/D EOC signal is then sent to the Rd/W En and the $\overline{W}$ inputs of the RAM through the MUX, U14.

Again, the specific RAM mode of operation must be determined, but there is usually an edge and a duration requirement, as well as a requirement that the data be present for a defined length of time before the Write edge is applied. It is seen that a time delay has been inserted in the A/D EOC line leading to the RAM to ensure that the data is available when the RAM is clocked. The HC157 MUX is included because the RAM Rd/W En and the W lens must be used both by the SP and the computer.

The 16 SP address lines and the 16 Comp address lines are both applied to the RAM address lines in the same manner as the RAM data lines; also, as in the data lines, they are interlocked by the tri-state controls so that they cannot operate at the same time.

When the computer is reading or writing into the RAM the 6-function select lines must have the proper access code. The decoding is provided by U_{10}, the 8 input NOR gate. The inverters on the input are selected to provide all Lo's on the input when the correct code is applied and this in turn provides the required Lo to the Rd/Write En input of the RAM. Since this enable line is required for Read or Write, the required OR function is provided by the AND gate U9.

Most computers require an acknowledge, or handshake, as it is sometimes called, from the equipment being addressed. If a function takes a relatively long time, the acknowledge signal must not be transmitted until it is complete. In many cases, however, the defined action is very fast and the incoming decoded signal can be returned for this purpose. This is accomplished in this circuit with the tri-state buffer U11.

There are times when the μP enable signal must be turned off at a precise time in the cycle of the directed function. A D f/f (a J–K f/f can also be used) is very useful in this situation. The μP signal edge is used to shift the D input to the Q output and then a signal change at the required time is used to reset the f/f. A means must also be established to ensure that the f/f is in the correct state to accept the μP signal, that is, there must be a reset.

Proceeding to the transceivers U3 and U4, it is seen that in the Read mode, transmission must be from B to A and in the Write mode from A to B. It is very important to observe that it is the decoded Rd signal that must be used for the Read function. It must be remembered that the computer Rd line is not dedicated to this particular operation and if it is not used with the specific decode logic the outputs of the transceiver will be improperly placed across the active computer data bus and cause a malfunction. The decoded Read signal for the transceiver is developed by the OR gate (AND function) U12.

All unused inputs of CMOS chips *must* be attached to a specific logic level. There are times, however, when there are many lines (e.g., the bus lines of a computer) that become open when the computer board is removed, and these lines must have terminating resistors for that occasion. Since this can clutter up a schematic, the resistors are often left off the main schematic and are instead contained in an auxiliary wiring table. In many cases, it does not matter whether the input is tied to a Hi or a Lo, but in cases where it does these terminations are part of the circuit logic and must be shown on the main schematic.

The resistor to the +5 line shown at the Comp Rd input of U9 is an example of this definite requirement. This Comp Rd line goes directly to the RAM where it could conflict with the Write input during the SP mode.

As long as we are discussing input terminations for CMOS circuits, it is well to point out that even unused gates must be terminated. For example, if three of four gates in a quad NAND gate are used, the two inputs of the unused gate must also be terminated. If these inputs are left open, that gate could either oscillate or stay in the middle and draw an excessive current.

REFERENCES

[1] *AN-340, Natl. Semiconductor*, p. 251.
[2] *Transistor Speed Up Using Schottky Diodes, Application Bulletin 13*, Hewlett-Packard, Palo Alto, CA.
[3] R. S. Hsiah, Divide by 3 Circuit, *Electon. Des.*, Nov. 11, 1982.
[4] M. B. Greenberg, Counter has Symmetrical Output Though the Input Signal is Asymmetrical, *Electron. Des.*, Sept. 27, 1974.

GENERAL REFERENCES

H. S. Stone, *Microcomputer Interfacing*, Addison-Wesley Reading, MA, 1982.
P. Horowitz and W. Hill, *The Art of Electronics*, Cambridge University Press, Cambridge, UK, 1981.
C. J. Sippl, *Computer Dictionary and Handbook*, Howard W. Sams, Indianapolis, IN, 1982.

FIVE

Transformers

One important decision that a circuit designer must make about a transformer is whether it should be purchased or designed and constructed. Fortunately, this decision is not very difficult.

Low-frequency transformers and audio transformers should rarely be built, since they require many turns, often of small gauge wire. In addition, there are a large variety of off-the-shelf items to choose from. Even for nonstandard values, specialty shops can generally produce small quantities at reasonable prices. Another type of transformer that is readily available in many variations is the pulse transformer. These are generally intended for higher than audio frequencies and are specified in a different manner. To a certain extent these specifications can be used as a guide to broadband or tuned circuit application, though a few additional tests are usually required.

A wide range of RF and high-frequency broadband transformers are easy to design and build but difficult to find as off-the-shelf items. A few words about basic transformer theory must be said before discussing specific design.

If a closed path, of any magnetic material, has a coil of N_P turns wrapped around it as in Fig. 5.1a, it has the characteristic of Fig. 5.1b. Assuming that there is no residual flux, the flux density B increases from zero as the current through the winding is increased. There is a saturation level above which no appreciable change in flux occurs as the current or magnetizing force H is increased. This is one of the design limits. As the current is decreased, the flux maintains a residual value and traces out the curve shown in Fig. 5.1b. This is called the hysteresis loop and represents a power loss, per unit volume, that is a function of the area of the core, frequency, flux density, the material, and the way the material is manufactured. There is a second loss in the iron due to induced currents flowing in the material.

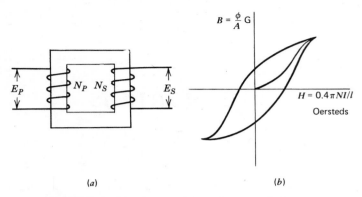

FIGURE 5.1 Fundamental transformer relations.

This is called the eddy-current loss and is also a function of the material and the operating conditions.

The slope of the curve is the permeability μ. The permeability of air is unity, so that μ represents magnetic conductivity relative to air. $\mu = \Delta B/\Delta H$ where B is flux lines φ per square centimeter of the magnetic area and is called gauss. H is the magnetizing force called oersteds and is defined as

$$H = 0.4\pi \frac{NI}{l} \quad \text{Oe}$$

$$B = \frac{\varphi}{A} \qquad \text{G}$$

where l = length of the magnetic path (cm), A = area of magnetic circuit (cm^2), N = turns, and I = amperes.

A voltage is induced in a coil if the magnetic flux through that coil changes. Specifically

$$E_{\text{ind}} = N \frac{d\varphi}{dt} (10)^{-8} \text{ V} \tag{5.1}$$

This means that if there were a change of 100 lines in 1 μs, $100(10)^{-8}/10^{-6} = 1$ V would be induced for each turn. When a voltage is impressed on the primary of a coil, this induced voltage is of the same sign and opposes the applied voltage, thereby limiting the current flow. This is shown in Fig. 5.2a.

Approached in a different manner, with a sine wave applied, the coil is said to have a reactance X_L which opposes the current flow.

$X_L = 2\pi f L$ and for the condition of perfect coupling, that is, all of the flux lines are passing through all of the turns:

$$L = \frac{0.4\pi N^2 \ \mu A (10)^{-8}}{l} \quad \text{(H)} \tag{5.2}$$

If the flux φ in Eq. 5.1 is a sine wave, that is

$$\varphi = \varphi_{max} \sin 2\pi f t$$

then

$$\varphi = -N \int \frac{d(\varphi_{max} \sin 2\pi f t)}{dt} (10)^{-8}$$

from which

$$\varphi(ft) = -N\varphi_{max}(2\pi f) \cos 2\pi f t (10)^{-8}$$

The cos term is simply a phase relationship, so to obtain the rms value, divide by $\sqrt{2}$:

$$E_{rms} = \frac{2\pi}{\sqrt{2}} f N \varphi_{max}(10)^{-8}$$

We now have, for a sine wave,

$$E_{rms} = 4.44 f N \varphi_{max}(10)^{-8} \tag{5.3}$$

If a pulse is applied, $\varphi = E$, and we have

$$\int E \ dt = -N \int d(\varphi_{max})(10)^{-8}$$
$$Et = N\varphi_{max}(10)^{-8}$$

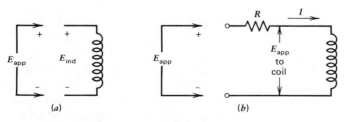

FIGURE 5.2 Induced voltage relations. In (b), E_{app} to coil $= E_{app} - IR$.

or

$$N = \frac{Et(10)^8}{\varphi_{max}} \tag{5.4}$$

It is seen here that the amplitude and width of a pulse are interchangeable. For example, if a transformer can pass a 10 V pulse 1 μs wide pulse, it can also pass a 1 V pulse 10 μs wide.

Equation 5.3 can be expressed for a square wave by recognizing that $4.44 = 4(0.707)/(0.636)$, where 0.707 is the effective value of a sine wave and 0.636 the average value. Since the effective value and the average value of a square wave are the same, we have for a square wave

$$E = 4fN\varphi_{max}(10)^{-8} \tag{5.5}$$

A variation convenient for our intended designs is obtained by converting E_{rms} to E_{peak} and using the substitution $\varphi_{max} = B_{max}A$. Thereupon,

$$B_{max} = \frac{16E_{peak}(10)^6}{fNA}, \qquad \text{for a sine wave} \tag{5.6}$$

and

$$B_{max} = \frac{25E_{peak}(10)^6}{fNA}, \qquad \text{for a square wave} \tag{5.6a}$$

Equation 5.3 contains a subtle and important bit of information. Magnetic flux is a function of current. If the wire carrying the current is wrapped in a coil around a magnetic path, this flux is greatly increased. It is, however, the voltage that determines how much flux must be developed. The impedance of the winding adjusts itself so that the proper current is drawn to produce the required flux. If the required voltage demands a flux density in the saturation region of Fig. 5.1b, a short circuit condition develops, with possible damage to the transformer and circuit. It can be further seen that as the frequency decreases, the flux must increase. Accordingly, a transformer is designed for the lowest anticipated frequency. There are high-frequency limitations, but with regard to Eq. 5.3, the higher the better.

If Eq. 5.3 is again reorganized, we have A = area of a transformer core = $E_{rms}(10)^8/4.44fNB_{max}$. Now the observation is made that there is no allowance for power. The answer to that question is that, as far as the core alone is concerned, its size is independent of power. The core losses are fixed by Eq. 5.3 and are independent of load. When a current flows in the secondary, it demagnetizes the core, and the primary must draw more current to reestablish the level of the no-load flux, but no changes in core loss, permeability, or flux density have occurred.

In practice it is well established that as the power level is increased, the size of the core must increase. The losses incurred by the transformer because of an external load occur completely as IR in the windings. This leads to overheating and poor regulation. Regardless of the method of transformer construction, the core in some manner surrounds the coils. Put another way, the core must provide a window for the necessary coil area and the core must become larger to go around the increasing coil size. The flux density B_{max} for a big transformer is essentially the same as for a small transformer. Accordingly, as the core area increases, the number of turns in the primary winding must decrease.

The estimated core size of a transformer, for a given frequency, is determined by its volt-ampere capacity rather than by its power output. The relationship between size and volt-ampere capacity can be demonstrated in the ideal case as follows.

If magnetizing and core losses are neglected, a normal transformer has the relation $N_1 I_1 = N_2 I_2$. Each winding generally uses one half of the window area. Accordingly,

$$N_1 I_1 = N_2 I_2 = K_1 A_{CU} \qquad (5.7)$$

$\varphi_{max} = A_{FE} B_{max}$, and for a given material, B_{max} can be considered a constant. Also if we limit this equation to a single frequency, Eq. 5.3 can be rewritten as

$$\frac{E_1}{N_1} = K_2 A_{FE} \qquad (5.8)$$

Upon multiplying Eq. 5.7 by Eq. 5.8, we obtain

$$E_1 I_1 = K_3 A_{CU} A_{FE} \qquad (5.9)$$

In other words, on a general basis, the volt-ampere rating of a transformer is proportional to the product of the copper (or window) area and the iron area. Appendix IV contains some useful graphs from Magnetics, Inc. These relate the product of core area and winding area to power and frequency. Section 9.8 gives a design that uses these curves to select a core size. To optimize some designs it may be necessary to have a nonstandard ratio of core area to window area. A laminated core, if applicable, allows some flexibility, but for other core types the available ratios are definitely limited.

Let us now backtrack a bit to round out this discussion. Figure 5.2b shows the case where the coil contains resistance. This is an effective resistance that consists basically of copper losses and the core losses of the magnetic material. The effect of this resistance is to reduce the voltage that is applied to the pure inductance.

In general linear circuit analysis, the inductive reactance X_L is designated in ohms and combined with resistance on a vector basis to form impedance, which is also designated in ohms. This all works out very nicely, but in truth X_L is not a voltage drop like IR. It is alternately a storage element and a voltage generator, and a nonlinear one at that. This must be kept in mind when designing transformers and inductors to avoid mistakes of oversimplification.

5.1 CONVENTIONAL TRANSFORMER CONNECTIONS

The transformers to be designed in this book are generally driven by a transistor, as shown in Fig. 5.3. The input signal could be a sine wave, a square wave, or a complex wave such as speech, which is contained in a band-pass region.

In Fig. 5.3a there is a quiescent DC component flowing through the primary. This in turn establishes a steady-state magnetic flux in the transformer core. This flux must be in the linear position of the magnetization curve, as shown in Fig. 5.1b. When the AC signal is superimposed, the flux and current are related by the minor hysteresis loop, as shown in Fig. 5.3c. If the primary of the transformer is center tapped and operated in a push–pull fashion, as in Fig. 5.3b, the net quiescent flux is zero and the dynamic range and linearity of the transformer are substantially extended.

When a second coil is wound around the magnetic path, a voltage is induced in this coil. If all of the primary flux passes through the secondary turns, the magnitude is $E_S = E_P N_S / N_P$ and the transformer is said to have unity coupling.

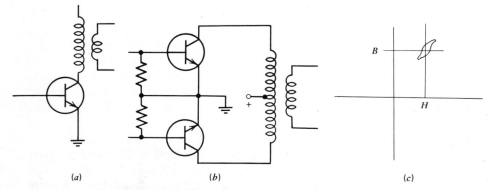

(a)   (b)   (c)

FIGURE 5.3 Conventional transformer operation.

When the coefficient of coupling is unity and the winding capacitances are negligible, an impedance Z_S that is placed across the secondary winding is reflected to the primary winding as $(N_P/N_S)^2 Z_S$. As the coupling becomes less than unity, the transfer rapidly becomes more complex. This is because each winding develops a leakage reactance that is in series with the load.

5.1.1 High-Frequency Considerations

The first transformers considered here use toroidal cores and consist of a small number of turns that can conveniently be hand wound. They are meant for either broadband or tuned primary applications. These applications require that the coefficient of coupling be as close to unity as possible. Double-tuned circuits that require specific coupling coefficients are not covered in this book. (Reactance coupled tuned circuits are, however, covered in Chapter 8). As core materials, a range of ferrites and powdered iron are used. The ferrite materials have a higher permeability and a poorer temperature coefficient than the powdered iron materials. Powdered iron can be used for higher frequencies. In both materials, with an increase in frequency capability the permeability goes down and the temperature stability improves.

A great deal of technique and experience is required to wind the coils of a transformer to obtain the low distributed capacitive and leakage reactance required for extended high-frequency performance. This information is not covered in this text but there are many fine books that specifically discuss these techniques. References [1], [2], and [3] are a few examples.

The core material is determined by the frequency. For high-frequency low-power amplifiers, core size is usually a matter of convenience. 0.375 in. O.D. is a good choice because it is not too large but still big enough to make the winding easy. The reason for this flexibility is that flux density is rarely a problem with this class of transformer. For example, if a 0.375 O.D. core is wound with 10 turns and is used at 1 MHz with a 15 V power supply, we have

$$B_{\max} = \frac{16E_P(10)^6}{fNA} = \frac{16(15)(10)^6}{(10)^6(10)(0.076)}$$
$$= 316 \text{ G}$$

Since moderate saturation occurs in the range of 2000 to 3000 G, depending on the material, this value is quite conservative. If linearity is important, measurements must be made to determine how much flux density is tolerable. Generally, for a highly linear operation a feedback circuit should be used if at all possible. In the case of maximum power level, dissipation charts from the manufacturer are necessary for a preliminary calculation. Such a chart is given for Ferroxcube 3C8 in Appendix IV, where the core loss in mW/cm^3 is given as a function of frequency and flux density. The effects of power overload are observable in the distortion, heating, and loss of Q.

It is important to check the magnetic bias due to the DC current as well as the AC flux. For example, 15 mA flowing through a coil on a 3C8 core of 0.375 O.D. would produce

$$\text{Magnetizing force, } H = \frac{0.4\pi NI}{l} \tag{5.10}$$

$$= 0.4\pi N(0.015)/2.16$$

$$= 0.0087 \, N \text{ Oe}$$

The core data sheets show that in this example the value is very small.

For the low-power RF transformers being considered here, the number of turns generally is not large. This results in a great deal of latitude in the choice of the wire size. In many cases the choice is mechanical—making certain that the wire is not too stiff or fragile for easy handling.

When there are only a few turns of large diameter on the core, the unloaded Q is generally determined by the core losses.

There is a chart in Appendix IV that relates the AC resistance and DC resistance of the winding as a function of wire size, and frequency for straight conductors. Unfortunately, the actual AC resistance of a winding is far more complex, depending upon both the coil structure and magnetic flux path.

The best way to determine if parallel wires are necessary to reduce the skin resistance is to conduct tests and build up a reference table that will be valuable for future use.

As a starting point, however, there is a rule of thumb that has been proven to be of some merit. A wire size larger than #20 should not be used at a frequency above 20 KHz; it does not seem to make much difference if the applied voltage is a sine or square wave.

For close coupling the primary and secondary windings should be wound close to each other, bifilar or the secondary on top of the primary. This increases the interwinding capacitance, however, which in turn reduces the high-frequency isolation of the transformer. The expected inductance and unloaded Q of the primary are given in tables furnished by the manufacturer.

5.1.2 Design Procedures

The conventional transformer design procedures in this book are given in the form of examples. Section 2.3.5 deals with the low-power RF application. Section 9.8 contains two designs: one drives a capacitive load and the other is a high-power application.

5.1.3 Test Procedures

The inductance and Q of a coil are measured as shown in Fig. 5.4. An estimate is made of the capacitance required to resonate the coil at the operating frequency. This is connected in parallel with the coil and the frequency is varied until e_o is a maximum. The value of R is not critical, but for best accuracy it should be several times the anti-resonance impedance. The inductance is then calculated from the relation

$$f_r = \frac{1}{2\pi\sqrt{LC}} \qquad \text{or} \qquad L = \frac{1}{(2\pi f)^2 C}$$

A reactance slide rule such as the Shure Brothers RSR-1 is highly recommended for making this and similar calculations quickly and with reasonable accuracy. These slide rules are generally available in hi-fi and acoustical centers.

The Q can be determined by measuring the -3 dB frequencies and using the relationship $Q = f_r/\Delta f$. This is, however, the circuit Q and includes R acting in parallel with R_P. R should be at least 10 times larger than R_P or a second calculation is required to obtain an accurate coil Q. If the series resistor R can be made high enough to neglect its effect, this is the easiest test. There is, however, a small amount of capacitance in parallel with a resistor, which may have to be taken

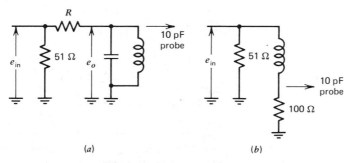

FIGURE 5.4 Test circuits.

into account. For example a 100 kΩ $\frac{1}{4}$ W resistor has about 0.25 pF, which produces a $f_{+3\,dB}$ frequency at 6.1 MHz.

When the tank circuit is loaded by a reflected resistance from the secondary inductance, this resistance appears in parallel with the primary inductance. Because of this the method above can be used to calculate the loaded Q, even though it may be very low. For good efficiency, the unloaded Q, however, should be substantially greater than the loaded Q.

The self-resonance is measured as shown in Fig. 5.4b. Since the resonance is in the parallel mode, a null is obtained at the frequency of the resonance. The 100 Ω resistor is typical. It should be low enough so that the probe capacitance does not cause a roll-off prior to the resonant frequency and high enough so that the null signal can be observed.

Wideband applications are much more restricted by the leakage reactance and coil capacitance than are the tuned amplifiers. A tuned amplifier, in this respect, is quite a tolerant circuit. To a large extent it simply absorbs the stray parameters with a slight shift in the discrete tuning capacitor. For wideband applications, ferrites are much to be preferred over powdered iron because of higher permeability and consequently better coupling. Fortunately, the temperature coefficient is not as important in broadband applications as in narrowband tuned circuits. If bandwidths over a couple of decades are required in the RF range, the transmission line transformers should be considered. They are discussed in Section 5.2 on unconventional transformers.

5.1.4 Pulse Transformers

As previously mentioned, pulse transformers are available in great abundance, so there is no need to delve into their design procedures here. The discussion that follows shows how the transformers are used in the applications for which they are designed and in some applications for which they are not designed.

The ideal transformer used as a coupling device in Fig. 5.5a is mathematically identical to the more common RC coupling shown in Fig. 5.5b.

The RC circuit in most practical conditions can be considered as ideal, but the transformer has many real limitations and complications. To understand the transformer, it is well to review the action of the more familiar RC coupling and use this as a starting point.

With a sine wave input the output of the RC network is down 3 dB ($0.707E$) when $X_C = R$. As the frequency is lowered, the output falls at a limit of 6 dB/octave. The phase of the output approaches an asymptotic value of $+90°$. With a step function input the output falls in an exponential manner, as shown in Fig. 5.6.

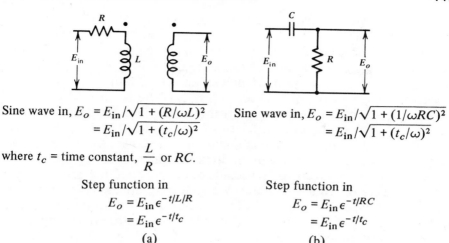

Sine wave in, $E_o = E_{in}/\sqrt{1 + (R/\omega L)^2}$
$$= E_{in}/\sqrt{1 + (t_c/\omega)^2}$$

where t_c = time constant, $\dfrac{L}{R}$ or RC.

Step function in
$$E_o = E_{in}\,\epsilon^{-t/L/R}$$
$$= E_{in}\,\epsilon^{-t/t_c}$$

(a)

Sine wave in, $E_o = E_{in}/\sqrt{1 + (1/\omega RC)^2}$
$$= E_{in}/\sqrt{1 + (t_c/\omega)^2}$$

Step function in
$$E_o = E_{in}\,\epsilon^{-t/RC}$$
$$= E_{in}\,\epsilon^{-t/t_c}$$

(b)

FIGURE 5.5 Comparison of inductive and capacitive coupling. $\epsilon = 2.718$.

Figure 5.6*a* indicates the response for an extended time so that the second and negative-going step function also starts from a 0 V output condition. At time $= RC$ (or L/R for the inductive circuit) the output is down to 36% of its initial value. At time $= 5RC$ the output is down to less than 2% of the initial value. If the pulsewidth is reduced, the falloff looks like a straight line and is generally called droop or tilt. Figure 5.6*c* shows the droop for several different time constants.

The ideal transformer has the redeeming features that as a coupler it can isolate and change voltage and impedance levels or go to push–pull, as the case may be. A load on the secondary winding does not change the analogy to the RC circuit. The secondary resistance is reflected to the primary where it is combined with the source resis-

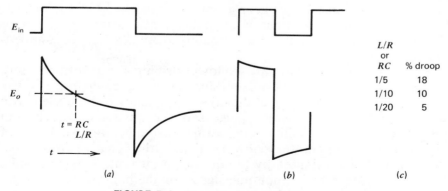

L/R or RC	% droop
1/5	18
1/10	10
1/20	5

(a) (b) (c)

FIGURE 5.6 Response to a pulse input.

tance by Thévenin's theorem. This gives a new time constant but no change in principle.

Although the ideal *RL* circuit is mathematically equivalent to the *RC* circuit, the practical applications are an entirely different matter. An *RC* circuit should be used unless an *RL* circuit can establish a specific advantage or, of course, unless it is the natural load.

The departures of the practical transformer from the ideal case are many and provide several restrictions on its use. The first is the assumption that the inductance is linear. In particular, as the magnetic core approaches saturation, the inductance falls to a very low value. This is generally given as a voltage time product for pulse transformers. This is often written as V/μs. It may appear as a rise time specified as volts per second, but it is not. A volt–second rating of 2 μs means that if you apply 10 V with a given source resistance, the pulse has less than the manufacturer's specified droop after 0.2 μs. 5 V would allow a 0.4 μs pulsewidth. This is for a maximum level condition, and the droop is caused by the loss of inductance. It has nothing to do with the droop defined by the equations shown in Fig. 5.5*a*. These equations assume a constant inductance and are not a function of the applied voltage.

The volt–second rating of an inductor can be best explained by the relation $E = L(di/dt)$. This states that if a constant voltage is applied to a pure inductance, the current increases at a constant linear rate. However, in a saturable reactor there is a large increase in the current when the inductance drops because of the saturation. The source resistance that is defined with a given pulse transformer then causes a sharp drop of voltage across the coil.

Since the time constant of an inductive circuit is L/R, minimum nonsaturating droop is obtained with a low impedance source such as in an emitter follower. This statement is worthy of further emphasis. It will be recalled that in dealing with a tuned transformer or choke it was desirable to use a constant current drive such as the collector of a transistor to keep from lowering the Q of the circuit. If the inductance is untuned a constant current drive will generate the derivative of the signal. For a broadband application a low-impedance source is required.

Figure 5.7*a* shows an emitter follower driving a transformer. Here the bypass capacitor must present an impedance comparable to the transistor output resistance at the lowest frequency to be passed. The resistor and emitter supply voltage sets the quiescent current and gives the stage DC stability. This form of drive has the weakness of all single transistor emitter followers. That is, the negative swing (positive for a PNP) is limited by the quiescent current. This first limits the low-frequency high-amplitude signals on the half-cycle being supplied by the emitter supply.

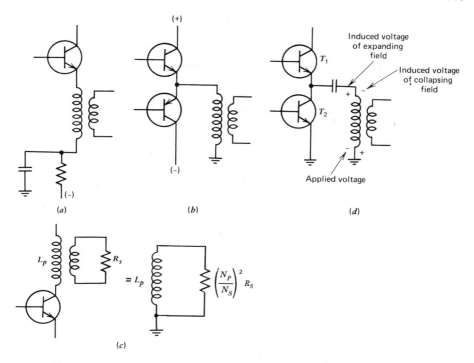

FIGURE 5.7 Additional transformer connections.

Figure 5.7*b* illustrates a complementary emitter follower driving the transformer. This avoids the saturation DC problem, but is more complex. There are, however, hybrid packages available that substantially reduce the space required. NSC, for example, has the LH0002 in a T05 package. This has a 6 Ω output resistance, but is down 3 dB at 30 MHz, which could in some cases be a limitation. Figure 5.7*c* shows a transformer driven from the collector. Now if the coupling is tight (close to unity), the secondary load resistance is reflected by $(N_P/N_S)^2$ to a load resistor in parallel with the primary inductance. In this manner adequate low-frequency response can often be obtained in a collector-loaded stage.

Figure 5.7*d* shows a transformer driven by the "totem-pole" output commonly used in T^{2}L circuits. The capacitor is necessary because when the output goes into its zero condition the negative induced voltage in the inductor is trying to turn Q_1 from its normally "off" condition to an "on" state. This greatly limits the negative swing. With a capacitor suitable for the desired pulsewidths this malfunction is corrected and proper operation occurs. Section 9.5 contains a circuit that uses a capacitor to couple a T^{2}L driver to a transformer.

Pulse transformers must have a wide frequency band to pass the required spectrum of a square wave. Consequently, the Q is generally sacrificed for other considerations. The PCA 7044 transformer, for example, had $f_{-3\,dB}$ frequencies of 1 MHz and 3.55 MHz when tuned at 1.95 MHz and driven from an approximate current source. This is a $Q = 1.95/3.55 - 1 = 0.76$.

When driving the primary of the PCA 7044 pulse transformer with the LH0002, the low-frequency roll-off was 9 kHz. The maximum amplitude at this frequency, however, was 150 mV p/p, after which severe distortion rapidly set in because of saturation (see Eq. 5.3). At 200 kHz, the full amplitude of the signal generator, 5 V, could be applied. The high-frequency cutoff was above 180 MHz. This was determined with a 50 Ω source directly driving the primary and a secondary load of 50 Ω in parallel with 10 pF.

The PCA data sheets give the interwinding capacity and the leakage inductance with an approximate equation $t_r = \sqrt{L_p C_w}$. For the 7044 transformer this would be

$$t = \sqrt{0.6(10)^{-6}(7)(10)^{-12}} = 2 \text{ ns rise time}$$

5.2 UNCONVENTIONAL TRANSFORMER CONNECTIONS

All of the transformers discussed in this section have a 1 to 1 turns ratio with unity coupling. This generally means a bifilar winding where the primary and secondary wires are wound in parallel around the core. In some cases, as is demonstrated later, a twisted pair is used. Therefore, the general expression for the mutual inductance $M = k\sqrt{L_P L_S}$ becomes $M = L_P = L_S$. When analyzing inductively coupled circuits it is very important to avoid confusion about the polarity of the induced voltage. Figure 5.8a is a conventional transformer connection. The dots above one of the primary leads and above one of the secondary leads indicate that the two sides have the same polarity. The dots signify either the two starts or the two finishes. The schematic of Figure 5.8a is shown in Fig. 5.8b. With the dots on the same side, the induced voltage, in the secondary winding, is of the same polarity as the IX drop in the primary circuit that produced the induced voltage. Figure 5.8c is the same transformer as Fig. 5.8a, just connected in a different manner. Figure 5.8d is the schematic representation of Fig. 5.8c.

Going around the loop of Fig. 5.8d we have

$$E_{in} - I_P X_L + I_S X_M - I_P R_P - I_P R_L - I_S R_S + I_P X_M - I_S X_L = 0$$

At a frequency where the transformer reactance is five times it resistance the impedance is only 2% greater than the reactance and the resistance terms can be dropped. The equation now takes the form

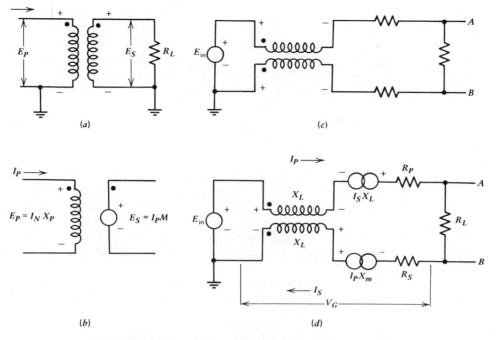

FIGURE 5.8 An unconventional transformer connection.

$$E_{\text{in}} - I_P X_L + I_S X_M - I_P R_L + I_P X_M - I_S X_L = 0$$

When the load R_L is not grounded, $I_P = I_S$ and, since $X_L = X_M$,

$$(-I_S X_L + I_P X_M) = 0$$

If a ground is placed at point B, some current is diverted from I_S, with the result that $(-I_S X_L + I_P X_M)$ equals a finite voltage that attempts to increase I_S. The net result is that a transformer connected in this manner restricts the amount of ground current that flows if point B is grounded. It is very hard to quantify exactly how much ground current flows under a given condition because this depends on the total symmetry of the transformer, exact unity coupling, and the selection of the frequency range. The frequency must be of a value to ensure that $X_L \gg R$ on the low end and that resonance is not approached too closely on the high end.

If point A is grounded, we have a standard transformer connection simply drawn in a strange manner. As a practical observation, a standard commercially available pulse transformer was connected on a copper-clad board with the input and point B both grounded and separated by 1 in. There was no observable difference of the output, displayed on a scope, between placing a ground on point A or on point B. The center of R_L can also be grounded for push–pull operation. Referring to Fig. 5.8d, it is seen that a difference in ground potential V_g between the input and the point B ground causes a current to flow through the primary and secondary inductances in the same direction. This effects a cancellation of the noise voltage. A straightforward analysis of this circuit [4] shows that V_N, the common mode noise developed across R_L, is given by

$$V_N = V_G \left(\frac{R}{R + \omega L} \right) \tag{5.11}$$

where R and L are the resistance and inductance of one of the windings. From this it is seen that there is no rejection of a common mode noise voltages at low frequencies. When $X_L = R$ the rejection is 3 dB and after that it continues to increase at 6 dB/octave until resonance with the stray capacitance is approached. At that time measurements must be made to determine the remaining degree of effectiveness.

It can be shown that transmission lines act in a similar manner. There is the same R and X_L relation, where $R = X_L$ is called the

TABLE 5.1
Measured Values of Shield Cutoff Frequency (f_c)

Cable	Impedance (Ω)	Cutoff Frequency (kHz)	Five Times Cutoff Frequency (kHz)	Remarks
Coaxial Cable				
RG-6A	75	0.6	3.0	Double shielded
RG-213	50	0.7	3.5	
RG-214	50	0.7	3.5	Double shielded
RG-62A	93	1.5	7.5	
RG-59C	75	1.6	8.0	
RG-58C	50	2.0	10.0	
Shielded Twisted Pair				
754E	125	0.8	4.0	Double shielded
24 gauge		2.2	11.0	
22 gauge[a]		7.0	35.0	Aluminum foil shield
Shielded Single				
24 gauge		4.0	20.0	

[a] One pair out of an 11-pair cable (Belden 8775).

cable cutoff frequency. Table 5.1 [4] gives the cutoff frequencies of several different cables.

At five times the cutoff frequency the coupling between the two conductors, coaxial or twisted pair, is about 98% effective. This is a low-frequency consideration, since the capacitance of the cable has not been taken into account. However, in contrast to the transformer, the distributed cable capacitance blends with the distributed inductance to form the frequency-independent characteristic impedance of the transmission line. This is discussed further in Appendix I on transmission lines and applied in the wideband transformers discussed in the next section.

5.2.1 Wideband Transformers

The transformers described here are generally called "transmission line transformers" and are capable of extremely wide bandwidth operation. Frequency ratios as high as 20,000 to 1 have been claimed under certain conditions of operation [5]. This section describes how these transformers work and outlines a simple design procedure. To explain how these transformers operate we must consider what happens in a transmission line.

Figure 5.9a represents a twisted-pair transmission line. Figure 5.9b is a schematic version of the same line and shows an input signal applied to one end. The line AB is coupled to line A'B' by both capacitance and mutual inductance. The net result is that the signal applied at A after a suitable length of line has been transversed induces an equal and opposite voltage on the other end of the line, producing the signals shown in Fig. 5.9b. The equations relating the length of line to the degree of coupling are quite formidable, but measurements indicate that a length of about 0.013λ is required for the 3 dB low-frequency cutoff. This cutoff is determined by grounding B in Fig. 5.9b and measuring the voltage at B'. (If B' is grounded, the arrangement is that of a terminated transmission line and the response is flat to DC). For example, if the lowest frequency to be coupled is 1 MHz,

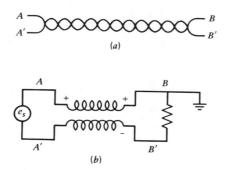

(a)

(b)

FIGURE 5.9 Coupling in a transmission line.

the wavelength λ is 300 m and the required length of line is 3.9 m. It is seen from this that as the frequency is lowered the line soon becomes excessively long. Furthermore, there is also an upper frequency cutoff, and when the transmission line is connected as a transformer, that value is about $0.125\lambda^3$, which leaves a bandwidth of $0.125/0.013 \cong 10$. This is hardly an exceptionally wide bandwidth performance.

To improve the low-frequency response, the transmission line is wound on a ferrite core. We now have a conventional transformer that is designed just like any regular transformer. A load can be placed across the secondary winding as shown in Fig. 5.10.

The transmission line at these low frequencies acts like a bifilar winding, that is, it is a tightly coupled secondary winding. Also, as shown in the preceding section, the transformer, because of its close coupling and symmetry, can be connected as in Fig. 5.9b.

The conventional transformer coupling does have a very limited high-frequency range. However, if it can maintain the frequency response up to the point where the twisted pair acts like a transmission line, a smooth transition occurs. The result is an extremely wideband transformer. The low-frequency cutoff of this transformer occurs when the inductive reactance equals the transmission line impedance. The impedance of the twisted pair used for the transformer in Section 9.4 is estimated to be 60 Ω (see Fig. 9.3). The inductance of a high-permeability core is $L = 0.4\pi N^2 \mu A (10)^{-8}/l$. With the Ferroxcube 266T125/4C4 core and six turns we have

$$L = \frac{0.4\pi(6)^2(125)(0.076)(10)^{-8}}{2.16} = 1.98\text{mH}$$

At 60 Ω this is a low-frequency cutoff of 4.7 MHz. Referring to Fig. 5.9b, the low-frequency cutoff is measured at B' with B grounded. This gave a value of 2.76 MHz. If B' is grounded and the output is taken at B again, the connection is that of a transmission line properly terminated and the response is flat to DC.

The low-frequency cutoff measurement was repeated with the 3 in. of twisted line required for the transformer, but without the core. This produced a low-frequency cutoff of 65 MHz. Winding the trans-

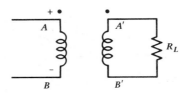

FIGURE 5.10 Conventional transformer connections.

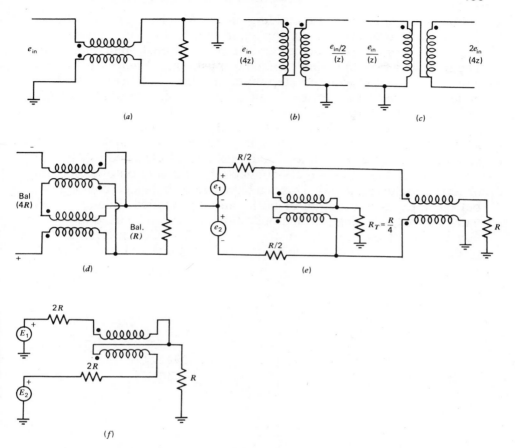

FIGURE 5.11 Unconventional transformer connections: (*a*) unity gain inverter; (*b*) step-down; (*c*) step-up; (*d*) series parallel; (*e*) 180° hybrid; (*f*) in-phase combiner.

mission line to six turns about a nonmagnetic core did not alter this value. Winding the transmission line around a Ferroxcube 266CT125/3B7 core produced a low-frequency cutoff of 85 kHz. This core is of the same physical size as the other core but the permeability is nominally 2300 instead of 125. Despite the fact that the permeability of this core begins to fall at about 0.8 MHz, there was no dip in the response curve prior to the 65 MHz cutoff of the straight transmission line. The response of these transformers was not measured above 65 MHz, but according to the 0.125λ predicted cutoff, the response should reach about 500 MHz.

This arrangement does have some specific limitations. For one, it does not block DC; second, it can be used only in certain discrete ratios. Figure 5.11 shows a collection of the various connections that can be made.

Figure 5.11*a* is the basic building block. All of the circuits shown use the same transformer. As applied in Fig. 5.11*a*, either output can be grounded or the load can be center-tapped for push–pull operation. The input can be either single-ended or push–pull. Figures 5.11*b* and *c* are 2 to 1 step-down and step-up connections, respectively. Two or more of these transformers can be cascaded to provide voltage ratios of 4 to 1, 8 to 1, and so on. A 3 to 1 voltage ratio connection is also possible, with expansion to 4 to 1, 5 to 1, and so on. A slight adjustable extension of the 4 to 1 impedance transformation (2 to 1 in voltage) to as high as 6 to 1 is described in Reference [6]. Figure 5.11*d* shows two transformers connected in parallel on one end and in series on the other end. This is a balanced-to-balanced connection, but the input or the output or both can be grounded. Figures 5.11*b* and *c* are only for single-ended operation. They can be used in push–pull circuits if one set of transformers appears in each line. At any rate, both circuits require the same number of cores. Figure 5.11*e* is

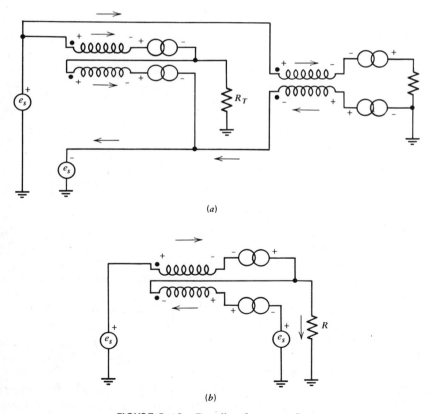

FIGURE 5.12   Details of current flow.

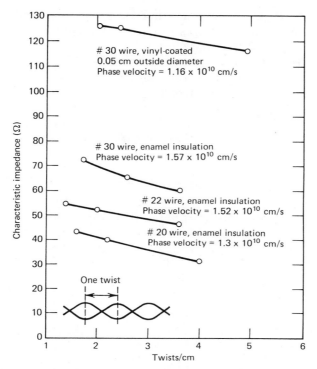

FIGURE 5.13 Impedance of twisted lines: characteristic impedance. "Reprinted from *Electronics*, August 16, 1973. Copyright © McGraw-Hill, Inc., 1973. All rights reserved."

really two separate circuits. The actual transformer is the same as Fig. 5.11*a*. The center part of the circuit is a high impedance if the two signal lines have equal and opposite voltage, but draws a current if there is an imbalance. This allows two favorable actions; first, it reduces the even harmonic distortion and, second, it reduces the load seen by one transistor if the other should fail [7]. (Failure of one half of a push–pull stage generates a large even harmonic distortion.) R_T should have one fourth the power rating of R. Figure 5.11*f* is the same circuit, but driven by two in-phase signals, which causes all of the power to go to the resistor at the center tap.

Figure 5.12 shows the relations of the induced voltages and currents in this circuit. First, push–pull voltages are applied. It is seen that the induced voltages in the balance circuit oppose the applied signal voltages, so that the current is going to be very small. The current instead takes the path to the output transformer where the induced voltage cancels the *IX* drop, thus offering very little opposition to the currents. In Fig. 5.12*b* in-phase voltages are applied to the circuit.

The induced voltages are now in a direction to aid the applied voltages and cancel the reactance drop so that the two currents are passed to add in the load resistor.

When transmission line transformers are used for impedance transformation, it is not possible to match the line with both source and load. The accepted compromise is $Z = \sqrt{Z_P Z_S}$. Fortunately, this match is generally not very critical. Figure 5.13 is a guide to making the proper line. References [6] and [9] give additional information on transformer construction and impedance levels.

REFERENCES

[1] W. M. T. McLyman, *Transformer Design Handbook,* Dekker, New York, 1978.

[2] R. W. Lande, D. C. Davis, and A. P. Albrecht, *Electronic Designers Handbook,* McGraw-Hill, New York, 1957.

[3] E. C. Snelling, *Soft Ferrites, Properties and Applications,* Chemical Rubber Co., 1969.

[4] H. W. Ott, *Noise Reduction Techniques in Electronic Systems,* Wiley, New York, 1976, p. 73.

[5] C. L. Ruthroff, Some Broad Band Transformers, *IRE,* Vol. 47, Aug. 1957.

[6] O. Pitzalis, R. E. Horn, and R. J. Baranello, Broadband 60 W HF Linear Amplifier, *IEE J. Solid State Circuits,* Vol. SC-6, No. 3, June 1971.

[7] O. Pitzalis and T. P. Cause, Broadband Transformer Design for RF Transistor Power Amplifiers, in *Proceedings of the 1968 Electronic Components Conference,* pp. 207–216.

[8] H. L. Krauss and C. W. Allen, Designing Toroidal Transformers to Optimize Wideband Performance, *Electronics,* Aug. 16, 1973.

[9] H. Granberg, *Broadband Transformers and Power Combining Techniques for RF, Motorola Note AN-749,* Motorola, Inc., Phoenix, AZ.

GENERAL REFERENCES

W. M. T. McLyman, *Magnetic Core Selection for Transformers and Inductors,* Dekker, New York, 1982.

D. DeMaw, *Practical RF Design Manual,* Prentice-Hall, Englewood Cliffs, NJ, 1982.

SIX

Interfacing and Interference

In various parts of this book the importance of the ground plane has been emphasized (see the Index). The problem becomes much more complex when circuits remotely located from each other must be interconnected. This is both because the various grounds can easily have a difference of many volts between them and because the greater lengths allow outside disturbances to be more effective. The circuits being connected often are shielded enclosures and the cables connecting them must also be considered as such. The extent to which interfering signals can couple into the cables must be carefully evaluated.

If certain basic rules are not adhered to, a given system may be unable to operate correctly. Unfortunately, many of the rules are broken before a knowledgeable person becomes aware of the problem. This leads to the following four rules:

1. A preliminary study of the basic interconnection requirements must be made early in the program. The results of this study should be clearly set forth in the system requirements so that the individuals responsible for hardware commitments and circuit design understand what they must do. Finally, there must be feedback to see if the interconnection requirements are being adhered to.

2. It is the circuit designer's responsibility to eliminate cables and connectors wherever possible. This should be the first phase of the design and must involve communication with the systems group so that possible trade-offs in space between different locations can lead to minimizing the cables. Last-minute thoughts or changes often create unnecessary cable problems.

3. An interface design for a harsh environment is costly in components, space, and power consumption, so even at the begin-

ning it is important not to overdesign. This chapter offers guidelines and solutions for various problems. The reader must decide how many of these problem areas need to be considered in a specific project, and to what degree.

4. Despite all the rules and thought processes involving basic shielding, even simple systems offer conflicts. This means that after all reasonable precautions have been taken, one evil must often be balanced against another to obtain the best system compromise.

As the interfacing conditions become more critical, it is necessary to use shielded cable properly and to define more carefully the various forms of interference. The following kinds of disturbances can be expected [1]:

1. Electric fields
2. Magnetic fields
3. Ground potentials
4. Reactance coupling
5. Common impedance coupling
6. Galvanic action
7. Electrolytic action
8. Triboelectric effect
9. Conductor motion

6.1 ELECTROSTATIC AND ELECTROMAGNETIC SHIELDING

Electromagnetic waves are propagated by the coexistence of an electric field and a magnetic field. The ratio of the strength of the electric field to the magnetic field is a constant.

However, when the electromagnetic energy is first generated, it may be either from a high-voltage source (electric field) or from a high-current source (magnetic field). It does not assume a balanced relationship until a distance of approximately $\lambda/6$ has been reached. For 10 MHz this would be 4.8 m. For fully developed electromagnetic waves both electric and magnetic shielding must be provided. Many interfering sources are fairly close, however; hence electric shielding and magnetic shielding are considered separately.

Electric fields divide directly according to the impedances involved. This is shown in Fig. 6.1. Figure 6.1b is a schematic representation of Fig. 6.1a. As the input impedance is lowered, the voltage received is reduced. Figure 6.1c shows a coaxial cable on the line to

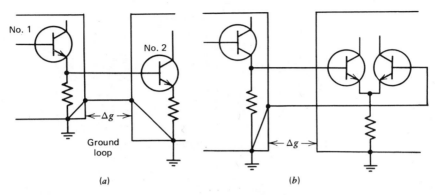

FIGURE 6.4   Ground potentials.

Since the differential amplifier is effective in minimizing pickup, it is well to take a closer look at these devices. There are both analog and digital differential receivers, and they are not interchangeable. In the analog device we are looking for such characteristics as

1. High common-mode rejection at all frequencies of concern
2. Low gain, usually about unity
3. Small package size
4. Low power consumption
5. Low input capacitance for high-frequency systems

The input resistance and bias currents are generally not very critical because of the low cable impedance. A low-gain receiver is important because it is desirable to transmit signals in a noisy environment at a high level.

The first thing to establish is that the standard op-amp is a poor differential receiver. This is illustrated in Fig. 6.5. The principal problem is that the gain is too high. This forces the use of a resistor on the noninverting side to ground. With a grounded transmitter this establishes a ground loop, which defeats the purpose of the differential receiver.

To consider the properties of the op-amp further, we look at a good device, the LF157.

The LF157 has a low-frequency common-mode rejection of 80 dB at 3 kHz, falling at 20 dB/decade as the frequency increases. In the useful frequency range of the amplifier the common-mode rejection is limited to the balance of the resistors. Special resistor packages can be purchased where the ratio balance is 0.1%, or better if required (Caddock and others), and this is the proper way to go. The ±1% standard resistors can be used, but the rejection ratio ranges from 30

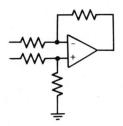

FIGURE 6.5   Op-amp as a differential receiver.

to 40 dB. Aside from this, the frequency response of even the better op-amps does not present a reasonable rejection above 1 MHz.

At lower frequencies there are monolithic instrumentation amplifiers (NSC LF152, BB 3660) that have 60 dB of rejection at 1 kHz for unity gain. These amplifiers do not require input resistors.

At lower frequencies there are video amplifiers such as Fairchild's μA733 and Motorola's MC1545. These amplifiers, however, require the undesired input attenuators to reduce their gain to a usable value. Though no real technical difficulties seem to exist, there are no suitable unity-gain monolithic video differential receivers on the market at this time. A discrete design is often the only solution to the problem.

A transformer can be used to isolate one chassis from another, but there are very definite limitations. However, when the ground loop voltages are power-line-frequency related and in ground-based equipment where size and weight are not problems, the transformer may be a good choice. For transformers the bandwidth is always a problem. The transformer not only passes the higher-frequency signals but also fails to reject the high-frequency common-mode signals (ground-loop voltages are common-mode signals) because of the interwinding capacitance. A grounded copper foil called a Faraday shield can be placed between the two windings to eliminate this feedthrough. This increases the capacitance of both windings to ground, although with detrimental effects on the high-frequency response.

Another manner of inductive coupling is the use of a longitudinal choke. The reader should refer to Section 5.2 on unconventional transformers at this time. Figure 6.6 shows such a connection. This can be a conventional transformer. Used in this manner, it rejects the common-mode current over its operating pass band. It does not isolate DC, which may or may not be an advantage. At the same time, it does not block the low-frequency common-mode voltages, which, unless it is a good-sized device, include the power-line frequencies. If a transmission line transformer is used in this application, greatly extended high-frequency operation is realized.

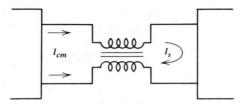

FIGURE 6.6   The longitudinal choke.

At higher frequencies and longer cable lengths, the problems become more complex. It is often recommended that a lengths greater than λ/20 it may be necessary to use multiple grounds (λ/20 at 1 MHz = 15 m) to guarantee that the shield remains at ground. This raises the question of what to ground it to. Unfortunately, generally there is no place along the length of the cable that is holding solid ground. It does, however, usually work out best if at frequencies above 1 MHz the shield is grounded at both ends. This may not be as bad as it sounds because the skin effect causes the noise currents to flow on the outside of the shield and the return signal current to flow on the inside of the shield, thus providing a degree of separation between them. To understand this it should be recalled that the reason that the signal current flows through the shield instead of alternate ground routes is the voltage induced by the mutual inductance with the center conductor. The center conductor is next to the inside of the shield and the noise is largely next to the outside of the shield.

The most difficult grounding problems occur with wideband transmissions. For one, there is simply more room for noise to enter and in the limiting case the resistor noise increases as the square root of the bandwidth. Of importance is the power-line frequency and its harmonics. If the low-frequency cutoff can be made 500 Hz or higher (for 60 Hz lines), this troublesome noise source can be filtered out. If the low-frequency roll-off is raised to several kHz, usually the normal blocking capacitors can do the job. Another benefit is the elimination of the noisy 1/f region. A good technique is to make the second ground on the shield by a capacitor. In this way the cable can have a single ground at low frequencies and a double ground for the high range.

6.3 GROUND LOOPS AND DIGITAL SIGNALS

All of the precautions about grounding and transmission in analog signals are also important in digital signals and operate in much the same manner. With analog signals rms noise affects the accuracy in a more or less proportional manner. With digital signals, however, the MSB is just as apt to be flipped as is the LSB, and the results can be much more serious.

Differential receivers and drivers are also used for digital signals to improve the noise immunity. The driver is commonly connected to the receiver by a shielded twisted pair, and the receiver is a sensitive comparator with its reference set at the midpoint of the high and low signal. The Fairchild 9614 dual driver and 9613 dual receiver are a typical pair. These devices are limited to about 10 MHz and draw a substantial amount of quiescent current, 34 mA for the 9614 and 30 mA for the 9613. The SN74S140, a single-ended device, can drive a 50 Ω line up to about 40 MHz. A normal Schottky gate or a comparator is then used as a single-ended receiver.

For computing equipment that operates in a laboratory environment and where the runs are short, ribbon cable is very popular. Here the emphasis is on reducing the noise source, since the cable is generally not shielded. With this type of cable it is a good idea to make every other line a ground to minimize cross-talk in the cable.

If properly shielded and terminated transmission lines were used for all digital lines, much of the troubles would be circumvented (see Appendix I). This is very costly in equipment, space, and power. However, when the speeds are such that ECL must be used, terminated transmission lines are defined and supported by that logic system. Large digital systems rely heavily on error-detecting codes and multiple transmissions to effect accuracy.

Most logic systems have low output impedances and high input impedances relative to the characteristic impedance of normal interconnections (50 to 200 Ω). In these cases a good rule of thumb is to limit the rise time of the pulse to four times the one-way delay time of the line [2]. As an approximation, the speed of the signal can be considered to be about 1.5 ns/ft.

6.4 SYSTEM CONNECTIONS

The limitations and complexity of providing satisfactory interconnections point again to one of the basic rules of system design: do everything possible to limit the number of cables between the subsystems. This involves some well-thought-out trade-offs among processing, space, power consumption, and other matters.

The problem of local ground potentials and loops is illustrated in Fig. 6.7. It must be emphasized that conditions outside the system itself can drastically alter the situation. The system should be designed for defined limitations of the environment or the development time

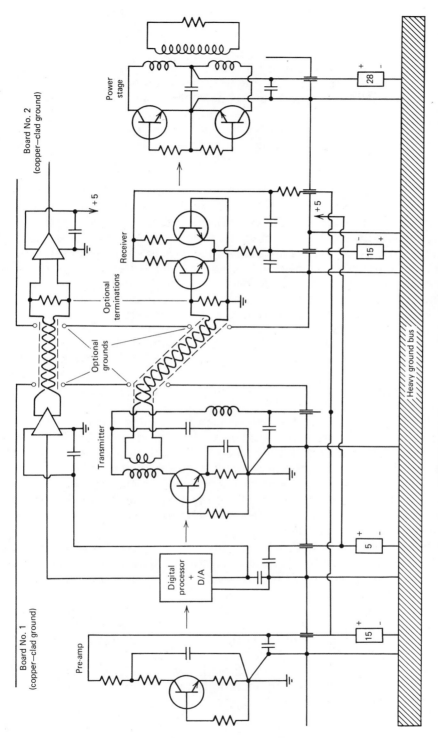

FIGURE 6.7 System grounding considerations.

and costs of the enclosures and interfacing circuits become prohibitive.

Figure 6.7 assumes only a reasonable voltage Δg exists between the two chassis. Part of this is due to the environment; the remainder depends on how the boards are constructed and the connection of the wires to those boards.

Board No. 1 shows a sensitive preamp and a digital processor that go to an analog driver and a digital driver. Board No. 2 has a digital receiver, an analog receiver, and a power amplifier. The two boards are fed by a common power supply.

An important factor in avoiding grounding problems is containment of the ground currents on the boards by proper layout of the components. The bypass capacitors are deliberately drawn to optimum points to localize these currents. For high-frequency circuits, however, the leads of these capacitors must be as short as possible to minimize inductance, and they are accordingly wired directly to the ground plane. Again, the little prethought regarding the orientation of the components greatly assists in this grounding compromise. Current localizing can never be made perfect, but striving to that end minimizes problems.

The same consideration must be given to the power lines. Within reason each section of the system is decoupled within itself and effectively has its own power leads. Sometimes it is necessary to cut the ground plane and make a discrete connection with a single wire at the proper place in order to control the current paths. At other times a single power lead attachment to the ground plane is satisfactory. This thought process must be exercised first and then the building decisions made. In addition to controlling the signal currents it is also important to keep them as small as possible. The use of source termination on *short* transmission lines aids in this respect and is generally preferred (see Section I.6 on transmission lines). The earth ground is generally made at the most sensitive part of the system to minimize the external fields in that area. There is also a desire to tie the power supply to the earth ground for safety, particularly if the power supply is operated without the grounded system unit. In some cases there may be little difference in performance with either ground or both grounds.

There are many options for connecting the signal leads between the two boards. In this case insulated shielded twisted leads with push–pull signals are used for both the analog and digital lines. *Both* ends of each shield are available for *optional* grounding. A terminating resistor is also conveniently available if system tests indicate a need for it. Some decisions cannot accurately be made before system testing, and a degree of flexibility is very valuable.

6.4.1 Isolated Power Supplies

The techniques of signal containment described with reference to Fig. 6.7 is fundamental to all systems. However, very often it is possible to have isolated power supplies, as shown in Fig. 6.8.

This is a simple and generally very effective way of minimizing coupling in ground lines. The resistor used to connect the analog and digital grounds is selected by testing in a representative noise environment. The higher the resistance, the lower the ground coupling and the poorer the noise rejection. The value of this resistance need not be very high and many times it can be shorted out. However, if the connection between the grounds is not limited to a single easy-to-reach point, there is often no solution to an unexpected problem.

6.4.2 Optical Isolators

If the coupling data between two boards is digital, as shown in Fig. 6.8, and the bandwidth is modest, electro-optical couplers offer an excellent means of avoiding the ground-loop problem. The HP6N34, for example, is a dual unit with a 10 MHz bandwidth. The required diode drive is about 12 mA and the receiver position takes mA from a 5 V supply.

A good idea is to use driver from the HCMOS family, or better, the newer ACMOS logic elements, as these are bidirectional drivers. This allows polarity changes, which always seem to occur, to be made in a convenient manner. It also affords the designer the luxury of consistently thinking in one logic form (e.g., high is always on) and then reversing the output drive direction to adapt to the actual systems demand.

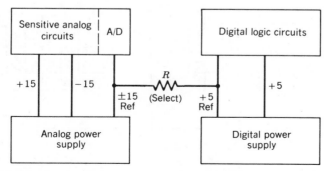

FIGURE 6.8 Separation of grounds by isolated power supplies.

6.5 MISCELLANEOUS FORMS OF COUPLING

Coupling by mutual inductance or capacitance occurs when two lines are placed close to each other, the noise or signal current in one line inducing a voltage in the other line. This commonly occurs in cabling. Sensitive lines and high-power lines should be in separable cables. Connectors are notorious for coupling signals. If digital or high-power lines must pass through the same connector, they should be on opposite ends of the connector with a number of ground pins between them to form a shield. All shields in a cable should be insulated unless they are specifically tied together and cannot touch another ground.

Common impedance coupling can occur anywhere because of oversight but is most common in ground and power-supply leads. Grounding has already been well discussed. Figure 6.9 shows correct and incorrect methods of connecting power-supply leads.

In Fig. 6.9b the currents of all three devices are coupled by the resistance of the common power and ground leads. There are also no local bypass capacitors to contain the high-frequency currents. This would be especially bad for T^2L, with its internal totem-pole pull-ups. These circuits have a small period of high conduction in the output stage during switching and can cause serious interference unless this current is contained with a local bypass. It is often overkill to wire every circuit as shown in Fig. 6.9a, and the series or "daisy-chain" power-line connections can be made provided that the local capacitor is maintained; 0.01 to 0.1 μF is generally a satisfactory range for these capacitors. The concept of Fig. 6.9a, however, must not be forgotten, and any conflicting components should not share a power-supply lead nor be too close to each other on the ground plane. For low-frequency signals small capacitors are not adequate. *RC* filters

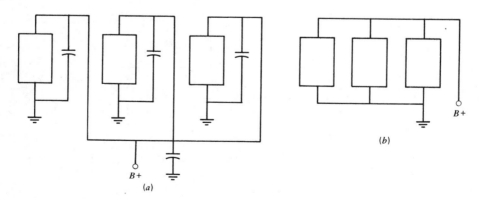

FIGURE 6.9 Power-supply connections. (*a*) correct; (*b*) incorrect.

TABLE 6.1
Galvanic Series

ANODIC END
(Most susceptible to corrosion)

Group I	1. Magnesium		13. Nickel (active)
			14. Brass
	2. Zinc		15. Copper
	3. Galvanized steel		16. Bronze
			17. Copper–nickel
Group II	4. Aluminum 2S	Group IV	alloy
	5. Cadmium		18. Monel
	6. Aluminum 17ST		19. Silver solder
			20. Nickel (passive)[a]
			21. Stainless steel
	7. Steel		(passive)[a]
	8. Iron		
	9. Stainless steel		
Group III	(active)		22. Silver
	10. Lead tin solder	Group V	23. Graphite
	11. Lead		24. Gold
	12. Tin		25. Platinum

CATHODIC END
(Least susceptible to corrosion)

[a] Passivation by immersion in a strongly oxidizing acidic solution. From Ref. [1].

with large tantalum capacitors must be used, and often local voltage regulators must be added to break up the coupling.

Galvanic action occurs when dissimilar metals are brought together. With a little moisture, a voltage is developed, producing noise and finally corrosion, which can lead to intermittent circuit performance and mechanical breakdown. Table 6.1 shows the galvanic series [1]. The further apart the metals are in the chart, the greater is the developed voltage.

Electrolytic action is a form of corrosion caused by current passing through two metals that are butted or pressed together. There must be an electrolyte which could be caused by some form of conductive pollutant. This differs from the galvanic action inasmuch as it can occur between similar metals.

The triboelectric effect occurs because of a change in the effective dielectric constant of a cable when the conductor moves relative to the fixed dielectric material in the cable. Certain low-noise cables have the dielectric coated with a conductive powder to maintain better contact between the outer conductor and the dielectric. The cable, in addition, should be securely tied down to avoid motion, and bends must be held to a gentle radius to avoid strains.

Conductor motion produces a result similar to the effect discussed above, but is due to movement in a magnetic field. The two effects are often called microphonics and occur under conditions of vibration where long high-impedance leads are involved. The problem at times requires extremely rigid mounting.

6.6 NOISE SOURCES

This is the other half of the noise problem. It is necessary to investigate the noise sources that are causing trouble and then determine what can be done about it. The outside sources of interference are so numerous and varied that any reasonable list would still be incomplete. It is well to try to identify the nature of the noise by examination with a scope. Magnetic sources can usually be identified by clipping the ground lead of the probe to the input so as to form a loop and examining the resulting signal. An electrostatic field would be detected by clipping the input of the probe to a short unattached wire and grounding the probe ground lead. The scope must, of course, have sufficient bandwidth to check for the frequencies of concern. Very high frequencies, beyond the scope range, quite often are demodulated by the circuit, thereby inserting a relatively low-frequency disturbance that seems to come from nowhere.

Interference caused by other parts of the same system are another matter and are as much a controlled design as any other part of the system.

High-frequency, high-gain circuits require local shielding or partitioning. This is aside from the grounding and decoupling concepts previously discussed. It is not easy to put a number on the gain and frequency levels that require a specified degree of planned isolation. Figures 2.14 and 2.15 show dotted lines where partitions are intended. If it is worthwhile to build a box, it is necessary to use a belt grinder to ensure that the top is flat and the lid fits securely. It is the maximum length of an opening that primarily determines the amount of leakage.

If the output of an amplifier delivers power to a remotely grounded load, the magnetic field is contained if both ends of the shield are grounded. The electric field is contained with only one ground. The reasoning is the same as in the shielding of an input line. However, the output stage, being of a higher level, is not as likely to be bothered with differences in ground potentials as are the input stages.

A high-frequency, high-rejection filter requires the same type of shielding. In this case the high-level signal is at the input.

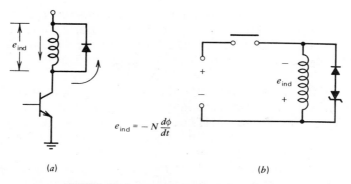

$$e_{ind} = -N\frac{d\phi}{dt}$$

(a)   (b)

FIGURE 6.10   Diode voltage suppression.

Whenever the current in an inductive circuit is turned off a voltage is developed that is inversely proportional to the time it takes to shut off the current. This voltage can reach large values that damage components and cause interfering signals in other parts of the circuit. Figures 6.9a and b show a transistor and a set of relay contacts breaking an inductive load, respectively.

When the current in an inductive circuit is decreased the induced voltage is in a direction to maintain that current, that is, it adds to the supply voltage. Accordingly, as the resistance of the transistor is increased, the voltage of the collector also increases and, without protection, can cause a breakdown. The diode placed across the inductor, as shown in Fig. 6.10a limits this voltage and protects the transistor. It does have a disadvantage: the decay time is increased, and if the inductance represents a relay the release time is greatly extended. The release time can be shortened by using a zener in series with the diode, as shown in Fig. 6.10b. The value of the zener is a design trade-off. The higher the zener voltage, the quicker the release and the larger the developed emf. It is important that this surge protection be placed close to the inductor to minimize the length of the radiating lines.

6.7 SUMMARY

For electrostatic shielding a shielded cable and ground at the receiving end should be used.

If the receiver and source are both grounded, grounding the shield of a cable at one end only gives no protection from a magnetic field.

Magnetic shielding is provided if both ends of the shield are grounded, but the effectiveness is reduced if noise currents flow in the shield. These currents are caused by differences in the ground potentials of the two chassis. The shielding is also less effective at frequencies below cable R/L breakpoint.

A twisted pair is more effective than coaxial cable against magnetic fields, but the same conditions and limitations apply.

For frequencies above 1 MHz best results are usually obtained with a ground at each end of the cable. Grounding one end by a capacitor breaks the ground loop for low frequencies.

To prevent radiation from a high-frequency line which is going from a grounded transmitter to a grounded receiver, both ends of the shield must be grounded.

Differential receivers offer much higher noise reduction than grounded receivers. However, the practical limits of the differential receiver must be carefully checked.

REFERENCES

[1] H. W. Ott, *Noise Reduction Techniques in Electronic Systems*, Wiley, New York, 1976.

[2] T^2L *Applications Handbook*, Fairchild, Camera and Instrument Corp., Mountain View, CA, Aug. 1973.

GENERAL REFERENCES

R. Morrison, *Shielding and Grounding Techniques in Instrumentation*, Wiley, New York, 1967.

H. S. Stone, *Microcomputer Interfacing*, Addison-Wesley, Reading, MA, 1982.

SEVEN

Filters

Filters are a very important part of electronic design. They separate desired signals from undesired noise. There are many types of filters, having a great range of transmission and attenuation characteristics, to choose from. The analysis and design of these filters are complex and tedious, and, in general, are beyond the capabilities of the nonspecialist engineer.

Fortunately, with the development of the computer and the efforts of many dedicated individuals, tables and graphs are now available that enable the average engineer to design filters for a wide range of applications.

This chapter, together with Appendix III, covers the basic knowledge and techniques required for these designs. Difficult and exacting filter requirements still require an expert and are beyond the scope of this book. The references given aid in further understanding.

This chapter discusses the design of three major types of filters. First, there is the classical passive *LC* filter design. Its basic theory and equations have been in existence for some time. Second, there is the active *RC* filter, which is relatively new, having grown up with the computer and the monolithic operational amplifier. The third type of filter is the tracking or switched capacitor concept; really a form of active filter, its applications are so unique that it deserves its own section.

For the most part, the active and passive filters complement one another without a large area of overlap. The active *RC* filter covers the low-frequency range, going down to a small fraction of a hertz. This is a practically impossible area for passive *LC* filters because of the large size and high cost of the components. Active filters do, however, begin to have difficulty with frequency response in the range of a few MHz. Fortunately, the passive *LC* filter is quite suitable in this part of the spectrum and for lumped parameters continues to be effective to about 200 MHz.

Beyond this the helical resonator and cavity along with other microwave techniques are the elements that must be used. This subject is not covered in this book.

The proper application of filters is a different subject which is largely covered by signal-to-noise analysis. It, likewise, is not included in this book, but a great deal of information is available from other sources.

The following three types of transmission characteristics are described and realized by the filters: The Butterworth–Chebyshev group, the elliptic, and several forms of constant delay designs. Specifically covered are a Butterworth–Thomson active filter and an equiripple passive filter.

The Butterworth is really a special case of the Chebyshev filter with no ripple in the pass-band. The Chebyshev filter tables (included in this book) are for 0.01 dB (0.1% pp) and 0.1 dB (1% pp) ripple. This is not very much, but there is a substantial improvement in the attenuation characteristics over that of the Butterworth. There is also a substantial increase in the time-delay errors. Some study of Figs. 7.1–7.8 would be worthwhile at this time.

The use of filters is most straightforward when one sine wave must be separated from another. It becomes more complex when the de-

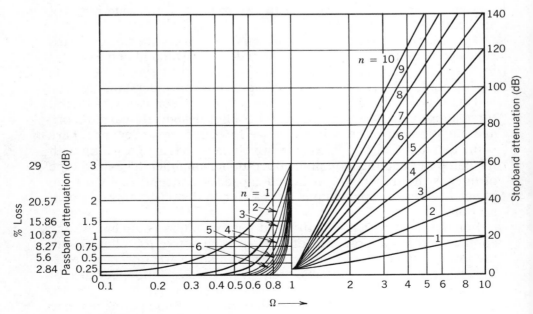

FIGURE 7.1 Attenuation characteristics for Butterworth filters.

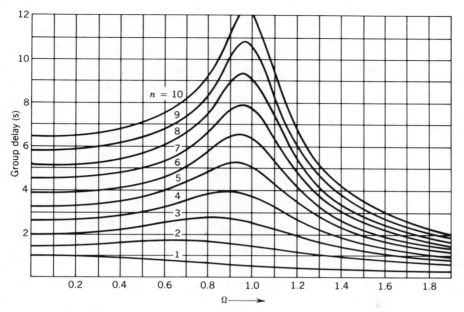

FIGURE 7.2 Group-delay characteristics for Butterworth filters.

sired signal has a unique waveform that must be preserved. In these cases not only must the harmonics be passed but their phase relationship maintained. A rule of thumb to pass a square wave through a band-pass filter is that the band-pass spectrum be $\frac{1}{10}f_0$ to $10f_0$ or $\frac{1}{20}f_0$ to $20f_0$ if better accuracy is required. There are, of course, no subharmonics involved, this being merely a means of preserving the phase characteristics of the high-frequency harmonics.

All filters have a delay, but when the delay is nonuniform for the necessary frequency components, phase distortion results. The group-delay Figs. 7.2, 7.4, 7.6, and 7.8 show this variation for the filters being discussed.

To pass these complex waveforms, the cutoff (-3 dB point) of the filter must be moved out far enough to satisfy both the phase and the amplitude requirements of the harmonics. This, of course, widens the noise transmission spectrum and is a problem when filters are used with complex signal forms.

The equiripple filter characteristics shown in Figs. 7.7 and 7.8 have a 0.05° phase ripple error. The attenuation is not as good as a Chebyshev, but it has a very superior time-delay characteristic, particularly for the higher-order filters. This means that the roll-off frequency of the filter can be closer to the fundamental frequency, thereby giving better noise rejection.

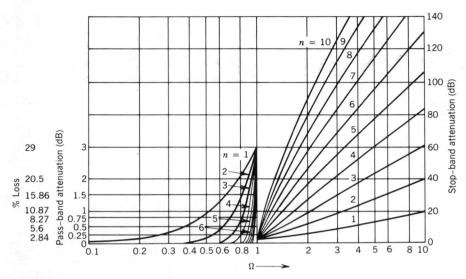

FIGURE 7.3 Attenuation characteristics for Chebyshev filter with 0.01 dB ripple (0.11%).

Except for the elliptic filters, the filters described in this chapter consist of series inductances followed by shunt capacitances. The differences in the characteristics are controlled by the specific values of these L's and C's.

In the asymptotic limit all the filters have the same slope, 6 dB/octave (20 dB/decade) per element or pole, as they are called. For example, a 3rd-order filter has a final roll-off of 60 dB/octave. This, of course, is true only as long as the L's remain inductive and the C's remain capacitive.

At this point it would be well to define the term "pole" as used in this text. The term comes from the mathematical representation of the filters, that is, when the denominator of a fractional expression becomes zero. A value of infinity is then produced, or, as it is called, a "pole." Although these polynomial expressions are not referred to in this text, the term has become so common that its use is practically required.

In a similar manner, a "zero" is produced when a term in the numerator becomes zero.

For our purposes a pole is produced when a reactive element is used to produce a frequency roll-off.

For example, an RC or an RL produces 1 pole and a 6 dB/octave roll-off. An LC produces 2 poles or a 12 dB/octave roll-off. In general, there is a 6 dB/octave roll-off for each pole in a filter. Again, these roll-offs are for the asymptotic condition. The initial roll-offs vary a great deal with the design of the filter.

Since all of the normalized filters are defined equal at the -3 dB corner, the difference is in the immediate area of this breakpoint. Figures 7.1–7.8 should again be reviewed at this time because this recognition of their properties is very important.

The elliptic filter is of a different nature, as indicated in Fig. 7.9. It, too, has a ripple in the pass band, but is then followed by a resonant trap, or "frequency of infinite attenuation." The higher frequency response does not continue down in the manner of the Butterworth and Chebyshev but consists of a series of peaks and valleys. For a given number of components the elliptic filter has the steepest slope following cutoff.

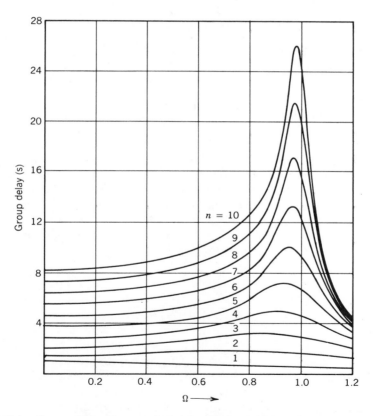

FIGURE 7.4 Group-delay characteristics for Chebyshev filter with 0.01 dB ripple.

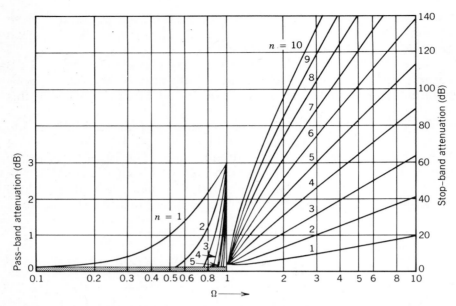

FIGURE 7.5 Attenuation characteristics for Chebyshev filter with 0.1 dB ripple.

This filter has another unique characteristic: a series of high attenuation points in the rejection region. These are often and improperly called points of infinite attenuation because of the cusplike structure of this part of the filter. The actual attenuation at these points depends upon the Q's of the circuit elements and the accuracy of the design and is accordingly difficult to predict. The number of cusps in the attenuation band increases with the order of the filter, but it is the first one that is normally of importance.

If the pass-band can stand some ripple and there is a specific nearby frequency requiring a high attenuation, the elliptic filter is an obvious choice.

7.1 PASSIVE FILTERS

The design tables for the passive filters are located in Appendix III. They are for low-pass filters only. The reason for this is that the high-pass, band-pass, and band-stop filters can all be obtained by transformations from properly defined low-pass designs.

These tables are also in a normalized form which gives a filter that has a 1 Ω impedance level and a cutoff frequency of 1 rad/s. The values in the tables are in henries and farads. For example, if we label the values in the tables as R, L, C, and ω and the desired values as R', L', C', and ω', we have the following relations:

$$L' = \left(\frac{R'}{R}\right)\left(\frac{\omega}{\omega'}\right) L \qquad (7.1)$$

$$C' = \left(\frac{R}{R'}\right)\left(\frac{\omega}{\omega'}\right) C \qquad (7.2)$$

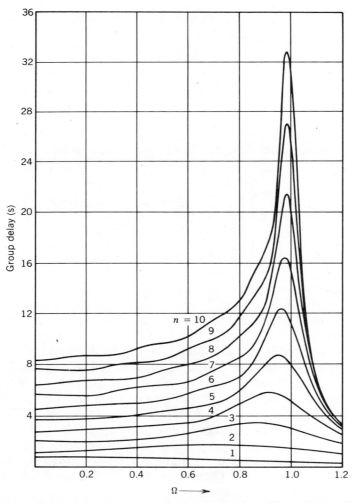

FIGURE 7.6   Group-delay characteristics for Chebyshev filter with 0.1 dB ripple.

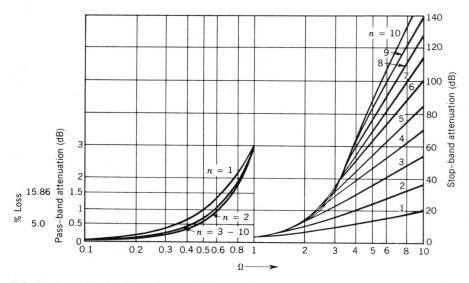

FIGURE 7.7 Attenuation characteristics for linear phase with equiripple error filter (phase error = 0.05°).

To illustrate, if the desired filter is to operate at 50 Ω and 25 MHz, we have

$$L' = \left(\frac{50}{1}\right)\frac{1}{2\pi(25)(10)^6} L = 0.318(10)^{-6}L \quad H$$

$$C' = \left(\frac{1}{50}\right)\frac{1}{2\pi(25)(10)^6} C = 127(10)^{-12}C \quad F$$

We see in Appendix III that there are several kinds of tables. The first set is called "lossless." This means that the coils are assumed to have infinite Q. These tables also are for source and load-terminated filters.

The next set of tables are called "uniform dissipation" networks. This means that the dissipation of all L's and C's is the same in a given filter, and there is a set of values for dissipation factors from 0 to 0.65 (see Appendix I for definitions of d and Q). These tables are meant only for low-pass filters that are to be transformed into band-pass or band-stop filters. They are correct for low-pass filters but require the addition of a resistor in parallel with each capacitor so that the capacitors have the same dissipation as the coils (a very worthless complication). Their necessity in the band-pass transformation is discussed in Section 7.1.6.

Next comes a set of tables called "lossy-L." These tables assume that the coils have finite Q and are specified for a dissipation from 0

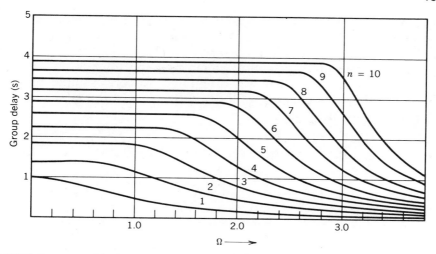

FIGURE 7.8 Group-delay characteristics for linear phase with error filter (phase error = 0.05°).

to 0.65. They also give a choice of source or load termination depending on whether the top or bottom schematics are used. Last is a set of tables for the design of elliptic filters.

One of the problems in designing filters is that the resulting parameters are often not practical values and the filters cannot be built without some kind of modification or compromise. The filter terminating resistance is an aid in getting the best average of practical components in the filter. If some unpractical components remain, various transformations and tricks of the trade can be used. For these

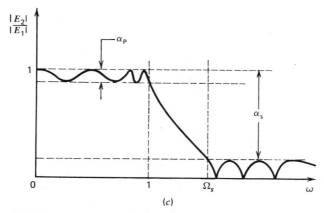

FIGURE 7.9 Elliptic filter transmission characteristic.

the reader is referred to other texts specializing in this subject. One last comment is that many of these impractical values result from transformation of low pass to band pass, particularly if the band pass is too narrow. This may simply mean that the filter is completely impossible in the form that was attempted. Several sample designs are included in this chapter to illustrate the use of the tables and to point out areas of difficulty.

7.1.1 Design Example: Filter 1, Five-Pole Butterworth Low-Pass Filter

Here $f_{-3 \, dB} = 15$ MHz. For a low-pass filter the lossless terminated filters or the lossy-L open termination design charts should be used. This filter is later combined with filter 2, a 5 MHz high-pass filter, to form a band-pass combination. To combine two filters directly without isolation or buffering, the input impedance of the second filter must properly terminate the first filter. Hence the terminated filter design is used. To further ensure that they do not interact with each other, the two filters must be of a low-ripple design such as a Butterworth and the pass-band must be at least 1 octave wide.

From Appendix III the normalized values of the five-pole lossless Butterworth filters are obtained and the transformations made in accordance with Eqs. 7.1 and 7.2. By trial and error it has been determined that 300 Ω would be an acceptable termination for both filters 1 and 2.

$$L' = \frac{300}{2\pi(15)(10)^6} = 3.18(10)^{-6}L.$$

$$C' = \frac{1}{(300)(2\pi)(15)(10)^6} = 35.4(10)^{-12}C.$$

$$
\begin{array}{ll}
C_1 = 0.618 & C_1' = 21.88 \text{ pF} \\
L_2 = 1.618 & L_2' = 5.15 \text{ } \mu\text{H} \\
C_3 = 2.000 & C_3' = 70.8 \text{ pF} \\
L_4 = 1.618 & L_4' = 5.15 \text{ } \mu\text{H} \\
C_5 = 0.618 & C_5' = 21.88 \text{ pF}
\end{array}
$$

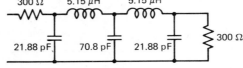

FIGURE 7.10 Five-pole low-pass Butterworth filter.

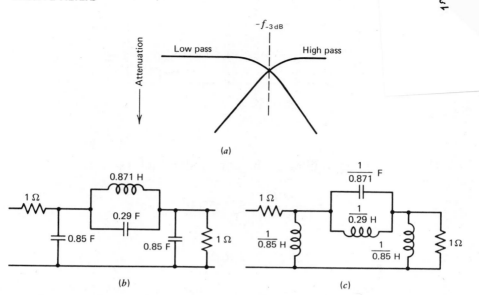

FIGURE 7.11 Low-pass–high-pass transformation: (*a*) symmetry of $f_{-3\,dB}$; (*b*) low pass; (*c*) high pass.

The resulting low-pass filter is shown in Fig. 7.10.

7.1.2 High-Pass Filters

This subsection shows the concept of the low-pass to high-pass transformation and the next one is a design example.

The transformation is very easy. Figure 7.11*a* shows the desired high-pass filter and its low-pass counterpart. The two are mirror images about the $f_{-3\,dB}$ point.

If Fig. 7.11*b* represents the normalized low-pass filter, the high-pass equivalent is made by changing all L's to C's and vice versa and then assigning reciprocal values as shown in Fig. 7.11*c*.

7.1.3 Design Example: Filter 2, Five-Pole Butterworth High-Pass Filter

Here $f_{-3\,dB} = 5$ MHz. The high-pass filter is constructed from the same normalized table as filter 1. To transform the low-pass design to a high-pass design, the L's and C's are interchanged and the values inverted.

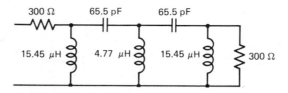

FIGURE 7.12 High-pass filter.

Using 300 Ω as in filter 1, the conversion factors are

$$L' = \frac{300L}{2\pi(5)(10)^6} = 9.55(10)^{-6}L$$

$$C' = \frac{C}{(300)(2\pi)(5)(10)^6} = 106(10)^{-12}C$$

Normalized Low-Pass	Normalized High-Pass	Conversion Factor	Component Value
$C_1 = 0.618$	$L_1 = 1/0.618$	$9.55(10)^{-6}$	15.45 μH
$L_2 = 1.618$	$C_2 = 1/1.618$	$106(10)^{-12}$	65.5 pF
$C_3 = 2.000$	$L_3 = 1/2.000$	$9.55(10)^{-6}$	4.77 μH
$L_4 = 1.618$	$C_4 = 1/1.618$	$106(10)^{-12}$	65.5 pF
$C_5 = 0.618$	$L_5 = 1/0.618$	$9.55(10)^{-6}$	15.45 μH

The completed filter is shown in Fig. 7.12.

7.1.4 Band-Pass Filters

One type of band-pass filter can be made by connecting the proper low-pass and high-pass filters in series as indicated in Section 7.1.1. Design examples 1 and 2 are therefore connected as shown in Fig. 7.13 to produce a band-pass filter. Since the filters have the same input and output resistance, the order in which they are connected does not matter. However, from a practical point of view it is always best to have a shunt capacitor as the output element of a filter. The filter generally has an impedance attached to it that has some shunt capacitance, and with this arrangement it can be absorbed as part of the filter.

If the cutoffs of the high- and low-pass filters were interchanged, a band-stop filter would result, as shown in Fig. 7.14.

The direct design of a band-pass filter is deceptively simple. The problems arise when the transformation produces values that are not physically realizable. Basically, the problem becomes more difficult

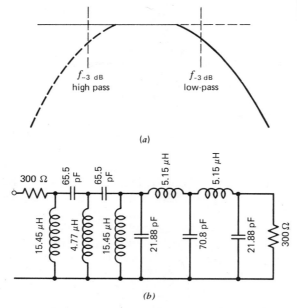

FIGURE 7.13 Combined band-pass filter.

as the band-pass gets smaller. This is discussed in the sections that follow. The design rules are as follows:

1. Design a low-pass filter whose *cutoff* frequency equals the *width* of the pass-band of the desired filter.
2. A capacitor is added in series with each coil to produce resonance at f_0, the center frequency of the pass-band.
3. A coil is added in parallel with each capacitor and again adjusted for resonance at f_0.

There is an alternative method to steps 2 and 3. When the filter is in the normalized form of 1 rad/s, the resonating elements are reciprocals of each other. The filter is therefore resonated in the normalized form and then corrected in the final version so that resonance is at f_0. This correction factor is $(BW/f_0)^2$ and is demonstrated in the sample problem on the band-pass filter.

7.1.5 Additional Requirements for a Band-Pass Filter

Aside from being restricted to the "uniform dissipation tables," as mentioned in Section 7.1, some other factors must be considered before designing a band-pass filter. When a low-pass filter is transformed

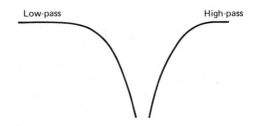

FIGURE 7.14 Band-stop filter (low pass and high pass).

into a band-pass filter, the inductors require a higher Q. For example, Fig. 7.15a shows a low-pass filter with -3 dB $= 1$ MHz and -30 dB $= 2$ MHz. In this example, the transformed filter has f_0 set at 5 MHz and will have a -3 dB bandwidth of 1 MHz and a -30 dB bandwidth of 2 MHz. The Q of the band-pass filter is $Q_{BP} = 5$ MHz/ 1 MHz $= 5$. The Q of the inductors Q_L now becomes

$$Q_L = (Q_{BP})(Q_{LP}) \tag{7.3}$$

for the band-pass filter, where Q_{LP} is the inductor Q that was used to design the original low-pass filter.

In some cases this requirement may be eased by the normal Q characteristic, since $Q = \omega L/R$ and is a function of frequency, as shown in Fig. 7.16. If A is 1 MHz and B is 5 MHz, the conditions are met by the same coil. However, if A is 1 MHz and C is 5 MHz the conditions are not met and a proper coil selection or design compromise is necessary.

A band-pass filter that is derived from a low-pass filter is a geometrically symmetrical filter and produces a symmetrical plot on a logarithmic graph. With reference to Fig. 7.15b, the center frequency is defined as

$$f_0 = \sqrt{f_1 f_2} \tag{7.4}$$

$$f_0 = \sqrt{f_3 f_4} \tag{7.5}$$

Also, from Fig. 7.15b we have the relations

$$\Delta f_{-3\,dB} = f_2 - f_1 \tag{7.6}$$

$$\Delta f_{-30\,dB} = f_4 - f_3 \tag{7.7}$$

If Eq. 7.6 is solved for f_1 and substituted in Eq. 7.4, we have

$$f_2^2 - (\Delta f_{-3\,dB})f_2 - f_0^2 = 0$$

This is a quadratic equation whose solution by the standard quadratic formula yields

$$f_2 = \frac{\Delta f_{-3\,\text{dB}} \pm \sqrt{(\Delta f_{-3\,\text{dB}})^2 + 4f_0^2}}{2}$$

$$= \frac{1 \pm \sqrt{1 + 4(5)^2}}{2} = 5.525 \text{ MHz}$$

(7.8)

for the useful root. Also

$$f_1 = f_2 - \Delta f_{-3\,\text{dB}} = 5.525 - 1 = 4.525 \text{ MHz}$$

And

$$f_4 = \frac{\Delta f_{-30\,\text{dB}} \pm \sqrt{(\Delta f_{-30\,\text{dB}})^2 + 4f_0^2}}{2}$$

$$= \frac{2 \pm \sqrt{2^2 + 4(5)^2}}{2} = 6.1 \text{ MHz}$$

(7.9)

Also

$$f_3 = f_4 - \Delta f_{-30\,\text{dB}} = 6.1 - 2 = 4.1 \text{ MHz}$$

Thus, on the low side a change of $4.525 - 4.1 = 425$ kHz produces 27 dB $(30 - 3)$ of attenuation and on the high side of the filter there is a change of $6.1 - 5.525 = 575$ kHz for the same attenuation. It can be observed from the equations above that the higher the Q of the filter, $f_0/\Delta f$, the more symmetrical the skirts are on a dB/cycle or linear basis. In any case, they average to twice the steepness of

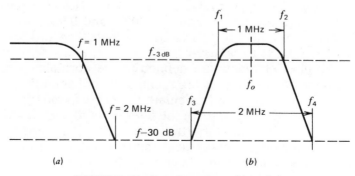

FIGURE 7.15 Band-pass consideration.

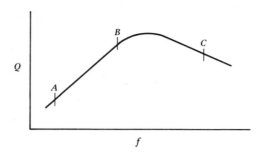

FIGURE 7.16 Q characteristics.

the low-pass filter. It can further be seen that this transformation is limited to relatively wideband or low Q's (perhaps 10) because the required inductor Q's become too high. As mentioned previously, there is also an increasing problem with being able to resonate the low-pass filter in the transformation, so that the problem of high-Q band-pass filters of this type gets rapidly out of hand.

If the Q of the inductors is less than the required value, the filter is degraded. Increasing the Q above the required value alters the characteristics somewhat but probably produces a better filter overall, so that this deviation is generally not very important.

7.1.6 Design Example: Filter 3, Five-Pole Butterworth Band-Pass Filter

The filter is to have a band-pass of 5 MHz and a center frequency of 10 MHz. The expected coil Q's are $Q_L = 70$. The Q of the band-pass filter is $Q_{BP} = f_0/\Delta f = 10/5 = 2$. The low-pass filter must be designed with a $Q_{LP} = Q_L/Q_{BP} = 70/2 = 35$. $d = 1/Q = 1/35 = 0.029$. A uniform dissipation network is required for a low-pass to band-pass transformation. Referring to Tables III.7 and III.8 in Appendix III we find that there are designs for $d = 0.02$ and 0.04. In a case like this it is better for the coil Q's to be too high than too low, so the chart for $d = 0.04$ is to be used.

When the filter elements are defined in the normalized form of 1 rad/s, the resonating elements are reciprocals of each other. Accordingly, we copy the chart and calculate the corresponding resonating elements. The impedance level of the filter is set to a value that makes a proper filter. This is done by trial and error. It is, however, necessary to evaluate only a few critical elements to make this judgment: the largest and smallest elements and whether they are in a series or in a shunt position.

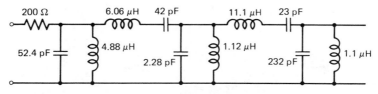

FIGURE 7.17 Band-pass filter $7\frac{1}{2}$–$12\frac{1}{2}$ MHz.

TABLE 7.1
Filter Calculations

Normalized Table Element	Resonating	Converted Resonating	Converted and Corrected Resonating Element	Converted Table Element
$C_1 = 0.3294$	$L_1 = 3.04$	19.5 µH	$L_1' = 4.88$ µH	$C_1' = 52.4$ pF
$L_2 = 0.9468$	$C_2 = 1.06$	168 pF	$C_2' = 42$ pF	$L_2' = 6.06$ µH
$C_3 = 1.443$	$L_3 = 0.693$	4.44 µH	$L_3' = 1.12$ µH	$C_3' = 228$ pF
$L_4 = 1.73$	$C_4 = 0.578$	91.9 pF	$C_4' = 23$ pF	$L_4' = 11.1$ µH
$C_5 = 1.461$	$L_5 = 0.684$	4.38 µH	$L_5' = 1.1$ µH	$C_5' = 232$ pF

Final filter values

The low-pass cutoff frequency is set to the band-pass which is 5 MHz. We try 200 Ω for R:

$$C' = \frac{C}{200(2\pi)(5)(10)^6} = 159(10)^{-12}C$$

$$L' = \frac{200L}{2\pi(5)(10)^6} = 6.4(10)^{-6}L$$

The correction factor for the resonating element in the final form is $(BW/f_0)^2 = (5/10)^2 = 0.25$.

The completed filter is shown in Fig. 7.17 and the basic calculations given in Table 7.1.

7.1.7 Adjustment Techniques

The information in this section applies, in varying degrees, to all types of *LC* filters. Filters having a tuned circuit and unfavorable ratios of *L*'s and *C*'s require closer scrutiny. The filter developed in Section

7.1.6 is analyzed as an example.

The largest shunt coil in this circuit is 4.88 μH. The tables in Appendix IV state that a 4.7 μH coil has self-resonance of 50 MHz, so that there should be no difficulty in the resonance adjustment.

The use of the inductor in a series element is generally a more restrictive case. This is because after resonance the inductor becomes a capacitor and that part of the filter has lost its defined function. The series-tuned element must remain inductive to maintain the theoretical high-frequency roll-off. In this circuit the largest series inductance is 6.06 μH. The nearest standard values in Appendix IV are 5.6 and 6.8 μH with self-resonances of 45 and 40 MHz, respectively. This is probably satisfactory for most applications, but each design must be judged by its own requirements. The magnitude of the standard values is not satisfactory, however. It is difficult to make a general statement on how accurate the components in a filter should be, but ±1% should be strived for. Chapter 5 contains design information on inductors and transformers and should be consulted if it is necessary to build the filter inductors.

Once the inductor is selected, the filter element should be adjusted to resonance by offsetting the capacitor if necessary. Another technique is to select the capacitor to the desired accuracy and then use an inductor with a few extra turns. The turns are removed as required to produce resonance. In higher frequency ranges where air core inductors are used the coil is sometimes squeezed or expanded by hand to effect the tuning. This is a common practice in low-cost commercial equipment. The coils must then be wound with heavy wire to maintain their shape. It is a better practice by far to use a solid coil form and cut off the unused portion.

If the filter resistance is lowered, so is the series inductance, which eases the problem. The drawback is that the power consumption goes up and the capacitors become larger.

The resonance of a capacitor is in the series mode and usually presents no problem in the series element because its inductance can be combined with the coil inductance. The capacitors in parallel resonance circuits present the same problem as the inductor in series resonance. Resonance information on capacitors is hard to find, but, fortunately, in reasonable frequency ranges it is easy to measure.

Figure 7.18 shows the technique. Since the series resonance is very low, the cable from the signal generator is properly terminated with the 51 Ω resistor. The frequency is simply varied until a null is reached. A high-impedance probe and a wideband sensitive preamp are required to obtain good measurements. The data in Fig. 7.18 are from dipped mica capacitors which are commonly used for passive filters. The table establishes the need for short leads in these connections.

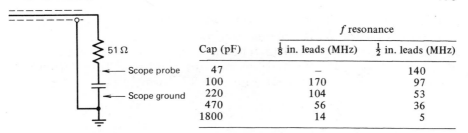

| | | f resonance | |
Cap (pF)	$\frac{1}{8}$ in. leads (MHz)	$\frac{1}{2}$ in. leads (MHz)
47	–	140
100	170	97
220	104	53
470	56	36
1800	14	5

FIGURE 7.18   Series resonance of a capacitor (dipped mica).

After the filter is built, incorrect values show up as various forms of distortion. Sometimes the corrections can be made after a little experimentation with the values, but often the relations are too complex and the design and components must be reexamined for errors.

7.1.8 Design Example: Filter 4, Capacitively Coupled Resonators

This filter has characteristics opposite to those of the low-pass to band-pass transformation described in Section 7.1.6. That is, it works well in high-Q, or narrowband, filters, but degrades rapidly when the Q becomes too low (perhaps 5). The filter has the form shown in Figs. 7.19 and 7.20.

There is an added complication for an even number of stages [1] which is not covered here. Therefore, the discussion below applies only to a filter with an odd number of stages.

This filter has a very convenient feature in that all the inductors can be made equal. They are then all resonated by the shunt capacitors to the center frequency f_0. These filters are not symmetrical, with the sharpest skirt being on the low-frequency side. As the bandwidth becomes wider, the difference becomes greater and the filter poorer.

The following example demonstrates how this filter is designed. A five-pole Butterworth band-pass filter is desired with $f_0 = 18$ MHz and a -3 dB bandwidth of 2 MHz. The available inductors have a

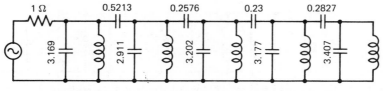

FIGURE 7.19   Normalized filter. All coils are 0.27 H.

Q of 60 (see Appendix IV). The filter Q is $18/(19 - 17) = 9$; therefore, a low-pass prototype is selected that has a Q, $Q_{LP} = Q_L/Q_{BP} = 60/9 = 6.66$ or $d = 1/Q_{LP} = 0.15$. The uniform dissipation low-pass filter is used just as in the normal low-pass to band-pass transformation. Accordingly, from Tables III.7 and III.8 in Appendix III we have

$$C_1 = 0.4104$$
$$L_2 = 1.151$$
$$C_3 = 1.681$$
$$L_4 = 1.894$$
$$C_5 = 1.113$$

The first step is to produce a normalized band-pass design. This is done in several steps:

1. The first shunt capacitor C_1 is multiplied by Q_{BP}. In this example $(Q_{BP})C_1 = 9(0.4104) = 3.69$ F.
2. Since we are still normalized at 1 rad/s, $L = 1/C = 1/3.69 = 0.271$ H.
3. Now the coupling capacitors are calculated:

$$C_{12} = C_1\sqrt{1/C_1L_2} = 0.4104\sqrt{1/.4104(1.51)} = 0.5213 \text{ F}$$
$$C_{23} = C_1\sqrt{1/L_2C_3} = 0.4104\sqrt{1/1.51(1.681)} = 0.2576 \text{ F}$$
$$C_{34} = C_1\sqrt{1/C_3L_4} = 0.4104\sqrt{1/1.681(1.894)} = 0.23 \text{ F}$$
$$C_{45} = C_1\sqrt{1/L_4C_5} = 0.4104\sqrt{1/1.894(1.113)} = 0.2827 \text{ F}$$

As mentioned before, the shunt tank circuits are all tuned to the same frequency. Accordingly, all the inductors are made equal. The shunt capacitors, however, must take into account the effect of the adjacent capacitors which consist of the two (or one on the ends)

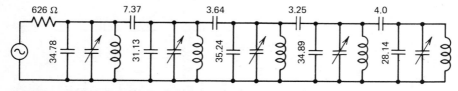

FIGURE 7.20 Completed band-pass filter. All coils are 1.5 μH; trim cap is 1–20 pF; capacitors are in pF.

coupling capacitors and the effective coil capacitance. (In this case the coil resonance is 120 MHz, which has an equivalent resonating capacitance of 1.2 pF, a negligible quantity.)

The normalized band-pass design now is as follows. Assume that $R = 600\ \Omega$. Then

$$L' = \frac{600(0.271)}{2\pi(18)(10)^6} = 1.438\ \mu H$$

To use standard 1.5 μH coils,

$$R_S = \frac{600(1.5)}{(1.438)} = 626\ \Omega$$

Then

$$C' = \frac{C}{2\pi(18)(10))^6(626)} = 14.13(10)^{-12}C$$

This results in practical values for the capacitors and, therefore, the source resistance is satisfactory. 10 pF is subtracted from each stage to allow for the center setting of the 1–20 pF trimmer. An additional 10 pF is subtracted from the last stage to allow for the load capacitance.

The normalized and final filters are as shown in Figs. 7-19 and 7-20, respectively. The measured data on the filter are as follows:

Low Side (MHz)	Relative (dB)	High Side (MHz)
18.000	0	18.000
17.287	-3	19.211
17.234	-6	19.289
17.09	-12	19.460
16.946	-18	19.650
16.780	-24	19.89
16.610	-30	20.16
16.393	-36	20.508
16.181	-42	20.88

7.1.9 Some Useful Transformations

Figure 7.21 shows a series of π, T, and mutual coupling transformations that frequently solve very serious component realization problems. When difficulties arise these transformations should be checked for a possible solution. An example is given in Fig. 7.22.

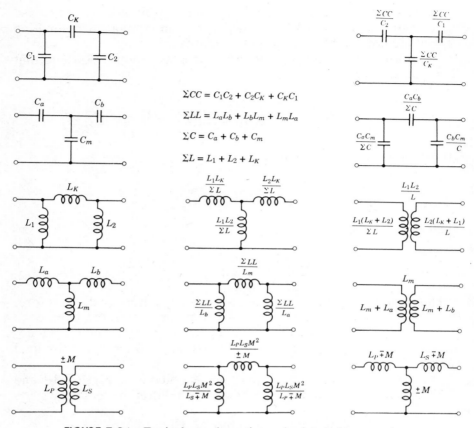

FIGURE 7.21 Equivalent schematics and related element values.

Under some conditions the dual of a filter may be more convenient than the original and is worth trying when a difficult situation is encountered. The rules are:

1. The magnitude of the parameters are unchanged.
2. Henries become farads and vice versa.
3. Series branches become shunt branches and vice versa.
4. Parameters in parallel are transformed into parameters in series and vice versa.
5. Resistances are transformed into conductances.
6. Voltage sources become current sources and vice versa.

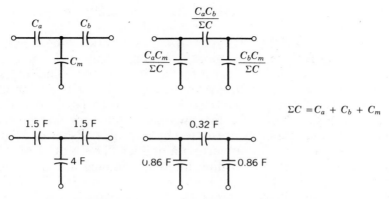

$$\Sigma C = C_a + C_b + C_m$$

FIGURE 7.22 Example of T to π transform.

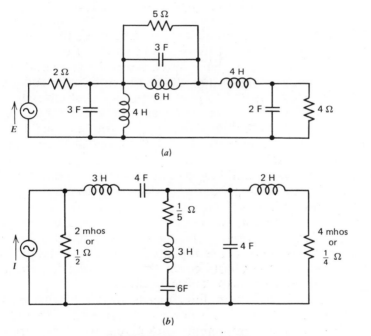

FIGURE 7.23 Dual circuits.

7.2 ACTIVE FILTERS

As previously mentioned, the choice between active or passive filters may occasionally require some thought, but as the frequency is lowered the active filters become the dominant choice. Passive filters might serve better in areas where space is no problem and a source of electrical power is not available. Even here, however, microwatt op-amps are available that can be used practically for the shelf life of the batteries.

There are many different types of active filters, some for general use and others for special purposes. Again the reader is encouraged to seek more specialized texts for further information. The filters that are described here cover many applications. Circuits designed and built from this information have worked very well. This is particularly true of the design tables for the low-pass–high-pass filters given in Appendix III and originally presented by Farouk Al-Nasser [2]. These filters use a unity-gain noninverting amplifier. The NSC LM310 is a good all-around choice with high input impedance and an excellent frequency response. For very low frequencies the JFET input type of operational amplifiers, such as the LF356 series, is recommended because their very low input current allows the use of large resistors. If the maximum in frequency response is desired, it is recommended that a double emitter follower be used employing a 2N3960 and a 2N4261 transistor. (A ferrite bead should be placed between the emitter of the first transistor and the base of the second to prevent oscillation.)

These particular design charts have several very good features. First, in the low-pass application all the resistors have equal values, with the capacitors selected to give the proper characteristic. In the case of the high-pass filter it is the capacitors that are the same. This means that if you have a filter already built you can easily shift to a new frequency by a change of the identical resistors (or capacitors in the high-pass case).

There are two basic building blocks in the technique that is presented here. They are simply connected in series to obtain the desired number of poles. Figures 7.24a and c are two-pole filters and Figs. 7.24b and d are three-pole filters (which are used only when an odd number of poles is required). The tables go up to 10 poles and, although the two-pole blocks are repeated, they do not have the same component values. The charts cover the Butterworth, several Chebyshev, and the Butterworth–Thomson filter.

The Butterworth–Thomson filter merits special discussion [3]. All filters have what is known as a nonlinear phase shift characteristic. That is, all frequency components of a given waveform are not delayed by the same amount of time. If a filter delays all frequencies in a complex wave by the same amount of time, the shape of the wave remains the same. The Butterworth–Thomson filter tables are given values of $m = 0.2, 0.4, 0.6,$ and 0.8. The function m is simply a scaling factor. When $m = 0$, the filter is a pure Butterworth; for $m = 1$ the filter is a pure Thomson. As the group delay becomes more uniform the frequency cutoff characteristics become poorer. This is illustrated in Figs. III.6 and III.7.

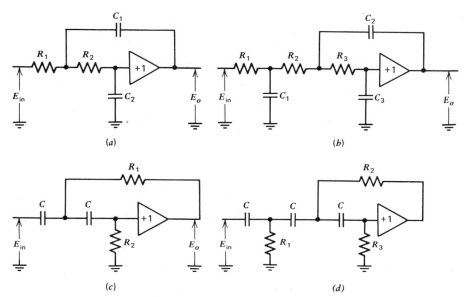

FIGURE 7.24 Passive filter building blocks. (*a*) Two-pole low pass. (*b*) Three-pole low pass. (*c*) Two-pole high pass. (*d*) Three-pole high pass.

Although these filters do not have a direct low-pass–band-pass transformation as do the passive filters, they are buffered, so that it is simple to connect a high pass and a low pass in series to produce the desired band-pass. The overlap of the cutoff points is the band-pass or, in the case of the band-stop, the separation of these cutoff points.

The scaling range of the filter depends on the characteristics of the buffer amplifier used. The high side of resistance level is determined by the input resistance and the bias current, while the low side of the resistance level is determined by output drive capability. This is fortunately a rather wide range so that the choice of the resistor is generally made to allow a favorable range of capacitors.

7.2.1 Design Example: A Seven-Pole Butterworth Low-Pass Filter

The normalized capacitor values are obtained from Table III.1. The resistance level and frequency are then selected and the corrections for the normalized capacitors is established

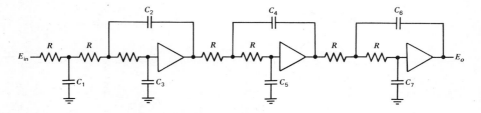

FIGURE 7.25 Completed seven-pole low-pass filter.

$R = 20$ kΩ, $f_c = 10^3$ Hz:

$$C = C_n/2\pi Rf = C_n/2\pi 2(10)^4(10)^3 = 7950(10)^{-12}C_n.$$

$$
\begin{aligned}
C_1 &= 1.38(7950)(10)^{-12} &&= 11{,}000 \text{ pF} \\
C_2 &= 2.52 &&= 20{,}000 \text{ pF} \\
C_3 &= 0.288 &&= 2{,}290 \text{ pF} \\
C_4 &= 1.11 &&= 8{,}824 \text{ pF} \\
C_5 &= 0.9 &&= 7{,}150 \text{ pF} \\
C_6 &= 4.49 &&= 35{,}700 \text{ pF} \\
C_7 &= 0.223 &&= 1{,}770 \text{ pF}
\end{aligned}
$$

Figure 7.25 shows the completed filter.

7.2.2 Design Example: A Seven-Pole Butterworth High-Pass Filter

For the high-pass filter the positions of the resistors and capacitors are interchanged. A convenient common capacitor is selected. The normalized resistors are the reciprocals of the capacitors given in the design chart.

$C = 10^{-9}$ F, $f = 10^3$ Hz:

$$R = R_n/2\pi fC = R_n/2\pi(10)^3(10)^{-9} = 1.59(10)^5 R_n$$

$$
\begin{aligned}
R_1 &= 1/1.38(1.59)(10)^5 &&= 115 \text{ k}\Omega \cong 120 \text{ k}\Omega \\
R_2 &= 1/2.52 &&= 63 \text{ k}\Omega \cong 62 \text{ k}\Omega \\
R_3 &= 1/0.288 &&= 552 \text{ k}\Omega \cong 560 \text{ k}\Omega \\
R_4 &= 1/1.11 &&= 143 \text{ k}\Omega \cong 150 \text{ k}\Omega \\
R_5 &= 1/0.9 &&= 176 \text{ k}\Omega \cong 180 \text{ k}\Omega \\
R_6 &= 1/4.49 &&= 35.4 \text{ k}\Omega \cong 36 \text{ k}\Omega \\
R_7 &= 1/0.233 &&= 682 \text{ k}\Omega \cong 680 \text{ k}\Omega
\end{aligned}
$$

Figure 7.26 shows the completed high-pass filter.

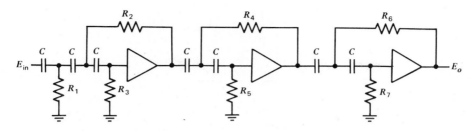

FIGURE 7.26 Completed seven-pole high-pass filter.

Band Pass Filter: $f = 10$ Hz, Gain $= H_0 = 1$, $Q = 10$

$\omega_0 = 2\pi(10) = 63$, Let $C = 0.1\ \mu F$

$R_1 = Q/H\omega_0 C = 10/2(63)(10)^{-7} = 1.56$ MΩ

$R_2 = Q/(2Q^2 - H)\omega_0 C = 10/199(63)(10)^{-7} = 7.9$ kΩ.

$R_5 = 2Q/\omega_0 C = 20/63(10)^{-7} = 3.17$ MΩ

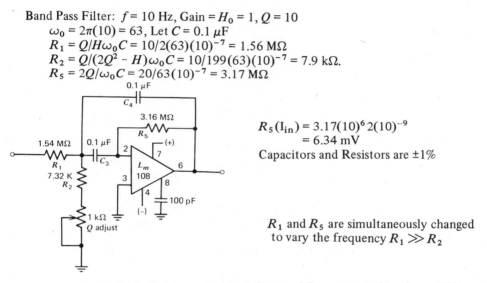

$R_5(I_{in}) = 3.17(10)^6 2(10)^{-9}$

$\qquad = 6.34$ mV

Capacitors and Resistors are $\pm 1\%$

R_1 and R_5 are simultaneously changed to vary the frequency $R_1 \gg R_2$

FIGURE 7.27 Band-pass filter. (From Reference [4]; courtesy of McGraw-Hill.)

7.2.3 Design Example: A Simple Band-Pass Filter

Although the high-pass and low-pass filters first described can be combined to produce a band-pass filter by appropriately selecting the two cutoff frequencies, this is often too complex for simple filtering jobs. The circuit described here [4] works well as a one-stage filter.

The completed circuit is shown in Fig. 7.27.

7.2.4 Design Example: A Simple Null Filter

A need often exists to attenuate one specific frequency sharply. For this case both the frequency and the filter must be very stable. Al-

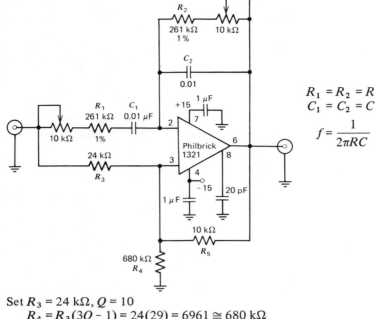

$$R_1 = R_2 = R$$
$$C_1 = C_2 = C$$

$$f = \frac{1}{2\pi RC}$$

Set $R_3 = 24$ kΩ, $Q = 10$

$$R_4 = R_3(3Q - 1) = 24(29) = 6961 \cong 680 \text{ k}\Omega$$

$$R_5 = R_3 \frac{(3Q - 1)}{3(2Q - 1)} = \frac{24(29)}{3(19)} = 12.2 \cong 12 \text{ k}\Omega$$

Data: -3 dB 57.5 and 64 Hz   Slow rate $= 3.6$ V/μs
          60 Hz null $= -55$ dB   1 MHz max. output $\cong 3V_{pp}$

FIGURE 7.28 Null circuit. (Courtesy of Allan Lloyd.)

though this is a band-stop filter by nature, a high-pass and a low-pass filter cannot be satisfactorily combined to perform this function. The design shown in Fig. 7.28 works very well. It is described in detail in Ref. [5].

REFERENCES

[1] P. R. Geffe, *Simplified Modern Filter Design,* Hayden, Rochelle Park, NJ, 1963.

[2] F. Al-Nasser, Tables Speed Design of Low-Pass Filters, *EDN,* Mar. 15, 1971.

[3] F. Al-Nasser, Tables Shorten Design Time For Active Filters, *Electronics,* Oct. 23, 1972.

[4] G. E. Toby, J. G. Graeme, and L. P. Huelsman, *Operational Amplifiers,* McGraw-Hill, New York, 1971, p. 291.

[5] A. Lloyd, Sharpen Active Null Networks, *Electron. Des.,* June 21, 1974.

GENERAL REFERENCES

GENERAL REFERENCES

For those interested in a greater selection of filter tables there are many sources available. *Radio Amateurs Handbook* contains valuable additional information and a good bibliography for other articles. Noticeable among these references are the works of Edward Wetherhold, who has auuthored many publications relating to filter design. A set of useful additional design tables is available for $4.00 from Edward Wetherhold, W3NQN 102 Archwood Avenue, Annapolis, MD 21401.

A. Zverev, *Handbook of Filter Synthesis,* Wiley, New York, 1967.

Radio Amateurs Handbook, American Radio Relay League, Newington, CT, 1984, p. 5.

E. E. Wetherhold, Simplified Passive LC Filter Design for the EMC Engineer, *IEEE Symposium on Electromagnetic Compatibility, IEEE Cat. No. 85CH2116-2,* Aug. 1985, pp. 575–584.

EIGHT

Resonant Circuits and Matching Networks

The resonant circuit, in its basic form, is a simple circuit. It can be either series or parallel, consisting of an inductive reactance and a capacitive reactance of equal magnitudes. In both cases the resonant frequency f_r is given by

$$f_r = \frac{1}{2\pi\sqrt{LC}} \quad \text{(Hz)} \tag{8.1}$$

where L is in henries and C is in farads. A sometimes handier form is

$$f_r = \frac{10^3}{6.283\sqrt{L_{\mu H}C_{pF}}} \quad \text{(MHz)} \tag{8.2}$$

Complications arise when resistance is taken into account and the circuit is connected to an arbitrary impedance by a choice of quite a few different techniques.

The exact equations expressing these variations rapidly become complex and inconvenient to use and consequently there are many practical approximations employed.

The method that I prefer consists of only one basic approximation for all of the resonant circuit combinations. This consists of using the serial-to-parallel and its counterpart, the parallel-to-serial, impedance transformations. This transformation is exact at the frequency of the transformation, normally resonance, but increases in error as the frequency is changed. For most conditions this error is small and a simple test for extended frequency characteristics defines the error. This test, in any case, is a prudent one because the effective coil resistance is a function of frequency and the self-resonance characteristics of both the inductor and capacitor often enter into the extended frequency characteristics sooner than expected.

It is very desirable to base the design procedure upon the inductive and capacitive reactances rather than using the inductance and capacitance directly. The insertion of frequency to determine the physical components is the final step. A word of advice at this point: It is a good idea to make a preliminary estimate of what the physical parameters will be to ensure that they are in a bracket of attainable values.

There are two reasons for dealing directly with reactances rather than the inductance and capacitance directly. Primarily, the calculations are easier, but of importance also, plus and minus reactances relate directly to each other and to the resistance. This makes sound judgment in component selection much easier.

The use of the transforms is discussed in the sections that follow (Sections 8.1 on parallel resonance, 8.2 on series resonance, and 8.5 on matching networks).

Specifically, all related elements are converted to their parallel form for parallel resonance and to their series form for series resonance. The transformation is shown in Fig. 8.1.

To derive the series equvalent of the parallel impedance we first form the expression for the parallel impedance Z_P. Capacitive reactance is used in the example.

$$Z_P = \frac{R_P(-jX_P)}{(R_P - jX_P)} = \frac{R_P(-jX_P)}{(R_P - jX_P)} \frac{(R_P + jX_P)}{(R_P + jX_P)} = \frac{R_P X_P^2 - jR_P^2 X_P}{(R_P^2 - X_P^2)}$$

This is a series expression and so we have

$$R_S = \frac{R_P X_P^2}{(R_P^2 + X_P^2)} = \frac{R_P}{\left(\dfrac{R_P}{X_P}\right)^2 + 1} \tag{8.3}$$

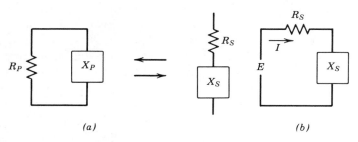

FIGURE 8.1 (a) Serial–parallel and (b) parallel–serial impedance transformation.

$$X_S = \frac{R_P^2 X_P}{(R_P^2 + X_P^2)} = \frac{X_P}{\left(\dfrac{X_P}{R_P}\right)^2 + 1} \tag{8.4}$$

To obtain the parallel equivalent of the series impedance we shall set forth the expression for the current of the series circuit I_S:

$$I_S = \frac{E}{Z_S} = \frac{E}{(R - jX_C)}\frac{(R + jX_C)}{(R + jX_C)}$$
$$= \frac{ER}{(R^2 + X_C^2)} + \frac{E(jX_C)}{(R^2 + X_C^2)}$$

This is the current in the resistive branch of a parallel circuit plus the current through the reactive branch. Accordingly,

$$R_P = \frac{(R_S^2 + X_S^2)}{R_S} \tag{8.5}$$

$$X_P = \frac{(R_S^2 + X_S^2)}{X_S} \tag{8.6}$$

By solving Eqs. 8.3 and 8.4 for X_P and R_P a variation of Eqs. 8.5 and 8.6 can be obtained which are useful in some circumstances. Thus, we have

$$R_P = \sqrt{\frac{X_S X_P^2}{X_P - X_S}} \tag{8.5a}$$

$$X_P = \sqrt{\frac{R_S R_P^2}{R_P - R_S}} \tag{8.6a}$$

Again a reminder, Eq. 8.4 through 8.6a are *valid at one frequency only*.

These equations are true also for inductive reactance. Because of this the transformations are also valid for any form of complex impedance. In these cases the impedance is broken down to the equivalent resistance and reactance for the *specific frequency of transformation*.

8.1 PARALLEL RESONANT CIRCUITS

The typical parallel resonant circuit is of the form shown in Fig. 8.2.

The resonant circuit is generally driven by a transistor, or vacuum tube, which has an effective dynamic resistance R_G.

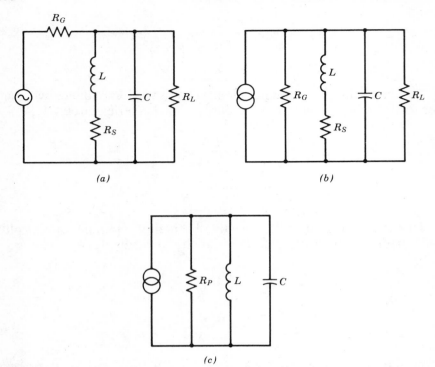

FIGURE 8.2 Typical parallel resonant circuit: (*a*) Voltage source; (*b*) Current source; (*c*) Equivalent circuit.

The word effective is used because in cases where a large dynamic range is involved, for example, class C operation, R_G is not a constant. Figure 8.2*b* is the Norton equivalent (Section 1.6) and more clearly shows that R_G is a parallel resistor and effective in establishing the circuit Q.

Part of C is also the output capacitance of the driver and, unfortunately, depends upon the drive level. Another part of C is the stray capacitance which is subject to change through mechanical instabilities.

R_L is the transferred load resistance which is the subject of a subsequent section.

The inductors have an effective series resistance which usually must be taken into account. The problem now is the combination of series and parallel resistances. The resulting equations are complex and tedious to use.

This is why the series and parallel conversions are used. When the elements are all in the same form, the circuit becomes quite manageable. We have now defined three parallel resistances which are combined to make the complete parallel resistance R_P.

The capacitor is generally considered lossless, but if not, the resistances in the equivalent circuit should also be converted to a parallel resistance.

As the frequency becomes higher and goes beyond the lumped parameter concept, the inductance and capacitor become complex distributed impedances and the procedures described here rapidly become worthless.

The parameter Q is used in resonant circuits to define the off-resonance half-power frequencies. Specifically,

$$Q = \frac{f_r}{f_{H(-3\ dB)} - f_{L(-3\ dB)}} \tag{8.7}$$

At resonance the capacitive reactance draws a current equal and opposite of that drawn by the effective parallel inductive reactance. The net current is zero and accordingly the total reactance is infinite. The impedance of the resonant circuit is therefore the effective parallel resistance R_P.

As the frequency moves away from resonance the impedance is lowered. It becomes inductive on the low side and capacitive on the high side.

The frequency response of the parallel resonant circuit is shown in Fig. 8.3 for several different values of Q.

The skirt response has three distinct characteristics, the distribution of which strongly depends upon the circuit Q.

For a very high Q, the slope just off resonance is near infinite. It then changes to 12 dB/octave, as both X_L and X_C are equally effective in changing the impedance. However, as the frequency departs further from resonance one of the reactances becomes so high that it does not affect the impedance and the slope changes to 6 dB/octave.

A low Q circuit almost immediately has a slope of 6 dB/octave.

From Section I.8 on complex algebra it is seen that the absolute magnitude of the impedance is

$$|Z| = \frac{R_P}{\sqrt{\left(\dfrac{R_P}{X_{\text{eff}}}\right)^2 + 1}} \tag{8.8}$$

where X_{eff} is the effective reactance. At resonance $X_{\text{eff}} = \infty$ and the impedance is R_P.

When $X_{\text{eff}} = R_P$,

$$|Z| = \frac{R_P}{\sqrt{2}} \quad \text{or} \quad R_P - 3\ \text{dB}$$

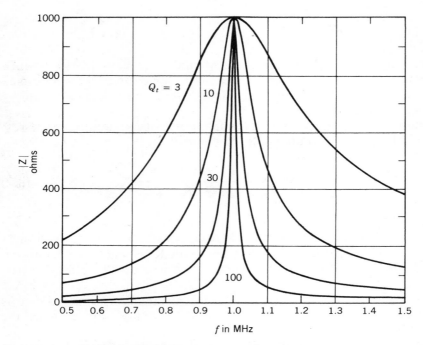

FIGURE 8.3   Parallel resonance frequency response.

From this it can be shown that the Q of a parallel resonant circuit is

$$Q = \frac{R_P}{X_L} \quad \text{(at resonance)} \tag{8.9}$$

This expression is exact for a parallel circuit and the expression $Q = X_L/R_S$ (at resonance) is exact for a series resonant circuit. Since the resistance of an inductance is a series element, the expression $Q = X_L/R_S$ is often used to express the Q of an unloaded parallel resonant circuit. This is an approximation that becomes more accurate as Q increases. A commonly accepted level of Q for this is 10 or greater.

Figure 8.4 shows a transistor driving a parallel resonant circuit.

The maximum gain of this circuit is R_F/R_E as described in Chapter 1. The bandwidth is $Q = R_P/X_L$ (at resonance). From this $X_L = X_C = R_P/Q$.

R_P, X_L, and X_C are all in parallel and therefore the current through the reactances is Q times the collector current. However, since the reactive impedances have opposite signs, this "tank" current merely circulates within the resonant circuit.

Because the resonant frequency is determined by $\sqrt{LC}$, there exists a wide range of L and C values that can be used in a resonant circuit. The selection of a specific set of values generally revolves around the properties of the inductor.

A starting point is the inductor specifications given in Appendix IV. The graphs give a good visual presentation of how the Q varies at a given frequency for different values of inductance.

There are three separate factors to consider in a resonant circuit. These are the gain (or impedance), the efficiency, and the bandwidth. The magnitude of the inductance and its Q are basic to all three considerations.

For a high impedance the inductance is made as high as practical. Usually the self-resonance and DC current capability are the limiting factors.

To determine the efficiency, the coil resistance is converted to its parallel form by the relation $R_P = QX_L$. Since R_P is in parallel with R_L (reflected or direct), the efficiency of the resonant circuit is given by

$$\text{Eff} = \frac{1/R_L}{1/R_L + 1/R_P} \qquad (8.10)$$

A high efficiency obviously means a high R_P or QX_L product. The Q charts in Appendix IV will help determine the maximum QX_L product.

Finally, since $Q = R_P/X_L$, the Q of the circuit can be increased by making R_P larger or X_L smaller. If there is no loading and the

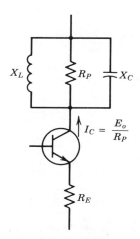

FIGURE 8.4   Parallel resonant amplifier.

source impedance is high enough to be ignored, the circuit Q is equal to the coil Q. This is in any case the maximum Q of the circuit. Generally, however, there is a source and load impedance that must be taken into account and accordingly R_P is fixed. This leaves the inductance as a variable to control the circuit Q. Reducing the inductance, while $LC = $ a constant, increases the circuit Q. There is naturally a lower practical limit of the inductance. When this becomes a factor other coupling techniques can be employed to extend the range of available Q; examples are matching networks and filters with uneven terminations.

Resonant circuits are also used purely to obtain gain and to define a frequency band-pass. Under these conditions a large inductance is desired because it has a large R_P and hence the circuit will have a high gain.

Care should be taken, however, to prevent the capacitance from being reduced to a level comparable to the stray circuit capacitance, or the band-pass accuracy will be affected.

8.2 SERIES RESONANT CIRCUITS

The typical series resonant circuit is of the form shown in Fig. 8.5.

Series resonance occurs when $X_L = X_C$, just as in the case of parallel resonance. Beyond that, the circuits are essentially opposites of each other.

The Q of the parallel resonant circuit is R_P/X_L. The Q of the series resonant circuit is X_L/R_S. This can be demonstrated as follows:

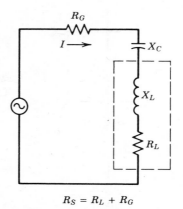

$$R_S = R_L + R_G$$

FIGURE 8.5   The series resonant circuit.

$$Q = \frac{f_r}{\Delta f(-3 \text{ dB})} \qquad \text{by definition}$$

The response of a resistance/reactive series network is down 3 dB when the net reactance X_n equals the resistance.

The reactance at resonance is given by

$$X_{Lr} = 2\pi f_r L$$

and

$$X_{Cr} = \frac{1}{2\pi f_r C}$$

In the *vicinity of resonance* a given change in frequency produces equal and opposite changes of the two reactances. Therefore,

$$X_n = 2(X_{(\Delta f/2)}) = X_{\Delta f} = R_S$$

Divide both sides by X_L at f_r and invert.

$$\frac{X_L}{R_S} = \frac{X_L}{X_{\Delta f}} = \frac{f_r}{\Delta f} = Q \qquad (8.11)$$

Since R_G adds directly to R_{XL} a low resistance source is required to maintain high Q. This is the opposite of the parallel resonant circuit which requires a high resistance source to maintain high Q.

Series resonance is a minimum impedance condition, whereas parallel resonance presents a maximum impedance. Series resonance is often used as "traps" to filter out selected unwanted frequencies. Examples of this are fixed-frequency amplifiers such as *IF* amplifiers where resonant capacitors are used to bypass the power supplies. For example, a typical 0.01 μF ceramic capacitor with $\frac{1}{4}$ in. leads is series resonant at 18 MHz and this is an improved bypass over the 0.85 Ω of capacitive reactance. By the same token, the wrong lead length produces a degraded filter, so care must be taken.

Although series resonance is a minimum impedance circuit, it thereby becomes a maximum current section. This current times either of the reactances can produce a very large voltage in a high Q circuit and consequently can be used as an amplifier.

The impedance transformation produced by the L matching network is a direct application of this condition.

Figure 8.6 shows an application as an amplifier.

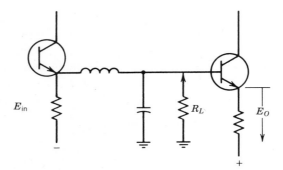

FIGURE 8.6 Series resonant gain stage.

$$\text{Gain} = \frac{E_o}{E_{\text{in}}} = \frac{I_R X_C}{E_{\text{in}}} = \frac{E_{\text{in}} X_C}{R_S E_{\text{in}}} = Q \qquad (8.12)$$

A low Q variation of the amplifier is the series peaking circuit (see Chapter 2) where a small amplification is produced at the basic RC roll-off of the amplifier. This gives a slight extention of the pass-band.

If a load resistor is involved, as shown in Fig. 8.6, the parallel-to-series transformation is used to obtain an effective series R. This resistance is added to the existing resistance, producing a new and lower Q.

In the series resonant circuit, $Q = X_L$ (resonant)$/R_S$.

The circuit Q can be increased by increasing the inductance (LC = a constant). However, as the inductance is increased, so is its series R. Inductors of the same design maintain a fairly constant Q as the inductance is changed. The benefit here is established when the resistance of the inductor is a small part of the *total* series resistance.

The shape of the series resonant curve is the same as that of the parallel resonant circuit shown in Fig. 8.4 except that the ordinate is current instead of voltage. Also, as the frequency is reduced from resonance, the current becomes capacitive and correspondingly inductive as the frequency is increased. This is the opposite of the parallel resonant circuit.

8.3 LOADED RESONANT CIRCUITS

When resonant circuits are involved in the transfer of power to some defined load, a method of coupling that load must be employed. This will affect both the Q and the tuning of the resonant circuit.

Discussed in this section and in Sections 8.4 and 8.5 are four different methods:

1. Reactance coupling
2. Tapped reactors
3. Coupled resonators
4. Matching networks

In addition, transformers (Chapter 5) and filters (Chapter 7) are also used as coupling techniques for resonant circuits. Applications and restrictions are further discussed in those chapters.

The examples are directed toward parallel resonant circuits because they are used more often. However, by reviewing the sections on parallel and series resonance, it will be seen that the principles can also be readily applied to the series resonant circuits.

8.3.1 Reactance Coupling

The simplest form of reactive coupling is a blocking capacitor connected directly to the load resistor. Figure 8.7 shows the connection.

In this case the capacitor serves only to block DC and there is no shift in the resonant frequency. The load is connected directly across the resonant circuit.

However, as the capacitor becomes smaller it begins to affect the signal transmission and can be used as a calibrated coupling element. An inductor can also be used but usually requires the addition of blocking capacitor.

For the coupling application a capacitor is convenient to use for the reactive element, particularly at those frequencies where a variable capacitor is a practical component. The value of the reactance

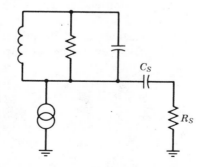

FIGURE 8.7   Capacitively coupled load.

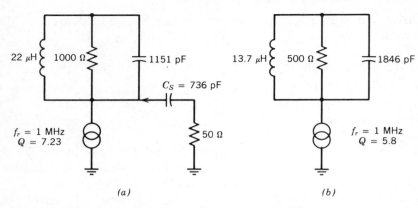

FIGURE 8.8 Reactance coupled circuit. (*a*) Circuit without load; (*b*) Equivalent loaded circuit.

is generally quite critical and it also transforms a reactance that affects the tuning. This is most easily compensated by a second variable capacitor in the tank circuit.

On the other hand, if some harmonic reduction is required, the inductive element becomes a useful low-pass element at these frequencies and in this case can be the preferred choice. Figure 8.8 illustrates the procedure.

It is evident from Eq. 8.5 that the parallel equivalent of a series resistor can only result in a larger value. In this application we wish to determine the value of C_S to transform a 50 Ω R_S to a 1000 Ω R_P.

Solving for X_S in Eq. 8.5 we have

$$X_S = \pm\sqrt{R_P R_S - R_S^2}$$
$$= \pm\sqrt{1000(50) - (50)^2}$$
$$= +217.9 \ \Omega \text{ which is 730 pF at 1 MHz.}$$

The $\pm$ means that the reactance could be either capacitive or inductive. Choosing the capacitive reactance and applying Eq. 8.6 we must calculate

$$X_P = \frac{R_S^2 + X_S^2}{X_S} = \frac{(50)^2 + (217.9)^2}{217.9}$$
$$= 229 \ \Omega$$

at 1 MHz, $C_P = 695$ pF

This now produces a total parallel capacitance of $(1151 + 695) = 1846$ pF and a new resonant frequency of 790 kHz.

Since it is desired to maintain the original frequency, the LC product of the tank circuit must be reduced. This allows some flexibility with Q, since $Q = R_P/(X_L$ or $X_C)$ at resonance.

Because the original Q was reduced by the addition of R_S, we shall elect to reduce the inductance to regain some of the lost Q. We can write the relation

$$\frac{0.790 \text{ MHz}}{1.0 \text{ MHz}} = \frac{\sqrt{L'C}}{\sqrt{LC}}$$

where L' is the new inductance

$$\therefore L' = (0.790)^2 \, (22) \qquad 000.0 = 13.73 \ \mu\text{H}$$

The original Q was $R_P/X_L = \dfrac{1000}{138.3} = 7.23$

The Q after loading was $\dfrac{500}{138.2} = 3.615$

The final Q is $\dfrac{500}{86.3} = 5.8$

A reminder: When selecting inductors, use the tables in Appendix IV to ensure practical values. For example, the 22 μH inductor has a Q of 80 at 2.5 MHz and is self-resonant at 22 MHz.

A test circuit was built using approximately the same values as the design example with good correlation.

An inductor will equal reactance was then substituted for the coupling capacitor. The two resulting responses at the 50 Ω load resistor are shown in Fig. 8.9.

It is clearly seen that the X_L coupling has superior high-frequency roll-off, whereas the X_C strongly favors the low-frequency side. The two curves are displayed from 1 MHz because the reflected coupling reactance was not canceled.

Figure 8.9 is normalized at 0 dB maximum output for ease of comparison. There is, however, a substantial signal voltage drop across the coupling reactor. This results in a much lower voltage across the 50 Ω load than that appearing across the tank circuit. This is as it should be. We are concerned with power here and not voltage.

Since $P = E^2/R$, and 50 Ω is 20 times lower than 1000 Ω, the voltage across it must be reduced by $\sqrt{20}$ from that of a 1000 Ω load.

There will be some power loss in a coupling inductor but the capacitive coupler loss should be essentially zero.

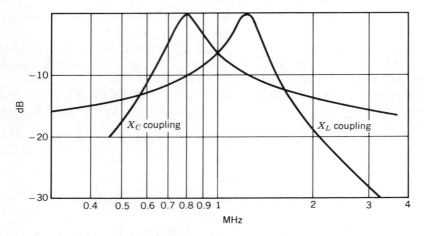

FIGURE 8.9 X_C vs. X_L coupling.

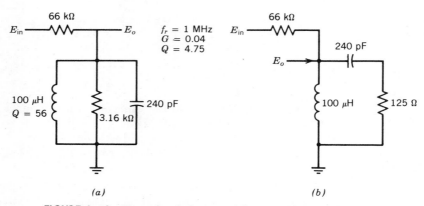

(a)   (b)

FIGURE 8.10   Test circuit for a serial to parallel transformation.

Figure 8.10 shows a second test circuit. This was used to compare the response of a parallel resonant circuit with a parallel resistive load to one where a series load was transformed by a capacitive reactance to be equal to the parallel load. The difference in response between the two circuits was barely more than measurement error (essentially the same to -30 dB (140 kHz to 7 MHz).

8.3.2 Tapped Reactors

Figure 8.11 shows three variations of how a resonant circuit can be tapped to couple to a load. Figure 8.11*a* shows the load tapped to one of the reactive sides of a resonant circuit. The tapped arm can

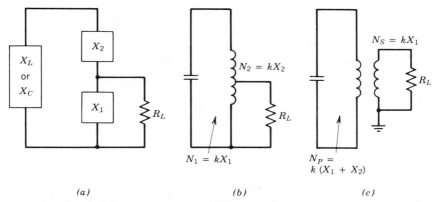

FIGURE 8.11 Tapping methods. (*a*) Reactance tap. (*b*) Auto X'fmr tap. (*c*) X'fmr tap. X'fmr = transformer.

be either inductive or capacitive. Figures 8.11*b* and *c* are included because they correlate in function to the reactance tap, although there are some differences which will be covered later. Chapter 5 discusses transformers and should be referred to if their use seems desirable.

When a resistance is connected from a tapped impedance it dissipates a power $= (E_{TAP})^2/R$. If an equivalent resistance is defined to be placed across the total circuit, it must dissipate the same power. Now, since power varies as the voltage squared, the transformed resistor must be increased by the square of the voltage ratio to maintain the equality.

Figure 8.12 shows three circuits tapped and with a load resistor.

The three circuits shown in Fig. 8.12 are of different impedance levels but have the same no-load voltage division, that is, 20:1, in common. The tap must present a reactance that is low compared to the load resistor if the no-load tap voltage is to be maintained.

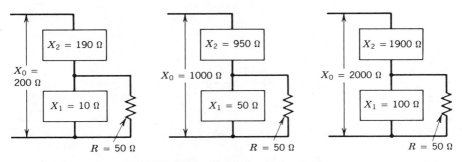

FIGURE 8.12 Tapped reactive lines.

Table 8.1 shows the effect of the load R_L on these circuits.

The parallel combination formed by the 50 Ω load resistance is first converted to the series equivalent R_S and X_S. X_S is then added to X_2 to produce the new total series reactance X_0'. These two values then make a final conversion to the parallel equivalent R_P and X_P. This procedure is outlined in Fig. 8.13.

Figures 8.13a and b are shown to alert the reader that the load resistor, shown in its usual schematic form, is across X_{C1} and not X_{C2}.

It should further be pointed out that X_L, which makes the collector load a resonant circuit, has no bearing on the transformation. The transformation is independent of anything that is connected to it.

Since the open-loop tap voltage is $\frac{1}{20}$ of the applied voltage, a 50 Ω R_L defines an equivalent R_P of $(20)^2 \times (50) = 20,000$ Ω. The 10 Ω tap reactance comes close to this, but, as can be seen, the other two are far off the mark. It is also noted that the parallel reactance changes very little so that compensation to correct the resonant frequency is minor. This shows that some of the calculations can be eliminated when one is familiar with a specific problem.

The two transformer connections, the autotransformer (Fig. 8.11b) and the isolated secondary (Fig. 8.11c) can be used to perform the same function as the separate reactors, but the mechanism of operation is different and their applications are broader.

Relating specifically to the inductive reactance for clarity, the reactance is a function of N turns around some kind of core or flux path. This relation is ideally $L = kN^2$. However, this fact is of no concern in separate inductors because the second reactance in the divider has a core and turns count that bears no relation to the other inductor. There is no common flux between the two inductors. It is the ratio of the impedance of the two inductors that must be maintained. In this case this is 19:1 for a division of 20.

In a transformer the primary and secondary, or tap, share the same flux. The transformer in this case is considered ideal (see Chapter 5 and Appendix I) and accordingly the voltage is proportional to the turns, while the impedance and transferred load impedance are proportional to the square of the turns.

TABLE 8.1
Effect of Load (R_L) on Tapped Circuit

R_L	X_1	X_2	X_0	R_S	X_S	X_0'	R_P	X_P
50 Ω	10	190	200	1.923	9.616	199.62	20,723	199.64
50 Ω	50	950	1000	25	25	975	38,050	975.64
50 Ω	100	1900	2000	40	20	1920	92,200	1920.8

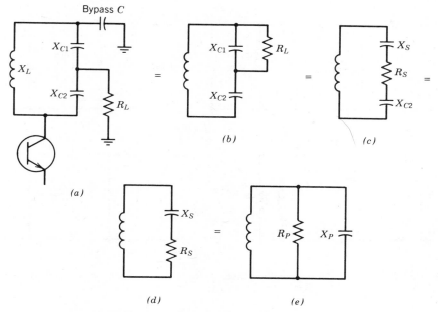

FIGURE 8.13 Tapped reactance conversion.

The illustrated reactance tap is a 20:1 division. This corresponds to a 20:1 turns ratio for the transformer which is a $20^2 = 400$ to 1 impedance ratio; $400 \times 50 = 20,000$, just as in the impedance tap.

A reactance tap can only couple power from a higher voltage to a lower one. In other words, it cannot amplify. The transformer tap can couple from either direction. Reactance coupling in the form of an L network, described in Section 8.5.1, can be designed to go in either direction and this should be investigated as a possible alternative to the transformer.

8.4 COUPLED RESONATORS

There are no hard and fast rules for coupling one resonant circuit to another; this is because there are applications for many of the varied results. Figure 8.14 shows the basic concept.

The coupling reactance can be either capacitive or inductive. If it is capacitive the asymptotic response below resonance is an RL of 6 dB/octave plus an LC of 12 dB/octave, which equals 18 dB/octave. Above resonance it is only the RC 6 dB/octave. With inductive coupling, the opposite is true: 18 dB/octave on the high side and 6 dB/octave on the low side.

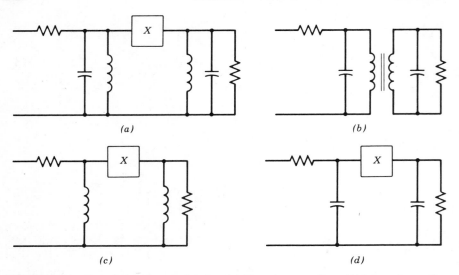

FIGURE 8.14 Coupled resonant circuits. (*a*) Reactive coupling. (*b*) Mutual coupling. (*c*) Below resonance. (*d*) Above resonance.

The mutual coupling is effectively an inductive coupling because a transformer with less than unity coupling can be approximated by a perfect transformer in series with its leakage reactance.

It should be pointed out that for two resonators, the slope is much steeper than for one resonant circuit and the Q is dependent upon both resonators, so that a greater attenuation can be obtained than with one tuned circuit.

If the reactance of the coupling element is high there is unwanted attenuation and the circuit is of little value. As the reactance is reduced the gain of the circuit increases and finally develops two peaks with an increasingly deep valley between the peaks. A condition of maximum gain before the two peaks emerge is called critical coupling. The coupling elements for this condition are, respectively,

$$X_{CC} = \sqrt{Q_1 Q_2}\, X_C \quad \text{and} \quad X_{LC} = \sqrt{Q Q_2}\, X_L \qquad (8.13)$$

where Q_1 and Q_2 are the loaded Q's of the two resonant circuits and where both resonant circuits have the same L's and C's. Since $X_L = X_C$ at resonance, the two forms of coupling reactances are also of equal magnitude.

If an increase of bandwidth is required while maintaining the steep slopes, a slight amount of overcoupling is effective at the price of some pass-band ripple. Tuning the resonant circuits at slightly different frequencies, that is, stagger tuning, also produces that effect.

The bandwidth of two identical resonant circuits with critical coupling is given by

$$BW \text{ of coupled resonators} = \sqrt{2}\, BW \text{ of one resonator} \quad (8.14)$$

If a series of n identical resonant circuits are connected by *isolated* stages the overall bandwidth BW_T is

$$BW_T = BW_1 \sqrt{2^{1/n} - 1} \qquad (8.15)$$

Consumer products containing tuned circuits commonly employ slug-tuned inductors with nonmagnetic flux return paths. These are usually enclosed by an aluminum shield. As the slug position is changed, the inductance, coupling, and Q are all affected. The design of this type of inductor is complex and requires much trial and error, the costs of which are amortized over many units.

There are many of these inductors, with and without mutual coupling, on the market. If this route is chosen some of the available units should first be tested for suitability to the application.

Torroids are generally not preferred in low-cost commercial equipment but are well suited to limited production engineering prototypes.

8.4.1 Design Example

Figure 8.15 illustrates the design of a reactive coupled resonator circuit. The 10 μH inductors have a Q of 40. The Q of each resonant circuit is set at 4. 10 μH has a reactance of 62.8 Ω at 1 MHz, and accordingly the load and source resistors are

$$R_P = X_L Q = 62.8(4) = 251.2 \; \Omega$$

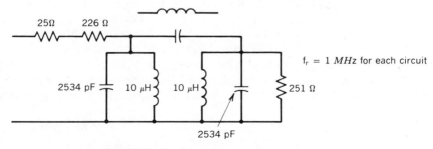

FIGURE 8.15   Reactive coupled resonator.

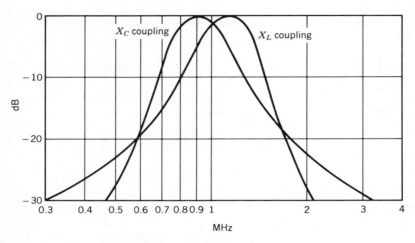

FIGURE 8.16   Coupled resonator.

This at 1 MHz is $C = 633$ pf or $L = 40$ µH. It is seen from Appendix IV that a 40 µH inductor would have an expected self-resonance of 16 MHz and could be of concern in some applications.

The signal source is a 50 Ω coaxial cable with a 50 Ω termination which is equal to 25 Ω and this is subtracted from the 251 Ω to produce the input resistor.

The series reactor for critical coupling is

$$X_{CPL} = QX_L \text{ (or } X_C) = 62.8(4) = 251.2 \text{ } \Omega$$

In practice component values are not always exactly as they should be and in this case the coupling reactance is generally adjusted as required to produce the correct result. For this design we are striving for a ripple-free top and a bandwidth increase of $\sqrt{2}$ (critical coupling).

Figure 8.16 shows the response of the design for both capacitive and inductive coupling. The nonsymmetrical response, as previously described, is evident. Also, it is seen that the capacitive coupling has lowered the resonant frequency, while the inductive coupling has produced an increase. This is because the series coupling capacitor has an equivalent parallel capacitance which lowers the resonant frequency. A reflected parallel inductance raises the resonant frequency. If the original resonant frequency is desired some trial and error may be necessary.

The preceding example illustrates a difficulty with the coupling inductance. This difficulty was apparent under conditions favorable to inductive coupling.

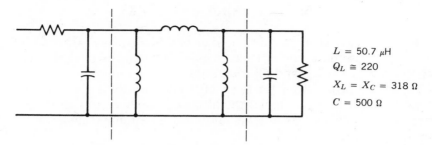

FIGURE 8.17 Inductively coupled resonator.

$L = 50.7\ \mu\text{H}$

$Q_L \cong 220$

$X_L = X_C = 318\ \Omega$

$C = 500\ \Omega$

Figure 8.17 shows a very practical requirement that is not as favorable.

$$\text{Set resonant circuit } Q = 20$$

$$X_{CPL} = QX_L = 20\,(318) = 6360\ \Omega$$

$$\text{At 1 MHz } X_{CPL} = 1012\ \mu\text{H}$$

Appendix IV shows that a 1000 μH inductor could be expected to have a self-resonance of 2.2 MHz, an unsatisfactory condition for most filters.

This condition can be corrected by making a π to T transformation (see Fig. 7.21). The transformation is shown in Fig. 8.18. The remainder of the circuit is unchanged. It is seen that the equivalent shunt coupling inductance is a very reasonable value.

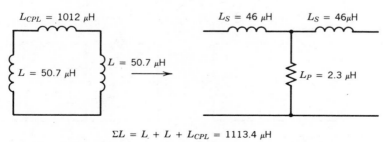

$$\Sigma L = L + L + L_{CPL} = 1113.4\ \mu\text{H}$$

$$L_S = \frac{L\,(L_{CPL})}{\Sigma L} = 46\ \mu\text{H} \qquad\qquad L_P = \frac{L^2}{\Sigma L} = 2.3\ \mu\text{H}$$

FIGURE 8.18 π to T transformation.

8.5 MATCHING NETWORKS

Matching networks are used to deliver *maximum power* from a source to a load. Maximum power transfer occurs when the source and load *resistances* are equal and all reactances are canceled.

Maximum power transfer is an efficiency of 50% which is not always desirable. For example, the alternators delivering utility power operate at a power-transfer level far below maximum transfer to maintain a high efficiency.

In lower-frequency *voltage* amplification, it is desirable to have the load impedance substantially higher than the source impedance to obtain a high transfer ratio. Unfortunately, as the frequencies rise the impedances become lower and voltage transfer must change to power transfer.

There are many techniques for obtaining a maximum power match. Discussed in this text are

1. Transformers, both tuned and broadband (see Chapter 5 on transformers)
2. Capacitive or inductive taps (see Sections 8.1–8.4 on resonant circuits)
3. Unbalanced filters (see Appendix III)
4. The L network and its variations

The L network and its variations and the π, T, and multiple L networks are the subject of this section. These four networks are shown in Figs. 8.19–8.22.

Capacitors and inductors are assumed to be lossless and nonresonant. Inductors are the most likely to cause problems. In these instances the inductor should be divided into its equivalent resistance

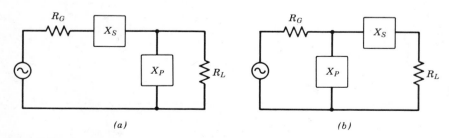

(a)   *(b)*

FIGURE 8.19 The basic L networks, Q set by terminations. (*a*) $R_L > R_G$; (*b*) $R_G > R_L$. X_S inductive and X_P capacitive = low pass. X_S capacitive and X_P inductive = high pass.

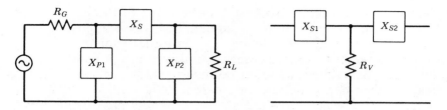

FIGURE 8.20   The π network, $Q > L$ network.

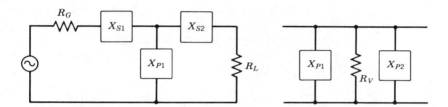

FIGURE 8.21   The T network, $Q > L$ network.

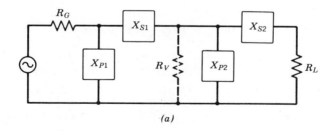

(a)

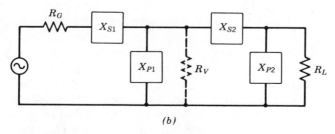

(b)

FIGURE 8.22   The multiple L networks, $Q < L$ network: (*a*) $R_G > R_L$; (*b*) $R_L > R_G$.

229

and reactance so that an estimate can be made of the losses. If the network is too lossy the impedance match may not be justified.

The transformations are defined for only the resonant frequency and because of this, off-resonance conditions are affected and frequency response checks should be made. This is of particular significance when harmonic rejection is required.

Although these networks are classified as low pass or high pass, the design procedures outlined here do not lead to standardized pass-band characteristics. They are intended as single-frequency couplers with selectable damping controlled by the circuit Q. They do, however, provide a very flexible coupling mechanism with a minimum of parts.

If well-defined pass-band and attenuation characteristics are desired, Appendix III contains tables of Butterworth, Chebyshev, and Bessel filters for mismatched terminations up to 10:1. These filters, however, have very little flexibility in absorbing reactive elements associated with the terminations.

A matching network serves only to couple the *resistive* portions of the two terminations (e.g., source and load). The associated reactances are absorbed or canceled in the matching network. The techniques of absorbing the reactive elements are as much a part of the design as the resistive match.

The design relations used for these networks are listed in Table 8.2. Their properties and use are explained and then a design example with response data is shown.

8.5.1 The L Network

The L network is the basis of the other three types and discussions of its design relates to this. The L section has four forms, which were shown in Fig. 8.19.

The low-pass form is by far the most used because it provides for harmonic attenuation. A noninterfering blocking capacitor can be used for DC if required. However, the same design rules apply to the high-pass version.

As indicated by Fig. 8.19, the parallel element must *always* face the higher resistance. This is because the parallel element changes the parallel resistance to a smaller series resistance that matches the other terminating resistance, which is, of course, the purpose of the design.

Another way of viewing the action of the L network is to recognize that it is a series resonant circuit. A fundamental property of this type of circuit is that at resonance the input impedance drops to minimum and the output impedance becomes a maximum (see Section 8.2). A simple example illustrates this point. Figure 8.23 shows the basic L transformation.

TABLE 8.2
Design Relations

L networks	$Q_S = Q_P = 2Q_n = \sqrt{\dfrac{R_{\max}}{R_{\min}} - 1}$	(8.16)
	$X_S = Q_S R_S$	(8.17)
	$X_P = R_P/Q_P$	(8.18)
π networks	$Q_n \cong \sqrt{\dfrac{R_{\max}}{R_V} - 1}$ or	(8.19)
	$R_V \cong \dfrac{R_{\max}}{(Q_n^2 + 1)},\ R_V < R_{\min}$	
	Q of L section with $R_{\max} \cong Q_n$	(8.20)
	Q of L section with $R_{\min} = \sqrt{\dfrac{R_{\min}}{R_V} - 1}$	(8.21)
T networks	$Q_n \cong \sqrt{\dfrac{R_V}{R_{\min}} - 1}$ or	(8.22)
	$R_V = R_{\min}(Q_n^2 + 1),\ R_V > R_{\max}$	
	Q of L section with $R_{\min} \cong Q_n$	(8.23)
	Q of L section with $R_{\max} = \sqrt{\dfrac{R_V}{R_{\max}} - 1}$	(8.24)
Multiple π	$R_{\max} > R_V > R_{\min}$	
	For minimum Q, $R_V = \sqrt{R_{\max}\,R_{\min}}$	(8.25)
	Q of all elements $= \sqrt{\dfrac{R_V}{R_{\min}} - 1} = \sqrt{\dfrac{R_{\max}}{R_V} - 1}$	(8.26)
Parallel to series conversion	$R_S = \dfrac{R_P}{(R_P/X_P)^2 + 1}$	(8.3)
	$X_S = \dfrac{X_P}{(X_P/R_P)^2 + 1}$	(8.4)

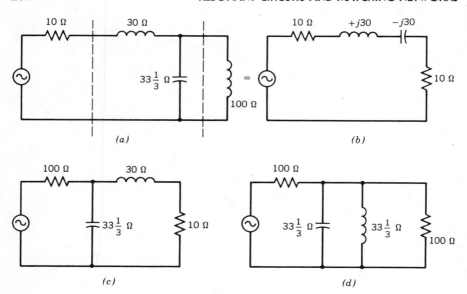

FIGURE 8.23 Basic L transformation. (*a*) Basic transform. (*b*) Parallel to series conversion. (*c*) Input reversed. (*d*) Series to parallel.

From Table 8.2 we use the relation

$$Q_S = Q_P = 2Q_n = \sqrt{\frac{R_{max}}{R_{min}} - 1} = \sqrt{\frac{100}{10} - 1} = 3$$

To understand this equation, it should be realized that a lossy capacitor has a Q defined exactly as that for a lossy inductor. For a series circuit $Q_L = Q_C = X/R_S$.

Equation 8.16 sets the Q's of the L and C in the L network equal. Although it is not directly evident, Eqs. 8.17 and 8.18 then establish that the circuit inductive impedance and the capacitive impedance are complex conjugates of each other (see Appendix I.8 on complex algebra). This establishes the match and it is demonstrated as follows:

$$R_S = \frac{R_P}{(R_P/X_P)^2 + 1} = \frac{100}{(100/33\frac{1}{3})^2 + 1} = 10 \ \Omega \qquad (8.3)$$

$$X_S = \frac{X_P}{(X_P/R_P)^2 + 1} = \frac{33\frac{1}{3}}{(33\frac{1}{3}/100)^2 + 1} = 30 \ \Omega \qquad (8.4)$$

It is also evident that the network resistance is double that of the individual loaded reactive elements, thereby resulting in a network Q that is $\frac{1}{2}$ of each of the loaded reactances.

If this circuit is driven from the high-resistance side as shown in Figure 8.23c, the series arm of $10 + j30$ is converted to the equivalent parallel form. We then have, from Eqs. 8.5 and 8.6,

$$R_P = \frac{R_S^2 + X_S^2}{R_S} = \frac{(10)^2 + (30)^2}{10} = 100 \ \Omega$$

$$X_P = \frac{R_S^2 + X_S^2}{X_S} = \frac{(10)^2 + (30)^2}{30} = 33\tfrac{1}{3} \ \Omega$$

With these values, as shown in Fig. 8.23d, it is evident that the maximum power transfer has been maintained. In other words, these circuits are bilateral.

The Q of the L section is determined by the terminating resistors alone. There is no flexibility.

8.5.2 The π Network

The π and T networks each consist of two L networks. It is handy to use an imaginary resistor R_V as an aid in the calculations.

In the π network, this virtual resistor is placed, in shunt, between two series reactors. It must have a value less than that of the smaller terminating resistor. Figure 8.20 illustrates the arrangement. Both L networks are designed using the same resistor. The two L sections, when connected together, then function as the desired π network (without R_V).

R_V is the mechanism by which a Q higher than the basic L network is designed. It is noted that the Q's of the two L networks are not equal. The L network facing $R_{\max}$ has the higher Q.

The Q of the total network Q_n has a Q based on the attenuation of the two L sections in series. That is, it is higher than either L network alone. Generally, the highest Q of the two L sections is used as a design basis for the total π network.

The Q of the inductance becomes more important as the total network Q becomes higher. This, of course, lowers Q_n and limits how high Q_n can be made.

It must be remembered that the virtual-resistor concept divides the π network into two L sections. The design technique is now in accordance with the L section design procedure.

In particular, it will be recalled that the L section Q is one half of the Q of each of its elements. Therefore, the L section design proceeds with a Q twice that of the final L networks. The final Q of the π network is then somewhat higher than the highest L section Q.

8.5.3 The T Network

Again, the rules are basically the same as the L network modified by the virtual-resistor concept. In this case, the R_V is facing the parallel elements and must have a value higher than $R_{\max}$, as shown in Table 8.2. Figure 8.21 shows the circuit arrangement.

In general, the π network is more useful than the T network because its outside elements are capacitive, which is more accommodating to the usual external circuits.

However, there are many instances where the T network results in more practical component values than the π network. If the π components are difficult, the T network should be tried.

8.5.4 The Multiple L Network

The multiple L network, as shown in Fig. 8.22, is used to obtain low Q matching. The form can be high or low pass, and again, the low pass is generally more useful.

The network also has one series end and one that is parallel. The choice of direction must be, as previously explained, such that the parallel element is across the larger terminating resistor.

Also as previously stated, the Q of these matching networks relates to the damping and overshoot characteristics at the intended match frequency. The high Q networks have an overshoot where the 3 dB bandwidth is similar to that of a resonant circuit. The low Q network merely smooths out this overshoot, producing no true increase in bandwidth.

There is another important factor that establishes a lower practical limit for the network Q (see Fig. 8.24). This data show the insertion

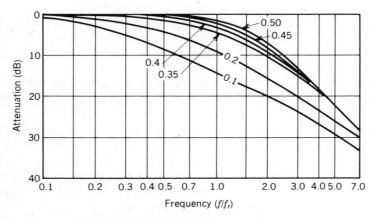

FIGURE 8.24 Losses of low Q circuits.

loss as a function of the Q of a two-pole network (L section). The response varies as the number of poles (or elements) is changed, but there is clearly a constraint on the lower limit of the network Q.

L sections can be added indefinitely, each stage producing more skirt attenuation and a smoother response to the desired signal. However, this process becomes laborious and the circuit lossy.

The multiple L matching network is of little value beyond two stages because an unbalanced Butterworth or Chebyshev filter can be designed with less effort and easily predictable results (see Chapter 7 on filters).

8.5.5 Design Example

Match the source and load of Fig. 8.25 with:

A. An L network.
B. A π network.
C. A T network.
D. A multiple L network.

A low-pass network is selected so that harmonic rejection is obtained. The circuit is to be matched at 2 MHz. A Q of 10 is selected for the π and T networks. The multiple L is designed for two stages and with a minimum Q. Frequency plots of the resulting designs will be made.

A: L NETWORK CALCULATIONS

This design includes reactive elements in parallel with the two terminations. They must be accounted for in the designs and each specific design will show how this is done.

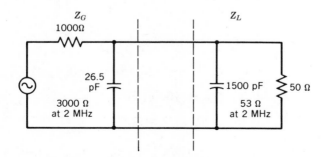

FIGURE 8.25 Design example.

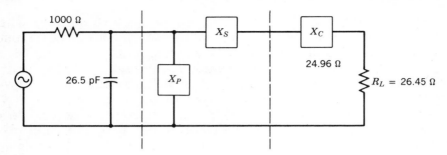

FIGURE 8.26 Developing L network.

In this case the reactances are capacitive, but any simple or complex impedancee can be handled in the same manner. The nature of this impedance is, however, a strong factor in determining the characteristics of the transformation as the frequency is changed.

The parallel element of the L network faces the higher termination, leaving the series element facing a shunt capacitor (Fig. 8.26).

The series element must absorb this reactance and to do this the reactance must be in its series equivalent. Accordingly we have

$$X_S = \frac{X_P}{(X_P/R_P)^2 + 1} = \frac{53}{(53/50)^2 + 1} = 24.96 \ \Omega \qquad (8.4)$$

$$R_S = \frac{R_P}{(R_P/X_P)^2 + 1} = 26.45 \ \Omega \qquad (8.3)$$

This series combination represents the values that must be used to establish the L network. The capacitance on the source side can be absorbed directly by the parallel arm of the L network.

We now have

$$Q_S = Q_P = \sqrt{\frac{R_{max}}{R_{min}} - 1} = \sqrt{\frac{1000}{26.45} - 1} = 6.07 \qquad (8.16)$$

and then

$$X_S = Q_S R_S = 6.07(26.45) = 160.5 \ \Omega \qquad (8.17)$$

$$X_P = R_P/Q_P = 1000/6.07 = 164.7 \ \Omega \qquad (8.18)$$

$$C_P = 483.2 \ \text{pF at 2 MHz}$$

As previously stated, the network Q will be one half of the branch Q, so a Q of about 3 can be expected for the completed circuit.

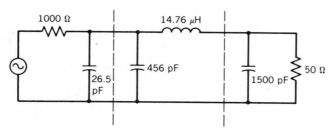

FIGURE 8.27 Final L coupled circuit.

Since this is a low-pass filter, X_S is inductive and X_P is capacitive.

Also, X_S must be increased by 24.96 Ω to absorb the series equivalent of the shunt load capacitance. The total $X_S = 160.5 + 24.96 = 185.19$ Ω which at 2 MHz = 14.7 μH.

Since 26.5 pF is already in the circuit, the total additional $C_P = 483.2 - 26.5 = 456.7$ pF.

The two shunt capacitors in the circuit could also be resonated by shunt inductors, and sometimes this is done, but it requires two extra parts and produces different off-resonance responses. These two capacitors have been compensated for at the matching frequency. However, their presence defines a change in the circuit from pure resistances and again the off-frequency response will be modified. Figure 8.27 shows the final L coupled circuit.

For comparison the values of the L network without the presence of the extra capacitors are 347 pF and 17.3 μH.

B: π NETWORK CALCULATIONS

Figure 8.28 shows the developing π network with the virtual resistor R_V in place.

Since a Q of 10 is desired for the complete π network, a design value of $Q = 20$ must be used for each reactance of the high Q L network. The high Q L network is next to R_{max}.

The virtual resistor is determined first. From Table 8.2 we have

$$R_V = \frac{R_{max}}{Q_{max}^2 + 1} = \frac{1000}{(20^2 + 1)} = 2.49 \ \Omega$$

$$X_{P1} = \frac{R_P}{Q_{max}} = \frac{1000}{20} = 50 \ \Omega$$

At 2 MHz, $C_{P1} = 1591$ pF

$$X_{S1} = Q_{max}R_V = 20(2.49) = 49.8 \ \Omega$$

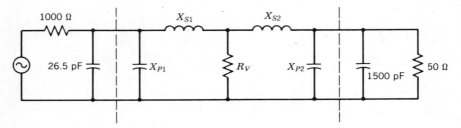

FIGURE 8.28 The developing π network.

Q for the second section is

$$Q_{\min} = \sqrt{\frac{R_{\min}}{R_V} - 1} = \sqrt{\frac{50}{2.49} - 1} = 4.37$$

$$X_{S2} = Q_{\min}R_V = 4.37(2.49) = 10.88 \ \Omega$$

$$X_{P2} = \frac{R_{\min}}{Q_{\min}} = \frac{50}{4.37} = 11.44 \ \Omega$$

At 2 MHz, $C_{P2} = 6954$ pF

The series inductors add so that

$$X_S = 10.88 + 49.8 = 60.68 \ \Omega$$

At 2 MHz, $L_S = 4.83 \ \mu H$

The terminating capacitors are subtracted from the two parallel arms and Fig. 8.29 is the final circuit.

If the parallel arms have a capacitance less than the terminating capacitor, the parallel element becomes an inductor set to resonate with the excess capacitance at the design frequency.

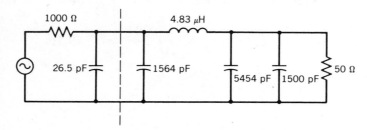

FIGURE 8.29 Completed π circuit.

C: T Network Calculations

Figure 8.30 shows the developing T network with the terminations converted to their series equivalent so that the reactive components can be combined.

Unlike the π section, the high Q L network is on the R_{min} side. This is because the terminating resistors are in series with the reactive element.

From Table 8.2 we have

$$R_V = R_{min}(Q_n^2 + 1) = 26.45(20^2 + 1) = 10,606 \ \Omega$$

$$Q_{min} = \sqrt{\frac{R_V}{R_{max}} - 1} = 3.28$$

$$X_{S1} = Q_{min} R_{max} = 3.28(900) = 2952 \ \Omega$$

$$X_{P1} = R_V/Q_{min} = 10,606/3.28 = 3234 \ \Omega$$

At 2 MHz $C_{P1} = 24.6$ pF

$$X_{S2} = Q_{max} R_{min} = 20(26.45) = 529 \ \Omega$$

$$X_{P2} = R_V/Q_{max} = 10,660/20 = 530 \ \Omega$$

At 2 MHz, $C_{P2} = 150$ pF

X_{S1} must be increased by 300 Ω to cancel the capacitive reactance of the termination.

$$\therefore X_{S1} = (2952 + 300) = 3252 \ \Omega$$

$$\text{At 2 MHz, } L_{S1} = 259 \ \mu\text{H}$$

Likewise,

$$X_{S2} = (529 + 24.96) = 554 \ \Omega$$

$$\text{At 2 MHz, } L_{S2} = 44 \ \mu\text{H}$$

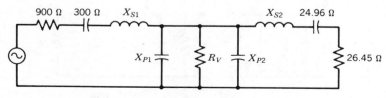

FIGURE 8.30   The developing T network.

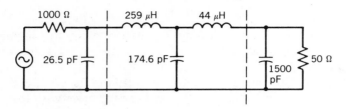

FIGURE 8.31   The final T network.

The capacitances add so we have

$$C = (24.6 + 150) = 174.6 \ \mu F$$

The final network is shown in Fig. 8.31.

D: Multiple L Network Calculations

Figure 8.32 shows the developing two-stage L network. From Table 8.2 we have

For min Q,

$$R_V = \sqrt{R_{max}R_{min}} = \sqrt{1000(26.45)} = 162.6 \ \Omega$$

from which

$$Q = \sqrt{\frac{R_V}{R_{min}} - 1} = \sqrt{\frac{162.6}{26.45} - 1} = 2.27$$

The two L networks comprising the complete network are determined as follows (note that the capacitive end is next to R_{max}):

$X_{P1} = R_P/Q = 1000/2.27 = 441 \ \Omega$, at 2 MHz $C_{P1} = 180$ pF

$X_{S1} = QR_S = 2.27(162.6) = 369 \ \Omega$, at 2 MHz, $L_{S1} = 29.36 \ \mu H$

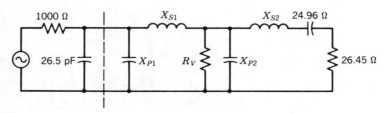

FIGURE 8.32   Developing two-stage L network.

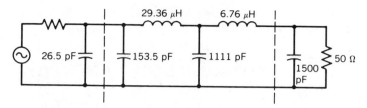

FIGURE 8.33   Final two-stage L network.

$$X_{P2} = R_P/Q = 162.6/2.27 = 71.6 \ \Omega, \text{ at 2 MHz} \quad C_{P2} = 1{,}111 \text{ pF}$$

$$X_{S2} = QR_S(2.27)(26.45) = 60 \ \Omega$$

Adding 24.96 Ω to cancel the load reactance,

$$X_{LS2} = 60 + 24.96 \ \Omega, \text{ at 2 MHz}, \quad L_{S2} = 6.76 \ \mu\text{H}$$

Figure 8.33 shows the final two-stage L network.

Figure 8.34 shows the relative response of an L, two-stage L, and a π or T network. The π and T networks are equivalent and therefore have the same response.

Since these matching networks are all of the low-pass form and have the same source and terminating resistors they will have the same DC gain. That is, $50/1050 \cong -26$ dB. This does not appear to be the case from the way the curves approach the low-frequency

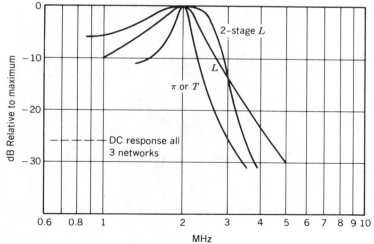

FIGURE 8.34   Relative response of coupling networks.

asymptote, but there are lower-frequency resonances involved that produce the misleading slopes.

8.6 OFF-RESONANCE CONSIDERATIONS

This subject is illustrated by a parallel resonant circuit, and some numerical calculations are made for the application of a square wave to a parallel *LC* circuit. However, the conditions shown here apply to all resonant circuits driven by an off-resonant single frequency.

The application of a steady-state single *fixed* frequency (by definition a sine wave) to a parallel *LC* circuit results in one of three possible conditions. This is illustrated in Fig. 8.35.

Resonance is the simple case. Here X_C and X_L cancel, leaving a pure resistance. This resistance represents the circuit dissipation. $R = QX$, and the reflected load is in parallel with the reactance.

Figure 8.35*b* represents the circuit at a frequency *below* resonance. Here the capacitive reactance is canceled by part of the inductive reactance, leaving a net parallel *RL* circuit. Likewise, for frequencies *above* resonance, there is a net parallel *RC* circuit.

For illustration, numbers generated in Section 9.8.1 are used as follows. Here $C = 2940$ pF, $L = 1.7$ mH, and the frequency is defined as the fundamental of the 20 kHz square wave, that is, a 20 kHz sine wave. Resonance is 71 kHz. The inductance required to cancel the 2940 pF of capacitance at 20 kHz is 22 mH. From the relation for two inductors in parallel,

$$L = \frac{L_1 L_2}{L_1 + L_2} \tag{8.27}$$

We can derive

$$L_1 = \frac{LL_2}{L_2 - L} \tag{8.28}$$

 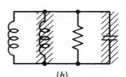 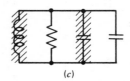

        (*a*)   (*b*)   (*c*)

FIGURE 8.35 Tuned circuit conditions: (*a*) at resonance resistive; (*b*) below resonance inductive; (*c*) above resonance capacitive.

The net inductance at 20 kHz is then

$$L = \frac{22(1.7)}{22 - 1.7} = 1.8 \text{ mH}$$

This is what the circuit will appear to be for a steady-state sine wave.

When a square wave is applied to an LC circuit, as in Section 9.8, the supporting harmonics are odd, and the equivalent circuits for these odd harmonics must be determined. To preserve the waveform, the source must have a low impedance capable of furnishing the current required by all of the harmonics. This, of course, produces a low Q which is necessary to pass the bandwidth required for a square wave.

In this case we evaluate the third, fifth, and seventh harmonics to complete the example. $f = 60$ kHz is still below resonance. To resonate 2940 pF requires 2.4 mH. L now equals

$$\frac{1.7(2.4)}{2.4 - (1.7)} = 5.8 \text{ mH}$$

The fifth harmonic at 100 kHz is above resonance and accordingly to resonate 1.7 mH requires 1500 pF, leaving 1440 pF as the load.

The seventh harmonic at 140 kHz requires 770 pF to resonate 1.7 mH, leaving approximately 2170 pF as the load.

$$1.8 \text{ mH at } 20 \text{ kHz} = 230 \text{ } \Omega$$

$$5.8 \text{ mH at } 60 \text{ kHz} = 2.2 \text{ k}\Omega$$

$$1440 \text{ pF at } 100 \text{ kHz} = 1.2 \text{ k}\Omega$$

$$2170 \text{ pF at } 140 \text{ kHz} = 540 \text{ } \Omega$$

The spectral construction of a square wave is given in Section I.3 from which we can calculate the harmonic currents as follows:

$$20 \text{ kHz } I_P = 20 \text{ V} \left(\frac{2}{\pi}\right) \bigg/ 230 \text{ } \Omega = 56 \text{ mA}$$

$$60 \text{ kHz } I_P = 20 \text{ V} \left(\frac{2}{3\pi}\right) \bigg/ 2200 \text{ } \Omega = 3.6 \text{ mA}$$

$$100 \text{ kHz } I_P = 20 \text{ V} \left(\frac{2}{5\pi}\right) \bigg/ 1200 \text{ } \Omega = 2.0 \text{ mA}$$

$$140 \text{ kHz } I_P = 20 \text{ V} \left(\frac{2}{7\pi}\right) \bigg/ 540 \text{ } \Omega = 3.4 \text{ mA}$$

This aids in determining the driving current required for a square wave applied to a tuned circuit. To determine the true current, the phase of the harmonics must be taken into account and a plot made of the resulting waveform. If power dissipation is to be determined, the rms value of the resulting waveform must be calculated or measured.

8.7 CABLE EQUALIZERS

Cable loss as a function of frequency is complex and specialized techniques must be used for its correction. Compensation for any substantial amount of loss cannot be made by the methods discussed in this book and requires the services of a specialist.

One such source of design services is given in Reference [1]. The following description of a design was submitted by Ken Sites, manager of the Nuclear Instrumentation Division of SAIC.

Cable equalizers have been in use for over 20 years and are essentially attenuators that represent the inverse loss of that presented by a coaxial cable. The combination of the equalizer and cable loss then provides a flat attenuation over the frequency range from DC to the upper 3 dB point.

The transfer function of a coaxial cable is frequency dependent, where the attenuation per unit length increases as a function of frequency. As a result, cable attenuation is not a flat response when a pulsed signal is transmitted through it. To optimize frequency response, the cable length should be as short as is practical and the quality of cable should be the best that can be afforded. Then the cable can be equalized to achieve the overall bandwidth that is required.

An example equalizer design is shown in Fig. 8.36. At low frequencies the cable attenuation is primarily due to the resistance of the cable conductors; at higher frequencies the loss is due to the reactance in the cable.

The equalizer is a passive device that is constructed in a three-stage bridge tee configuration. At low frequencies all three stages operate as a resistive attenuator. At high frequencies each stage is designed to decrease attenuation such that the composite response is the inverse of the cable response. The combined equalizer and cable response provides a flat attenuation from DC to the upper 3 dB point where the loss converges with the original cable loss curve.

Cable equalization can significantly improve the transmission line response but is limited by the total cable and equalizer loss. From a practical standpoint, equalizer designs up to 30 dB attenuation are reasonably easy to handle and in principle up to 60 dB attenuation

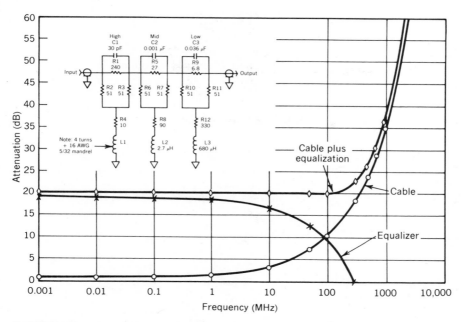

FIGURE 8.36 Example equalizer design for 122 m RG-223/U, 20 dB attenuation.

can be achieved. Since these are passive devices, we must realize that the 30 dB device works with about a 30 to 1 low-to-high frequency pass ratio. This ratio increases to 200 to 1 for the 60 dB design. As a result the design and fabrication procedures are critical in order to minimize feedthrough due to coupling and stray reactance. This problem is accentuated by high attenuation and high frequencies. Also, these problems lead to unfavorable phase shift, which may result in ringing or resonant effects that distort the throughput signal.

The bridge tee design is used because the network matches the coaxial cable impedance in both directions. Therefore, it makes no difference where the equalizer is located in a coaxial cable. From a signal-to-noise consideration it is preferable to place it at the output end so that any coupled low-frequency noise is attenuated within the equalizer.

Equalizer designs are usually handled by a computer process that defines the component values and the expected operating response. The design is based on input data that includes the calculated or measured impulse response of the cable and the desired attenuation or upper 3 dB frequency. Many designs involve a combination of several cable types, and in-line signal conditioning devices such as attenuators and couplers. It is best to measure the end-to-end response which then can be used to design the equalizer.

REFERENCES

[1] K. R. Sites, Manager, Nuclear Instrumentation Division, Science Applications International Corp. (SAIC), 3351 South Highland Dr., Suite 206, Las Vegas, NV 89109.

GENERAL REFERENCES

J. K. Hardy, *High Frequency Circuit Design,* Reston, VA, 1979.

H. L. Krauss, C. W. Bostian, and F. H. Raab, *Solid State Radio Engineering,* Wiley, New York, 1980.

C. Bowick, *RF Circuit Design,* Howard W. Sams, Indianapolis, IN, 1982.

NINE

Circuit and Component Applications

This chapter discusses how various circuit elements and building blocks are combined to function together. The circuits do not necessarily represent useful end items, but typify everyday design problems. Calculations are included when necessary and the design steps required to fulfill the intent of the circuit are outlined. The individual parts of the circuit are generally not discussed beyond the application at hand. The index should be consulted to find out where further information on a device is given.

9.1 VOLTAGE-CONTROLLED CRYSTAL OSCILLATOR

A crystal can be operated off its normal frequency over a range of about 0.1% (total change). This is a good method when a small but precise frequency variation is required. Figure 9.1 shows a circuit that uses a pair of hyperjunction varactors to convert a control voltage to the desired capacitance variation. This type of varactor has a useful capacitance change of 10–1 for a voltage range of 1–10 V. Two diodes are used because the midpoint is a convenient place at which to apply the control voltage and because the modulating effect of the RF voltage on the capacitors is largely canceled. The inductor is used to resonate, and thereby cancel, the unwanted residual capacitance. The midpoint of the control voltage then produces the midpoint of the frequency spread. The source follower is used in the input to minimize both the resistive and the reactive load on the crystal.

The gain of the second stage is given by

$$G = \frac{g_m R_0}{1 + g_m R_E} \tag{9.1}$$

R_0 is the tank resonant resistance in parallel with the FET drain resistance. The coil resonant resistance involves both the core losses and the high-frequency copper losses (skin effect). The simple test circuit included in Fig. 9.1 establishes this value as 10 kΩ.

The FET drain resistance is determined from the device E/I data as $r_d = \Delta E/\Delta I = 20$ kΩ. This leaves $R_0 = 6.67$ kΩ. The data sheets are also sufficient to establish that the transconductance is about 10 mmhos. The gain now becomes

$$G = \frac{10(6.67)}{1 + 10(.33)} = 15.6$$

The transformer step-down results in a system gain of 15.6/5 = 3.1, and the secondary divider reduces the total loop gain to about 1.5. The secondary divider was determined experimentally to produce optimum performance over the tuning range. The gain of 1.5 is a calculated open-loop value. During operation the gain must adjust, by limiting, to exactly unity for stable oscillation. If more gain had been required to ensure good starting conditions, the source resistance of the second stage could have been partially bypassed.

The bandwidth in the test setup was determined to be 94 kHz. In the actual circuit 10 kΩ is replaced by $r_d = 20$ kΩ and accordingly the bandwidth is something less than this. It is, however, sufficiently wide to accommodate the frequency change of 6590 Hz.

The FETs used are Signetics high-frequency MOS devices with a low C_{dg} of about 0.3 pF.

9.2 DIGITAL PROCESSING

This title is a catchall phrase. Figure 9.2 is part of a larger control system and is described here purely to show how the components function together. The pin connections are complete except for the power supplies and ground connections. This is often done on large schematics for signal flow clarity and also because the power supply is wired in first from a separate schematic. There is a 0.1 μF capacitor on each supply pin.

Starting with U1, we have a hex D f/f. This is a six-channel digital storage. When the clock goes from low to high, the contents of the input lines are placed on the output lines. The arrows are used to distinguish the input and output lines. Note also that six lines are converted to one line for convenience. One of the inputs is labeled MSB. This explicitly means that the line below it is the second MSB and so on to the bottom line, which is the LSB. This cable is connected on the other end of the line in the same order. The output lines of

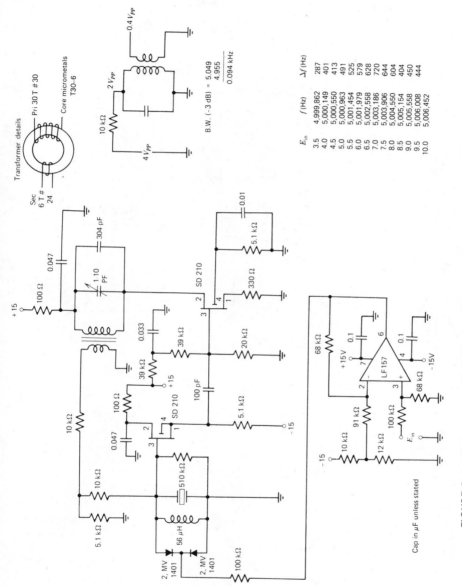

E_{in}	f (Hz)	Δf (Hz)
3.5	4,999,862	287
4.0	5,000,149	401
4.5	5,000,550	413
5.0	5,000,963	491
5.5	5,001,454	525
6.0	5,001,979	579
6.5	5,002,558	628
7.0	5,003,186	720
7.5	5,003,906	644
8.0	5,004,550	604
8.5	5,005,154	404
9.0	5,005,558	450
9.5	5,006,008	444
10.0	5,006,452	

FIGURE 9.1 Voltage-controlled X'tal oscillator. 5,006,452 Hz – 4,999,862 Hz 6590 Hz; $\dfrac{6590(100)}{5(10)^6} = 0.132\%$.

249

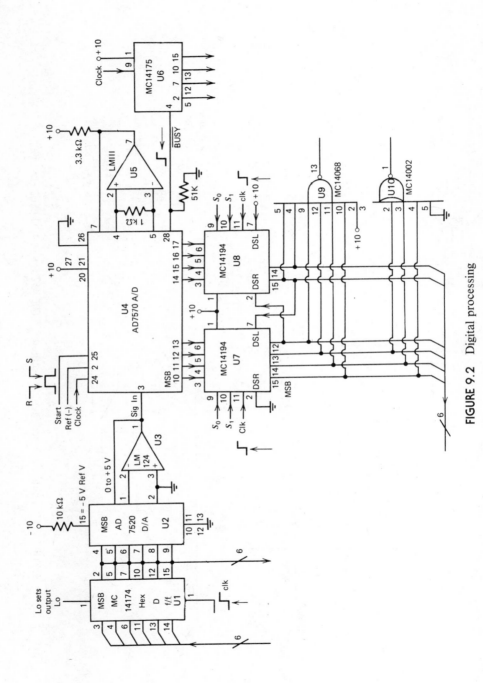

FIGURE 9.2 Digital processing

U1 may appear to be shorted together, but this is not the case. The connections are clarified by the /6 on the line which defines six separate wires. This is an important simplification because digital word lines can have many leads and go to numerous places in a system.

The 6-bit digital information is converted to an analog signal by U2. The 7520 D/A (Analog Devices) is used with one fourth of the quad op-amp LM124. Pins 10, 11, 12, and 13 are unused digital inputs and accordingly are grounded. The output of the D/A is $-V_{ref}$ for a maximum signal in, and goes to the signal input of the AD7570 A/D (Analog Devices). The A/D is connected so that it has a maximum digital output when the (+) signal input is equal in magnitude to its (−) voltage reference. The LM111 comparator is necessary for the AD7570 to fulfill the A/D function. When the START signal goes from low to high, the A/D is reset. The START signal must remain high for 0.5 μs after which a high-to-low transition starts the conversion. The MSB is resolved first and each clock cycle produces a new bit until LSB is developed and the conversion stops. There is a serial output (pin 8), if desired, as well as parallel outputs.

During the conversion period the $\overline{\text{BUSY}}$ output is low and goes to a high when the conversion is complete. U6 is a quad D f/f that is connected as a shift register (S/R). During conversion, the $\overline{\text{BUSY}}$ input to the S/R is low. Since the S/R clock is continuous, the outputs become all lows. When conversion is complete, the input to the S/R goes high, and each successive output goes high as the clock cycles. These outputs are then used in sequential logic to perform whatever functions are necessary to operate the system. It should be noted here that these outputs operate edge-sensitive logic as contrasted to state-sensitive logic. The MC14175 also has the output available in the complement form so that high-to-low-edge signals can be used.

The eight parallel outputs of the A/D go to two S/Rs connected in series. These are two-way S/Rs with both parallel and serial entry. The operation is controlled by the S_0 and S_1 inputs according to Table 9.1.

TABLE 9.1
Truth Table of the MC14194 Shift
Register

Clock	Mode	S_0	S_1
x	Hold	0	0
↑	Shift left	0	1
↑	Shift right	1	0
↑	Parallel entry	1	1

This is a very flexible arrangement. S_0 and S_1 are obviously the result of a system calculation and accordingly operate on the output of the A/D. Shifting a binary number one step to the left is a multiplication of 2, unless the MSB is a 1 and is lost in an overflow. Similarly, shifting 1 bit to the right is a division by 2. This likewise has a restriction: the bit entering the MSB position is a 0. U7 has the DSR input grounded so that a 0 will enter the MSB position. When the division is made, accuracy is lost as each LSB is dropped from the S/R. In this particular connection it was desired to have 1's enter the LSB position on the shift left operation, so that true multiplication is not being attained. U7 and U8 are connected so that on left shift the MSB of U8 enters the LSB input of U7, and on right shift the LSB of U7 enters the MSB of U8.

It is generally necessary to detect the S/R overflow and underflow conditions to maintain a desired operation. In this case an overflow is defined by a state of all 1's. This is detected by the NAND gate, U9. The underflow is defined as no 1's in the three MSB positions. This condition produces a 1 at the output of U10.

9.3 DIGITAL GAIN CONTROL

This is a low-frequency amplifier whose gain is controlled by the output of a digital processor. There is a fine adjustment of 1 to 512 and a coarse control of 1 to 1/64.

The fine control comes from an up/down counter, which is the output to the digital processor. Although not shown, a minimum and maximum count detector should be used with a circuit of this kind so that a maximum count cannot overflow to a minimum count and vice versa. This would be a set of word recognizers as described in the digital chapter and also shown in Fig. 9.2.

The truth table on Fig. 9.3 shows how the coarse gain is determined. For example, at the counter output of 0 0, the switches U5 and U6 are closed and the gain of the first stage is $1 + 34.8/4.99 = 8$. The second stage has 2.21 and 17.8 kΩ in parallel, which is $= 1.97$ kΩ. The gain is then $1 + 124/1.97 = 64$. The switches are schematically drawn like relays as a convenience. The DG307 switch was picked primarily for its low "on" resistance of 50 Ω. This represents $50(100)/2210 = 2\frac{1}{2}\%$ of the smallest resistor. When the switches are open, the amplifiers are at unity gain.

The LM108A op-amps were picked because of their low input current and low power consumption. The need for the low input current is brought about by the 1 MΩ resistor required for the low-frequency response. The maximum input bias current is 2 nA, which produces an output voltage of 125 mV at maximum gain. The 5.1 kΩ resistors

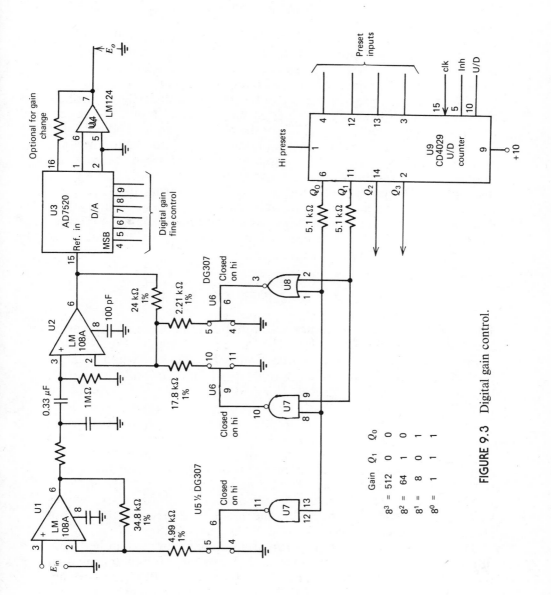

FIGURE 9.3 Digital gain control.

are placed in the clock lines as a testing convenience. This allows a ground of $+10$ V to be applied to the inputs of U7 and U8 without affecting the counter. For this application the resistors do not degrade the switching speed.

The unmarked *RC* at the output of U1 is an aid in controlling the switching spikes if needed. It restricts the signal bandwidth, however, so that its use depends on the nature of the circuit to be designed. In any event, the impact of the switching spikes must be evaluated.

A multiplying D/A converter can be used as a digitally controlled analog amplifier if the signal is put in the reference input. However, the specific D/A must be checked for the allowable range and polarity. The AD7520 is specified as a multiplying D/A and can accommodate an input range of ± 25 V. The output swing depends on the external op-amp and the supply voltages used with it. The AD7520 has an internal 10 kΩ feedback resistor, and with the internal 10 kΩ resistor ladder the D/A as shown in the schematic has a gain of unity. An external feedback resistor of 10 kΩ would double the gain. Maximum gain is produced when the digital inputs are all 1's. The output is proportional to the digital count.

9.4 POWER AMPLIFIER, 20–50 MHz

The guideline for this amplifier was reliability; hence a conservative approach is used in the design. The circuit is shown in Fig. 9.4.

Power developed by a resistive load is E^2_{rms}/R, but when a scope is used to observe a sinusoidal output, E_{PP} is handier and the relation $(E_{PP})^2/8R = P$ is more useful. For 6 W, $E_{PP} = 49$ V across the 50 Ω load. The transformer is of the transmission line type described in Chapter 5 and has a 2–1 voltage step-down. This means that there must be 49 V_{PP} at the collector of each of the output transistors. With a 24 V supply the maximum output on each transistor is 48 V_{PP}, so that it is clear that no more power can be obtained with this transformer connection and load. The harmonic level at 20 MHz and 6 W was -32 dB for the second and -26 dB for the third. These values were undoubtedly enhanced by the local feedback on the output stages. The maximum power at 50 MHz was 4 W.

The transistors are rated as tuned amplifiers under matched conditions. With a 28 V supply and the 0.3 W available for each transistor the rated output power per transistor is 9 W at 100 MHz. This application, however, is not tuned. It is broadband, which makes a considerable difference. The input and output capacitances cannot be resonated, and since they now discharge into a resistance instead of an inductance, there is a substantial power loss. Also the input and output impedances decrease as the frequency increases, further lim-

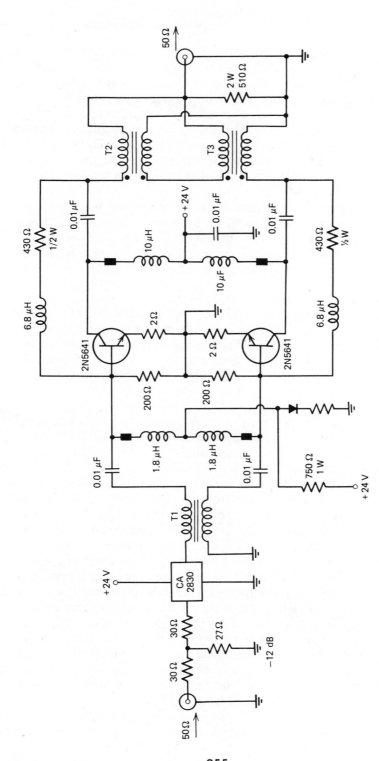

FIGURE 9.4 Power amplifier (6 to 4 W), 20 to 50 MHz T1, T2, and T3; 6 T of #24 twisted pair, wound six twists/in. Ferroxcube cores 266 T 125/4C4 (0.375 in. O.D.).

255

iting the power that can be obtained on the high end of the signal spectrum. The power gain of most RF power transistors falls at 6 dB/octave in their normal region of operation and that is when they are operating into matched tuned circuits. For this application, however, the band of operation is substantially below the nominal 175 MHz, so that the gain is higher but still falling as the frequency increases. Finally, the power supply was reduced from 28 to 24 V to increase the reliability. This may not seem like much, but since the power varies as the square of the voltage, this represents a power reduction of 26.5%.

The fact that this transformer cannot block DC forces the use of choke feeds for the power supply and a set of blocking capacitors. The choke can be a significant problem for a wideband amplifier. In this case the bandwidth is not very great, so that a conventional choke of 10 μH was satisfactory. The self-resonance of this choke is 35 MHz. At this point the impedance is very high, but will start to fall off rapidly as the frequency is increased. At 20 MHz the reactance of the 10 μH choke is 1300 Ω. This leaves 2600 Ω shunting the 200 Ω of reflected load resistance. This is quite adequate, but for a wider bandwidth a wideband choke constructed in the same style as the wideband transformers would have to be used (see Chapter 5). The chokes should have a low Q to minimize the possibility of spurious oscillations. The chokes available were of a high Q variety and so the ferrite beads were added in series as Q spoilers.

Local feedback in the form of an RL network is used to level the gain versus frequency response. The reactance of 6.8 μH equals 430 Ω at 10 MHz. The feedback impedance is accordingly rising and increasing the gain in the region of 20 to 50 MHz. The feedback is also effective in minimizing the distortion of the output stage. The amplifier had somewhat more gain than required, so that the 2 Ω emitter resistors gave a good gain-to-stability trade-off. Likewise, the 200 Ω base resistors help modify the large input capacitance. This is particularly helpful when local feedback is employed.

The bias is fed through choke isolators. A diode was used in the bias network to provide some temperature compensation, and although it is cemented to the heat sink, this is still not really adequate. The proper way is to use a diode that is built into the transistor case. Unfortunately, most power transistors do not have this feature. Transformer T1 is used as a phase splitter to convert the single-ended output of the CA2830 to the required push–pull for the output stage.

The CA2830 is one of a family of hybrid amplifiers marketed by TRW. It has a bandwidth of 1 to 150 MHz. This unit develops 600 mW across a 50 Ω load (15 V_{PP}) from a 50 Ω source of 0.3 V_{PP}. This makes an excellent and reasonably priced (about $40.00) power booster for a standard signal generator. It features good linearity and is very rugged. It must be used where power consumption is of no concern, however, since the device consumes 8 W to deliver 0.6 W of signal. An input attenuator pad is used to reduce the input signal to the required level. Appendix I contains a table for the calculation of T-pad attenuators.

9.5 HIGH-SPEED ANALOG MULTIPLEXER

Multiplexers for analog signals are readily available in compact DIP packages. These are usually dual devices that can be combined for more channels. Their switching times are limited, however, and when higher speeds are required it is often necessary to go to a discrete design. There are two common approaches to this problem. Figure 9-5a consists of gating a series of FETs on and off in sequence. This requires only a single-ended drive and is the more commonly used method. This application of FETs is described in Chapter 1. Figure 9.5b requires a push–pull voltage and generally uses more space and power, but it can be made to operate faster and has a more favorable ratio of maximum signal to switching spikes.

When a current flows in the direction of the arrow, the diodes are all turned on and a smaller current can flow from E_{in} to E_o. When the diodes are reverse biased, an input voltage that does not exceed the switching voltage is blocked.

The circuit shown in Fig. 9.6 is unique in the sense that it has a limited mode of operation, but within the limitation it is very compact and consumes less power than most systems with equivalent performance. The multiplexing system has six inputs, each of which is sampled for 50 ns. The rise and fall times are about 8 ns. Full output

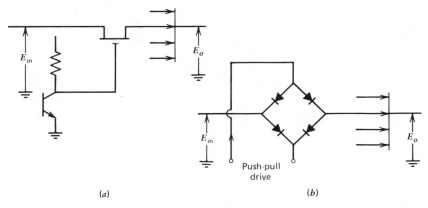

FIGURE 9.5 Basic multiplexers.

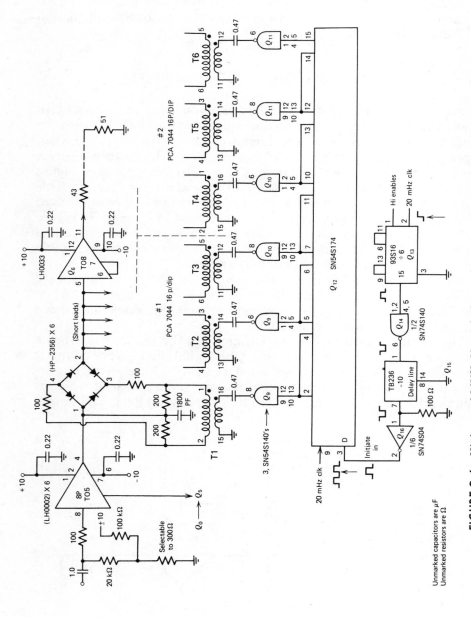

FIGURE 9.6 High-speed MUX. Unmarked capacitors are μF; unmarked resistors are Ω.

Unmarked capacitors are μF
Unmarked resistors are Ω

258

is 800 mV$_{PP}$ into a 50 Ω load. The switching spikes are about 5 mV maximum.

It is important that the driving impedance to the diode bridge be very low. This is a major factor in reducing the switching transients. The LH0002 used in the circuit, a NSC device, is a complementary emitter follower with an output impedance of 6 Ω and a frequency response of 30 MHz. The low output impedance of the normal operational amplifier is not completely satisfactory in this case because it cannot respond to the fast spikes, hence its output impedance remains high.

The principal limitation of the circuit occurs because of the use of transformers. This particular application has six inputs, and because a transformer cannot pass DC, the secondaries have the waveform shown in Fig. 9.7. The signal turn-on voltage is $E+$ and the turn-off voltage, which is now limiting the size of the signal, is $E-$.

The optimum arrangement occurs with two inputs where the turn-on and turn-off voltages are equal. It is doubtful that this would be an effective circuit if the inputs were increased above six.

One of the nice features of the circuit is that the six transformers are contained in two 16-pin DIP packages. The six SN54S140 drivers are contained in three 14-pin DIP packages. The balanced diode bridges come in a small plastic package and are convenient and compact, although relatively expensive at about $35.00 each.

The resistors in the secondary of the transformers were determined empirically and control the current level and damping. The capacitor assists in controlling the spike level, but does load the input signal and may need to be reduced if higher signal frequencies are encountered. There is a balancing option on the signal input buffer to balance the offset voltages. These input buffers must also be checked for temperature imbalance and selected units used.

The switching signals are developed in the SN54S174 D f/f connected as a shift register. The Initiate In signal is derived from Q_{13}, a divide-by-6 counter. This is a unique connection that produces an output pulse whose width is equal to the clock cycle. It is also required that the input to the S/R, Initiate In, precede the active clock edge by at least 5 ns. The best policy is to center the active clock edge with respect to the input pulse. Figure 9.8 shows the required waveforms.

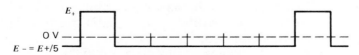

FIGURE 9.7 Turn-off/turn-on ratio.

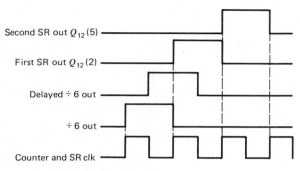

FIGURE 9.8 Circuit waveforms.

There are various ways of producing the required delays for the proper operation of edge-triggered logic. The most common method is by judicious selection of the basic components so that the timing is very close to being initially correct. Then just minor additions of a few gates for added delays complete the design. *RC* networks are sometimes used, but then the noise immunity and triggering levels may be adversely affected.

Figure 9.6 shows the use of a miniature *LC* delay line manufactured by Rhombus Industries. This device fits in a standard 14-pin DIP and has 10 taps for incremental delays. Though very handy, it requires a high-power driver for the generally low impedance of the delay line.

9.6 HIGH-VOLTAGE FEEDBACK AMPLIFIER

This is an older design, as evidenced by the μA709, that was used when small hybrid amplifiers of this type were not available. It does, however, contain general design considerations that are still applicable and is worth reviewing. Figure 9.9 shows the completed circuit.

9.6.1 The Output Stage

This is a complementary emitter follower connection that differs somewhat from the circuit shown in Fig. 2.5. It has no cancellation of the $e-b$ junction voltages; hence the special diode biasing system is necessary. There is, however, considerably greater power capability since the first emitter follower is directly driving the output stage. The NPN side furnishes the positive current and the PNP side the negative current. They are otherwise essentially equal, and only the NPN side will be described.

Q_2 sees a load of βR_L, which in this case is 40(900) = 36 kΩ. The 90 V signal requires Q_2 to furnish 90/36 $\cong$ 3 mA. It is good practice,

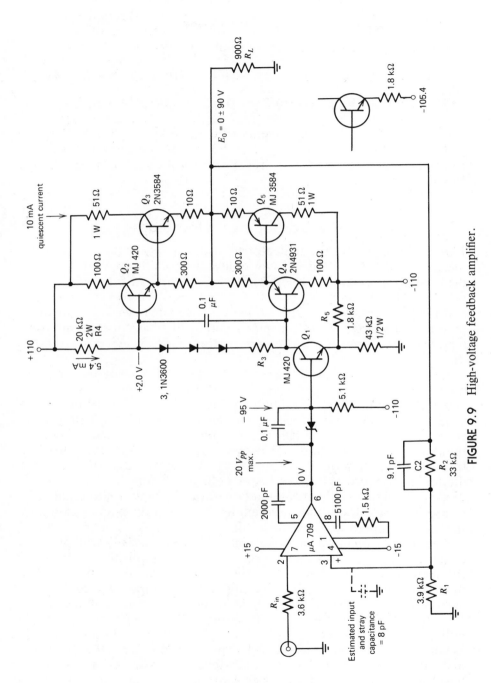

FIGURE 9.9 High-voltage feedback amplifier.

however, to have some residual current flowing through Q_2 to improve its operating characteristics. For this reason the 300 Ω emitter resistors are added. We have the relations

$$\text{When } E_o = 0 \text{ V}, Q_{3b} \text{ to } E_o = 0.6 + (10)(10)^{-2} = 0.7 \text{ V}$$

$$\text{When } E_o = 90 \text{ V}, Q_{3b} \text{ to } E_o = 0.6 + 10(10)^{-1} = 1.6 \text{ V}$$

This produces respective currents of 0.7 V/300 = 2.3 mA. And 1.6 V/300 = 5.3 mA through Q_2. The 2.3 mA is the minimum current through Q_2 and the 5.3 mA at full signal is not too great a penalty for this design.

9.6.2 Bias for the Output Stage

This is furnished by the collector load of Q_1. Q_2 requires 3 mA for the load and 5.3 mA for its own quiescent condition. With $\beta = 50$, the base requirement is (3 + 5.3)/50 = 0.17 mA. At full positive output the voltage across R_4 is $110 - (90 + 0.6 + 0.6 + 1) = 17.8$ V and 17.8/20 = 0.89 mA. This allows an adequate reserve for the drive requirements of Q_2. At full negative output, the base of Q_2 is approximately -90 V and the power dissipation of R_4 is $E^2/R = [(200)^2/2(10)^4] = 2$ W.

It is desirable that both the NPN and the PNP section be safely on the verge of conduction or possibly slightly conducting when the input signal is at zero. This is to minimize the crossover distortion. In this case three diodes and a resistor are used. Four diodes, if they were each incorporated in the transistor structure, would provide perfect temperature compensation. However, few transistors have this feature. The junctions of the transistors run hotter than the discrete diodes and accordingly have lower voltages. Four standard discrete diodes could be unsafe at full load operation. An alternative could be to use four Schottky diodes, which have a lower drop and essentially the same temperature characteristic.

The setting of the dead space or quiescent current, whichever is desired, should be done open loop. This is accomplished by breaking the feedback connection and putting a 3.6 kΩ resistor from pin 2 to pin 6 of the μA709. A sine wave is applied at the input, and the voltage across R_L is observed. R_3 is adjusted for the turn-on voltage. R_4 or R_5 probably have to be changed slightly for symmetry of the turn on voltage.

One last consideration on dead space. Section 3.1.9 shows that distortion is greatly reduced by the feedback connection, so that a reasonable amount of dead space may not be of any concern when the loop is closed.

9.6.3 Level Translation

To use a monolithic chip, the μA709, it is necessary to employ two sets of power supplies. In addition, there is an offset of 95 V to be balanced. The zener connecting the μA709 and Q_1 does this nicely. It is necessary to bypass the zener because its impedance increases with frequency. There is $(110 - 95)/5.1 \text{ k}\Omega = 3 \text{ mA}$ through the zener. This represents a safe $3(95) = 285 \text{ mW}$ of dissipation and puts the zener in a range of good operation. This is more than enough current for the base requirements of Q_1.

9.6.4 Stability Considerations

The emitter bias network in the transistor inverting stage Q_1 is equivalent to 1.8 kΩ from a source of -105.4 V (see biasing techniques in Section 1.2). The load resistance is 20 kΩ in parallel with the input resistance of Q_2 ($\beta R_E = 50(300) = 15 \text{ k}\Omega$). This is equal to 8.6 K. The gain is then $8.6/1.8 = 4.7$. If we rather loosely estimate the combined gain of the two emitter followers as 0.85, the loop gain is $(4.7)(0.85) G_1 = 4G_1$ or about 12 dB greater than G_1, the op-amp gain. Figure 9.10 demonstrates the stability considerations.

The compensating networks of the μA709 in this circuit are set so that the performance is about equivalent to the μA741. That is the high frequency roll-off is a straight 6 dB/octave reaching unity gain at about 1 MHz. The first RC roll-off in this circuit occurs with the

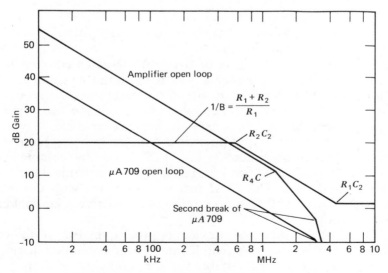

FIGURE 9.10 Amplifier gain vs. frequency.

20 kΩ resistor (reduced to 8.6 kΩ by loading). Based on limited information in the data sheets, the estimated capacitance is about 17 pF. This sets the break frequency at 1.3 MHz, and at this point the combined roll-off response is 12 dB/octave. Figure 9.10 shows an open-loop gain plot of the μA709 and that of the complete amplifier. It is seen that 1/β crosses the open loop safely above the R_4C breakpoint. The second-order effects of the R_1C_2 corner and those produced by R_1 and the input capacitance of the μA709 are beyond the frequencies of concern for this amplifier, but could well be a concern in another design.

The actual stability of the completed amplifier is easily checked, and this should definitely be done. A square wave is applied at the input and the output response observed. The frequency of the square wave should be varied, but a starting point is to place the fifth harmonic at the intersection of the two curves. The object here is to see how much trouble the harmonics are having. If there is a marginal factor of safety, excessive ringing occurs and the 1/β curve must be raised to increase the stability. This decreases the closed-loop frequency response, but it is the natural trade-off. There was no difficulty with this design, although C_2 was added to optimize the response.

The feedback in this amplifier is going to the noninverting op-amp input, but there is an inversion by Q_1, so that the feedback is in reality going to the inverting input of the overall amplifier.

9.7 A 10-MHz AND 10-kHz CRYSTAL-CONTROLLED CLOCK

Figure 9.11 shows a simple circuit that is included primarily because of its usefulness and flexibility.

The basic oscillator consists of two NAND gates coupled to the crystal, as described in Chapter 4. The remaining two gates are used as buffers. The NSC MH0026 is one of the better clock drivers presently available. It must be AC coupled in accordance with the manufacturer's specifications. It is used in this case as a T^{2}L driver, but it is flexible in that the output pulse is driven from the $(+)$ to the $(-)$ supply voltages. A maximum swing of 22 V can be obtained. The device is nominally rated for 5 MHz maximum, but this depends on the voltage and load. The 39 Ω resistor combines with the output impedance to form a 50 Ω source resistance to drive a coaxial cable (see Section I.6).

The DM8520, another NSC device, is programmable so that other divisions can be obtained. A switch can be used for added flexibility. However, the logic is not suitable for a thumbwheel switch, and if this is desirable, a Fairchild 9316 counter would be more suitable.

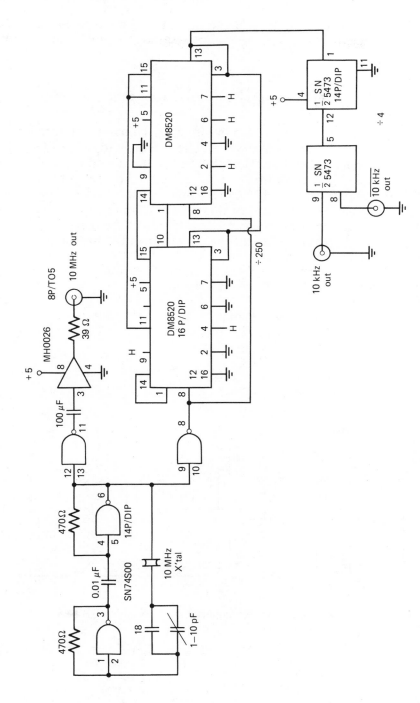

FIGURE 9.11 10 MHz and 10 kHz clock.

A flip-flop is generally used at the output of a counter to obtain a square wave. At this low a frequency, a line driver is usually not required.

9.8 A 20-kHz 150-W AMPLIFIER

The completed amplifier is shown in Fig. 9.12. This is a high-efficiency amplifier for a 20 kHz square wave. The intent is to drive the transistors from hard conduction to total cutoff. If the "on" resistance is zero and the "off" condition is infinite, and if the rise and fall times were zero, the transistor efficiency would be 100%. The degree to which the transistors fall short of this goal determines the power that must be dissipated by the transistor. In addition to the thermal ratings, the voltage and current limits of the transistor must be adequate for the defined task.

A MOSFET manufactured by International Rectifier, the IRF530, has the following important characteristics:

$$VDS = 100 \text{ V max.}$$
$$R \text{ (on)} = 0.18 \ \Omega$$
$$I = 10 \text{ A max.}$$

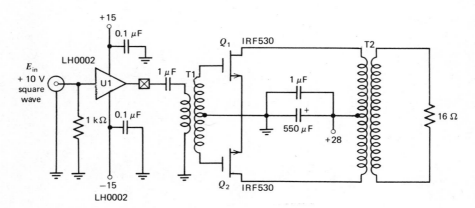

FIGURE 9.12   20 kHz 150 W amplifier. X, Ferroxcube 3B bead.

T1	T2
P = 21 T #23	P = 24 T #20 CT
S = 42 T #27 CT	S = 24 T #20
Core = Ferroxcube	Core = Ferroxcube
1408-3E2A	3622-3E2A

$$C_{GS} = 900 \text{ pF}$$
$$C_{GD} = 150 \text{ pF}$$
$$C_{DS} = 500 \text{ pF}$$
$$\text{Power} = 75 \text{ W at } 25° \text{ case temperature}$$

In addition, the transistor requires about $+8$ V on the gate for hard turn-on.

This amplifier is a good example of a design that would be unreasonably difficult for a complete analysis. Instead, we make some approximations of the limiting conditions and then check the results for possible further modifications.

9.8.1 Design of the Input Transformer

Since the input signal is ± 10 V and $+8$ V is required for full conduction of the transistor, T1 has a secondary with twice the total turns of the primary so that the voltage to each gate would approach ± 10 V. The load on the secondary consists of C_{GS} and C_{GD}.

When the gate of Q_1 or Q_2 is at $+10$ V, the drain is at 0 V. When the gate is at -10 V, the drain is at $+56$ V, and the gain is accordingly $56/20 = 2.8$. Due to the Miller effect (Section I.4), C_{GD} is multiplied by $(1 + G)$. Accordingly, the load capacitance per side is $900 + 3.8(150) = 1470$ pF. Figure 9.13 shows how this capacitance is reflected back to the primary. Half the reactance means twice the capacitance or 2940 pF.

These figures will be used to estimate the transformer input current in the discussion that follows. This is an approximation, but a more rigorous analysis does not seem reasonable. A deviation from this simplified model should, however, be kept in mind. The FET does not turn on until the bias is a few volts positive, and accordingly the Miller capacitance is not effective until that point. This means that the input capacitance has a step-function component that is not accounted for. This effect is, in general, quite noticeable and can cause extra ringing and general circuit misbehavior.

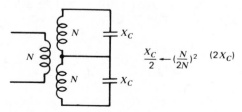

FIGURE 9.13 Reflection of output capacitance to the primary.

To minimize the transistor dissipation, the transition from conduction to the "off" condition should be as short as possible. However, if this edge is too sharp, spikes and ringing develop because of leakage reactance and various capacitive effects. This could possibly lead to transistor failure. 20 kHz represents an "on" time of 50 μs for each transistor, so that perhaps a rise time of 2 μs would be an appropriate value. The implication here is that the transformer should be carefully wound and the input wave shape controlled to ensure good operation.

In this case, the initial selection of the core size is not at all evident. We select a Ferroxcube pot core of type 1811 with type 3E2A ferrite material to make our basic calculations. The important parameters are:

$$
\begin{aligned}
A &= 0.433 \text{ cm}^2 \\
V &= 1.12 \text{ cm}^3 \\
l &= 2.58 \text{ cm} \\
L &= 7500 \text{ mH/1000T} \\
B_{max} &= 2000 \text{ G} \\
\mu_{-3 \text{ dB}} &= 1.5 \text{ MHz}
\end{aligned}
$$

The window area of the bobbin is 0.029 in.^{2}.

Referring to Chapter 5, for a square wave we have the relation

$$
N = \frac{E(10)^8}{4fB_{max}A_C} = \frac{10(10)^8}{4(2)\,(10)^4(2000)\,(0.433)} \cong 15 \text{ turns}
$$

It is important to recognize that the correct number of turns to produce the selected value of flux does not necessarily produce the desired inductance. If a greater inductance is required, Eq. 5.2 shows that more turns are needed, which results in a lower flux density, as shown by Eq. 5.3. This is satisfactory, but if less inductance is required, the frequency must be raised or the applied voltage reduced to maintain a safe flux density.

Equation 5.2 is generally not used to determine the inductance and in its place the manufacturer will specify the inductance of a specific core for a given number of turns. In the case of the core at hand there is a stated inductance of 7500 mH with a coil of 1000 turns. This is a square relationship and so for 15 turns we have

$$
\left(\frac{15}{1000}\right)^2 = \frac{L}{7500} \qquad \text{or} \qquad L = 1.7 \text{ mH}
$$

Section 8.6 on off-resonance conditions used the numbers generated in this design and develops the input currents required by the transformer.

$$I_P \ \ 20 \text{ kHz} = 56 \text{ mA}$$
$$I_P \ \ 60 \text{ kHz} = 3.6 \text{ mA}$$
$$I_P \ 100 \text{ kHz} = 2.0 \text{ mA}$$
$$I_P \ 140 \text{ kHz} = 3.4 \text{ mA}$$

Examination of these data indicates that the resonance should be lowered. This reduces the large 20 kHz current for a small increase in the harmonic currents. Doubling the inductance to 3.4 mH would require that the turns be increased by $\sqrt{2}$ and would result in a flux density of $2000/\sqrt{2} = 1400$ G:

$$15(\sqrt{2}) = 21 \text{ turns in the primary}$$

Half the bobbin winding area is 0.014 in.^{2}. Accordingly, from Appendix IV, we have

$$\text{IWD} = \sqrt{\frac{0.014}{21}} = 0.026 \text{ in.}$$

#23 gauge wire with an IWD of 0.024 in. is used. The secondary has 42 turns with a center tap. Accordingly, insulated wire diameter,

$$\text{IWD} = \sqrt{\frac{0.014}{42}} = 0.018 \text{ in.}$$

#27 gauge wire with an IWD of 0.0153 is used.

9.8.2 Design of the Output Transformer

To estimate the size of the output core, we refer to Fig. IV.6. Here it is seen that a 43627-PC pot core is required. This is equivalent to the Ferroxcube 3622 pot core, which is the largest core available in the high-permeability 3E2A material. The specifications on this core are as follows:

$$A = 2.02 \text{ cm}^2$$
$$V = 10.7 \text{ cm}^3$$
$$l = 5.32 \text{ cm}$$
$$\text{Winding area of bobbin} = 0.116 \text{ in.}^2$$
$$L = \text{mH/1000 T} = 17,500$$
$$mlt = 2.92 \text{ in.}$$

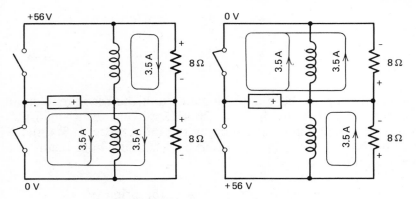

FIGURE 9.14 Equivalent circuit of T2.

On the power stage we are a bit conservative and choose $B_{max} = 1500$; accordingly, we have

$$\frac{N_P}{2} = \frac{E(10)^8}{4fB_mA_C} = \frac{28(10)^8}{4(2)(10)^4(1500)(2.02)} = 12 \text{ turns}$$

One half of the primary has an inductance of

$$L = 17500 \left(\frac{12}{1000}\right)^2 = 2.52 \text{ mH}$$

Referring to Fig. 9.12 it is seen that the drains are changing ± 28 V with respect to the $+28$ V power supply. This means that we have a square wave with an amplitude of 28 V impressed across one half of the primary. The total primary turns are 24 with a center tap.

7 A is selected for the maximum transistor current. Figure 9.14 shows a schematic of the output MOSFETs and the loaded primary of the output transformer. To draw 7 A, the load to the power supply must be 28 V/7 A = 4 Ω. As seen from Fig. 9.14, the conducting MOSFET drives its load directly, and the load of the nonconducting MOSFET as a 1:1 autotransformer. Accordingly, half of the conducting MOSFET current is used to drive its 8 Ω reflected load directly. The other half of the current is used to counter the demagnetizing effect of the reflected primary load that is across the nonconducting FET. Put another way, each conducting FET sees both loads in parallel. In this case 8/8 = 4 Ω.

The load power in a lossless system can be looked at in several ways:

1. From the power supply (28 V) (7 A) = 196 W
2. Two times the power of each half = $2(28)^2/8$ = 196 W
3. The power across the full primary = $(56)^2/16$ = 196 W

The secondary turns are determined by

$$\frac{N_P}{N_S} = \left(\frac{R_P}{R_S}\right)^2 \quad \text{or} \quad N_S = N_P \left(\frac{R_S}{R_P}\right)^2$$

For this problem, a unity turns ratio was desired. This means that the secondary load is 16 Ω, and to develop 150 W we need, under load,

$$E_{\text{rms}} = E_P = \sqrt{(16\ \Omega)\ (150\ \text{W})} = 49\ \text{V}$$

(for a square wave $E_P = E_{\text{rms}}$).

The wire size for both the primary and secondary turns is determined in the usual manner. One half of the bobbin winding area is 0.058 in.^{2}; accordingly, IWD = $\sqrt{0.058/24}$ = 0.05 in. and #18 gauge has a 0.0421 in. diameter and would be a usable selection.

This wire has 6.4 mΩ/ft and in the special case of a 1:1 ratio the output current can be considered as passing through the primary and secondary resistance in series. Therefore, the total winding DC resistance is

$$\frac{(48\ T)\ (2.92\ \text{in.}/T)}{12}\ (0.0064\ \Omega/\text{ft}) = 0.08\ \Omega$$

This is a DC Cu efficiency of 16/16.08 = 99.5%, which however, is of little consequence as the AC resistance will be considerably higher. Nevertheless, because of winding difficulties the wire was reduced to #20.

The symmetry of the two halves of the primary winding is very important. If these two halves are not the same, uneven heating and distortion occur. The most serious effect, however, is the aggravation of spikes and feedback problems that can lead, in many cases, to unexpected destruction of the transistors at ratings far lower than expected. A bifilar winding is an absolute must for a transformer used in this manner.

To make a bifilar winding, two wires of sufficient length are wound on the bobbin at the same time. The finish of one winding is then connected to the start of the other winding to form the center tap. This is illustrated in Fig. 9.15.

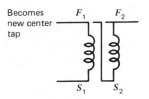

FIGURE 9.15   A bifilar winding.

9.8.3 Test Results

The completed amplifier had the following output data:

R_L	E_L	$I_{28\text{ V}}$	W_o	W_{in}	Eff
20 Ω	50 V	5.7 A	125	160	78%
15 Ω	50 V	7.5 A	166	210	79%

An amplifier driven by a square wave must always be checked for spikes that could cause a breakdown. Failure by transient breakdown can easily occur. Unfortunately, the solution is not as easy. A series *RC* circuit with the proper time constant and connected across the load is commonly used to absorb the spike energy. Zeners are often used, the rise and fall times can be increased slightly, the external circuitry may have to be modified, and finally the transformer may have to be rewound to reduce the internal capacitance and leakage reactance.

Observation of the current waveform should always be made for any new transformer design. Figure 9.16 shows the current entering the center tap of the output transformer. This is a very proper waveform. Each transistor is conducting on alternate lobes in a well-bal-

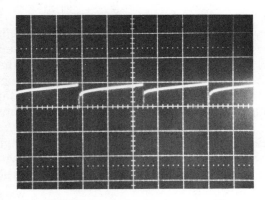

FIGURE 9.16   Normal current T2.

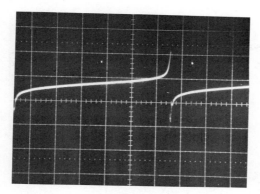

FIGURE 9.17   Saturating current T2.

anced manner and the interval in between is small, indicating good switching time.

It will be noticed that the top of the current lobes has a positive slope. This current increase is due to the increasing saturation as described in Section 5.1.4. For Fig. 9.17 the frequency was carefully lowered until the sharp increase in current started. It is evident that disaster is not far away. This photograph was taken at 8.5 kHz, representing a satisfactory margin of safety in the flux density.

Figure 9.18 shows the current in the ground lead of the driver for T1. This oscillatory current is to be expected because a high Q resonant circuit is being driven. Some damping resistance from each gate to ground is probably in order. The scale of the current in this photograph is 50 mA/sq. The last photograph, Fig. 9.19, shows the same data at 8.5 kHz and also the start of strong saturation.

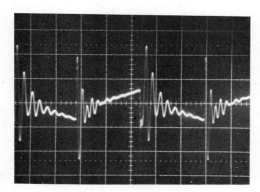

FIGURE 9.18   Normal current T1.

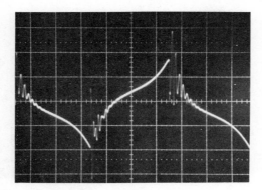

FIGURE 9.19   Saturating current T1.

Although the current into T1 is oscillatory, the output voltage waveform is a good, clean square wave. This results from the tight coupling of the transformer and the low impedance of the driver.

The blocking capacitor is necessary because even a small offset voltage causes a large current to flow through the low DC resistance of the transformer.

A final word of caution. High-permeability materials such as the 3E2A must have their butted surfaces completely free of dirt or small particles and must be very firmly held together. If these precautions are not taken, the inductance is drastically lowered.

9.9 A CURRENT MODE AMPLIFIER

This is an interesting and informative design because it uses an op-amp to emphasize some of the characteristics that are not apparent in other applications. Specifically, we are talking about the virtual ground and the relationship of $1/\beta$ to the closed-loop gain A_{CL}.

Some signal sources are defined as constant current devices, generally with some associated capacitance. A device of this type is the Indium Antimonide (InSb) photovoltaic detector. The unit in this case has a dynamic resistance of 2 MΩ and a capacitance of 200 pF. Figure 9.20a shows the schematic representation and Fig. 9.20b is the transformation to the more useful voltage source obtained by the application of Thévenin's theorem. Figure 9.21 shows the amplifier using the equivalent input.

This detector is often operated at cryogenic temperatures and then a MOSFET is generally used as a source follower to lower the impedance of the signal so that a cable can be driven to connect to the main electronics outside of the dewer. In this case the frequency -3 dB point is determined by the 2 MΩ and 200 pF capacitor, which is then 400 Hz.

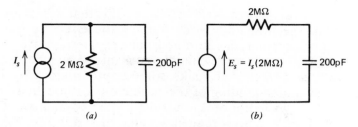

FIGURE 9.20 Detector equivalent circuits.

If an op-amp can be used as shown in Fig. 9.21, the frequency roll-off is very much extended by means of the virtual ground at pin 2. The magnitude of the impedance of the virtual ground is calculated exactly like the Miller Effect (Appendix I.4). When a voltage e is applied at the input side of R, there is a voltage $-A_{OL}e$ applied at the output side of R_F. This reduces the impedance that the input voltage sees to $R_F/(1 + A_{OL})$. At DC the gain of this amplifier is about 100 dB or 10^5.

Then $10^6/10^5 = 10$, which numerically produces an $f - 3$ dB roll-off of 78 MHz. This is far from a realizable number as will be directly shown, but it remains substantially higher than the 400 Hz produced by a simple high-impedance pick-off.

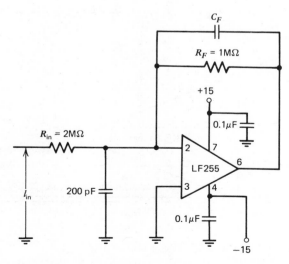

FIGURE 9.21 Equivalent current mode amplifiers.

The major discrepancy of the 78 MHz cutoff is that A_{OL} is inversely proportional to the frequency. Determining the effective roll-off of A_{CL} is a trial-and-error procedure and not very certain at that. It is a parameter that is much more suitably determined by measurement.

It is, however, practical to make some approximate calculations so that a better understanding of the problem is established.

Figure 9.22 shows a plot of A_{OL} for the LF255 op-amp and the $1/\beta$ feedback function. The low-frequency value of $1/\beta$ is $1 + R_F/R_{in} = 1.5$ or 3.5 dB. Without the 200 pF capacitor the projection of this $1/\beta$ to its intersection, with a continuing -6 dB/octave slope, of A_{OL} would produce an $f - 3$ dB $= 1.7$ MHz.

The β function is first determined from the circuit shown in Fig. 9.23. It will be recalled that this calculation is made without the presence of the amplifier. From this, $1/\beta$ becomes $1/0.667 = +3.5$ dB, as previously determined, and the corner frequency remains the same except that it denotes a $+6$ dB/octave slope rather than a -6 dB/octave slope. This results in an intersection with A_{OL} of 12 dB/octave, an unstable relationship. Table 9.2 shows the results of some spot checks taken on the circuit of Fig. 9.21.

The response of the amplifier without the 200 pF capacitor is substantially short of the projected 1.7 MHz. No effort was made to analyze this further as it was of no importance in the application at hand. The A_{OL} is without doubt steeper than 6 dB/octave at the in-

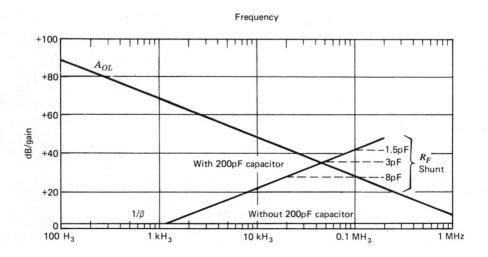

FIGURE 9.22   Response of Fig. 9.21.

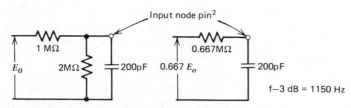

FIGURE 9.23 Determination of β and 1/β. (*a*) Direct circuit. (*b*) Thévenin equivalent circuit.

tersection with 1/β and, further, the high values of the resistors will aggravate the second-order capacitive effects.

The effect of the R_F shunt capacitor is also very predictable in nature, although not in exact numerical relationship. As 1/β is allowed to come closer to a 12 dB/octave relative slope with A_{OL} the peaking becomes more intense, indicating that complete instability is not far away. The optimum value of 3 pF is actually just about at the break-

TABLE 9.2
Data on Amplifier Performance

Closed Loop Without 200 pF Capacitance

+6 dB peak at 280 kHz
Back to l.f. level at 425 kHz
−6 dB at 560 kHz
−12 dB at 890 kHz

Closed Loop with 200 pF Capacitance (No Capacitor Across R_F)

+6 dB	38 kHz
+12 dB	46.5
+16.4 dB peak	51
+12 dB	55
+6 dB	61
Back to l.f. level	75
−6 dB	85

With Compensating Capacitance Across R_F

C		
1.5 pF	+6 dB peak at 47.5 kHz	−3 dB at 72 kHz
2.5	+1.8 ↓ 39	66
4.3	No peak	55
8	↓	24.5

point, which is a little higher than expected. Considering that none of the parameters are precalibrated this is not at all surprising.

The same result can be obtained, with less effort, by applying a square wave and tuning the capacitor for optimum response. A small trimmer allows for easy fine tuning of production units.

Again the frequency of the square wave is adjusted to show the ringing clearly. A good sharp rise time is required, but at these frequencies it is not at all difficult.

9.10 HIGH-SPEED LOW-POWER TRANSIENT RECORDER

The purpose of this system is to record high-speed transient waveforms aboard a spacecraft, where available power is very restricted. The design presented here shows a method and considerations to achieve a good balance between a fast response and low power.

In general, high-speed circuits require high currents. Voltage must be maintained at levels to operate the circuits effectively and to allow the required dynamic range. This application is limited to currently available components and accordingly the voltage are as low as practical within these constraints.

The system is composed of two basic parts: signal detection (Fig. 9.24) and signal processing (Fig. 9.25). Overall operation and capabilities are discussed first; following that are detailed design considerations of the separate functions that comprise the system.

In this example there are 16 inputs, each of which is buffered and go to a 16:1 power combiner so that a common signal processor can be used. Each signal line has a detector and latch so that the source of the processed signal can be determined. In this instance the chance of two signals occurring in the same processing period is unlikely, but in any event, this error would be recorded and the data judged accordingly. These particular data can be of either or both polarities; thus, the system is able to detect and record this type of event. For unipolar events a substantial part of the system can be eliminated.

In the problem at hand the true rise time of the input signal was not established because the recording instruments available could not resolve much better than 2 ns. This also limited the instruments used in the development of this system. There was also no evidence that any of the rise times were much slower than the designated 2 ns design goal.

In applying the concepts put forth in this design, different input bandwidths will require design modifications. Areas sensitive to these definitions are pointed out in the detailed design discussions.

There is a test input for each signal line so that a functional check for proper operation can be made. The latch reset, which prepares the system for a new event, is common.

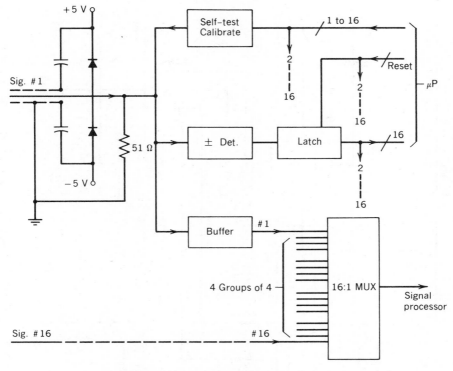

FIGURE 9.24   Signal detection system.

There are many possible methods of signal processing. If size and power were of no concern, probably a high-speed oscilloscope with a photographic attachment would be used to record the entire transient. This is a privilege, however, that this project could not support. In any event a method is illustrated here and the emphasis is on specific circuit design techniques that complement the other material in this book.

The signal processing method used in this application consists of recording the peak amplitude and the integral of the event.

The signal detection functions defined in Fig. 9.24 are discussed first.

9.10.1 Diode Peak Suppression

The input diodes are employed to clip excessively high signal peaks that are beyond the range of the measurement capabilities of the system and might possibly damage some of the components.

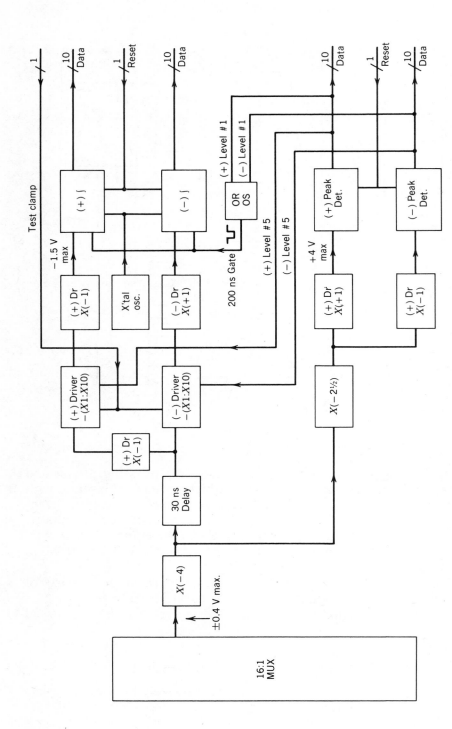

FIGURE 9.25 Signal processing system.

Most semiconductors, particularly diodes, can withstand very large currents when the pulse durations are very small. This information is normally not given in data manuals and the manufacturers must be consulted to see if this data is available. Figure 9.26 gives an example of the kind of ratings that can be expected for short pulse durations.

The bypass capacitors for the diodes are shown on the schematic because they are as much a part of the design as the diodes. They

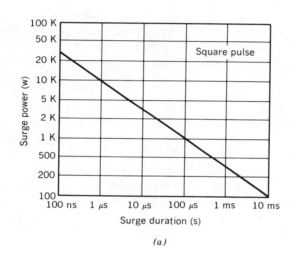

(a)

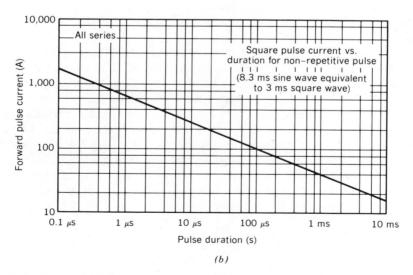

(b)

FIGURE 9.26 Diode characteristics. (*a*) Power rating of 5 W zener Unitrode U25706 series. (*b*) Current rating of 0.5 A diode Unitrode UTRI0.

are specifically low-inductance RF devices. The location of the ground side of these capacitors is very important, as the large surge currents must find their way back to the signal source via the coaxial cable ground. This current must not be allowed to flow into the circuit grounds, since possible damage unwanted coupling could occur to more sensitive components.

9.10.2 ± Signal Detector

This circuit is shown in Fig. 9.27. The amplifier is designed to produce a sharp positive edge of at least 20 mV in amplitude for a range of positive or negative inputs from 20 mV to 4 V. There is no attempt to reproduce the input waveform, as the leading edge function can be obtained with less current and a smaller number of parts than a true wideband amplifier.

The positive input pulses are favored by an NPN transistor and the negative inputs by a PNP. The transformers are connected so that the positive pulse through the NPN produces a positive output and the negative pulse through the PNP also produces a positive output. There is sufficient polarity emphasis by the transistors that the net positive signal through the OR'ing diodes reaches at least 20 mV in 2 ns with the defined minimum signal (min. sig).

The transformers are shown as a group of four in a standard 16-pin DIP package. However, subsequent tests revealed that there was sufficient coupling between detectors sharing a package to cause false triggering. Restricting the transformer package to one detector solved the problem. The transformers are available as two in an 8-pin DIP package.

The diodes are high-speed Schottky devices and their offset voltage is balanced by a similar diode common to all four of the detector circuits in the quad arrangement used in this construction.

The emitter bypass capacitors and their physical placement are very important in this type of application, as the gain is basically the collector impedance divided by the total emitter impedance. The external part of this impedance is the capacitor. The 2.4 kΩ resistor serves only to define a stable quiescent operating current. The capacitors are small 50 V ceramics with short leads and are grounded very close to the ground side of the 51 Ω input resistors. This is standard procedure for high-frequency circuit and is described further in Chapter 10.

9.10.3 Signal Latch

The signal detector provides an output capable of tripping the signal latch. All the latches are then polled by the μP to determine which

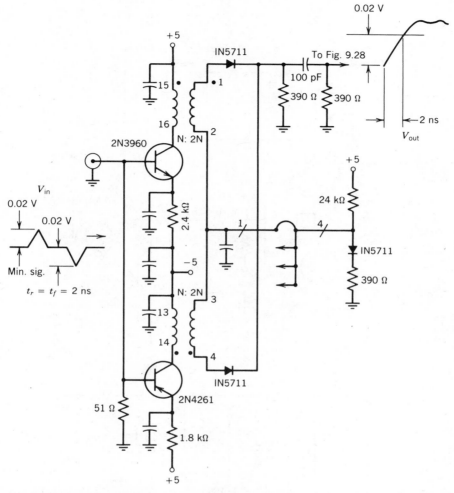

FIGURE 9.27 Bipolar detector. Transformer is $\frac{1}{2}$ PCA7044; all unmarked caps = 0.01 μF. Gain $Z = \pm 20$ mV$_{in}$ to +20 mV$_{out}$.

signal is present. All the latches are reset simultaneously when the processing is finished.

This latch is also used in the peak detector of the signal processing section (Section 9.10.7) to be described later. Figure 9.28 shows the circuit, the operation of which is as follows: The latch utilizes a high-speed comparator, the MVL407 manufactured by Le Croy Research Systems. The 20-pin DIP package contains four separate comparators from which the concept of a subsystem with four units has evolved.

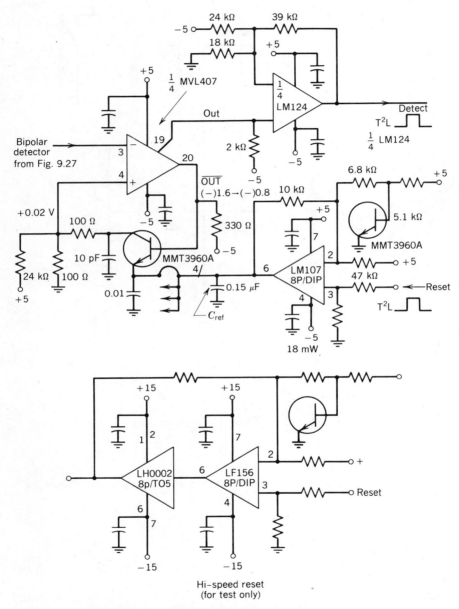

FIGURE 9.28 Signal latch. Bypass caps = 0.22 μF.

When the positive input from the signal detector exceeds the 20 mV reference on the noninverting side of the comparator, the comparator changes states on its output leads. There are two outputs complementary to each other and operating at ECL logic levels, that is, Hi = −0.8 V and Lo = −1.6 V. Accordingly, the positive input pulse changes the $\overline{\text{OUT}}$ signal from −1.6 to −0.8 V. The MMT3960A NPN transistor is then biased from off to on which in turn clamps the +0.02 V reference on the positive input to a negative value. This "hysteresis" action prevents the comparator from returning to its original state when the input signal drops to zero. Since the input signal cannot go below zero, the comparator remains in the latched condition until the reset pulse is received.

The LM107 op-amp sets the bias point as well as transmitting the reset pulse for all four comparators in the quad assembly. This bias must be carefully set for proper operation, but, once set, is satisfactorily stable. The bias source, as seen from Fig. 9.28, comes from two inputs, one of which has an MMT3960A transistor connected as a diode shunt. This is for temperature compensation of the base–emitter junction of the MMT3960A transistor that is in the comparator feedback loop. The calibration was arrived at empirically.

It will be noticed that the signal to the μP does not come from the same pin that is used in the feedback circuit. It is very important to minimize the loading on the feedback circuit to obtain the fastest possible response. The construction of the feedback path of the circuit must be very short point-to-point wiring, which involves the leads from pins 4 and 20. It is seen that there is a 100 Ω resistor coming from pin 4 to a 10 pF capacitor to ground. This is detrimental to the desired speed, but unfortunately, necessary to stabilize the comparator. Nevertheless, the comparator does respond consistently to a 20 mV 2 ns wavefront.

The MMT3960A is a miniature high-performance version of the 2N3960 transistor. The buffer and reset op-amps are not shown, as their positions are not critical. A socket is used in the development model to ease the difficulty of changing the comparator, if that becomes necessary, and to test for the interchangeability of that comparator.

In the flight model a socket is not used, but a plastic foam is necessary to package the subsystem. Whatever is gained by removing the socket is surely lost by the increased dielectric constant of the encapsulating material. There is no bonding product with a dielectric constant as low as air, but selecting a suitable product with as much air (bubbles) content as possible helps. In the design at hand, outgassing is not a concern, but where it is, additional problems are created.

A high-speed reset circuit, shown in Fig. 9.28, is used in place of the LM107 for test purposes. The low-power LM107, satisfactory for

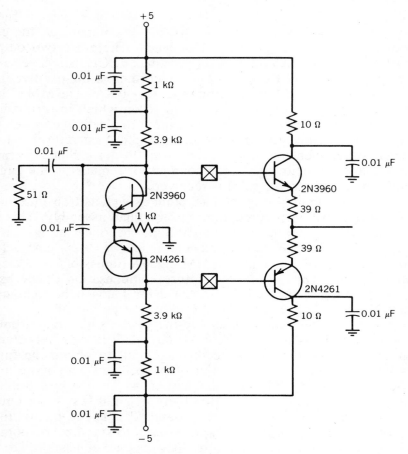

FIGURE 9.29   Buffer amplifier (AMP). X Ferroxcube ferrite bead.

mission operation, cannot recharge the 0.15 μF reference capacitor at a rate suitable for testing the circuit with an oscilloscope.

9.10.4 Buffer Amplifier and 16:1 MUX

These two circuit elements are combined because the system consideration is for the transmission of the signal from the source to the input of the signal processor (output of the MUX).

The buffer amplifier schematic is shown in Fig. 9.29. The circuit is a complementary emitter follower which produces equal drive capability for both positive and negative inputs. The same transistors types are connected as diodes to provide a temperature-compensating bias for the output stage. This provides a match superior to that ob-

tained by simply using diodes. The four transistors are mounted in a
block of thermally, but not electrically, conductive material. BeO
would be best, but this is poisonous and difficult to machine.

The ferrite beads are used to suppress parasitic oscillations that
commonly occur in high-frequency transistors, particularly when two
semiconductor junctions are connected together.

The quiescent current is determined empirically to obtain a suitable
rise time with a minimum current drain. The maximum gain–bandwidth product f_t occurs at about 20 mA for these transistors. This is
completely out of consideration.

The total current drawn by the circuit is 2 mA. Figure 9.30 shows
a typical response of the buffer and of the output of the MUX when

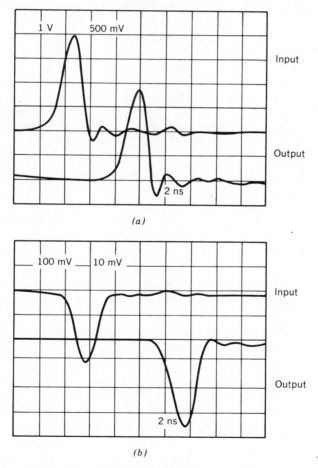

FIGURE 9.30   Pulse response buffer and MUX: (a) buffer; (b) buffer and MUX.

driven by the buffer. Positive and negative waveforms were about the same when tested over a range of $0-+125°F$. The bandwidth of the oscilloscope and its preamp was 350 MHz (1 ns rise time) and although it is difficult to determine the rise time of the buffer–MUX, it would seem to be on the order of 1.5 ns.

The MUX used in this test has a bandwidth of 2–250 MHz. A custom design of 0.2–250 MHz has been procured for further tests; this represents the state of the art in this type of device. The increase in the lower limit of the bandwidth was necessary to avoid differentiation of the longer pulses, which would give false data and must be avoided. The power splitter employs inductive coupling and may not be suitable for wider bandwidths.

The output of the MUX is terminated in 50 Ω and reflects 50 Ω to each of the 16 inputs, providing that all of the inputs are sourced by 50 Ω. Accordingly, the buffer amplifiers have an output impedance of 50 Ω.

Tests indicate that the output transistors, as they are biased, have the required 50 Ω source resistance when a 39 Ω resistor is inserted in series with the output. For purposes of DC stability it is better to place the resistors directly in series with the two emitters, as shown in Fig. 9.29. (Note: one transistor is on at a time.)

The maximum gain of this type of circuit with no load on the output is unity, which it closely approaches. The 50 Ω load, that it does see, reduces this gain to 0.5. The MUX has a stated insertion loss of 1.5 dB, which translates to a voltage gain of 0.84. This is defined, however, for 16 lines driving the output. When only one line is driving, the other 15 lines output that signal reduced by 30 dB. But since there are 15 extra outputs, the losses increase and the resultant voltage gain of the MUX becomes 0.2. This is a gain of 0.1 for the buffer driving the MUX.

There is another important characteristic of the amplifier–MUX combination and that is cross coupling. A signal into one input of the MUX is guaranteed to be down 30 dB as it emerges from any of the other inputs. The amplifier has a measured reverse gain, output to input, of -33 dB. The net cross coupling is therefore -63 dB or a reduction of 1400. Since the established signal range is 4 V/0.02 V = 200, cross coupling is not a problem.

9.10.5 Self-Test and Calibration

A system of self-test and calibration is important for all unattended systems. The question of how much to provide can be a difficult decision.

The technique presented in Fig. 9.31 is one of several proposed for this system. It is observed that the circuit requires no quiescent

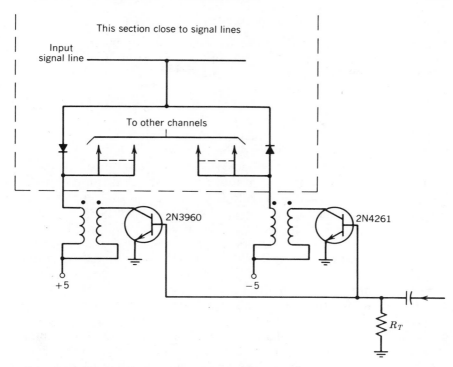

FIGURE 9.31 Self-test and calibrate circuit. X'fmrs are dual versions of PCA7044; diodes are IN5711.

power. The signal from the μP comes via a terminated coaxial cable to ensure the high-frequency content of the transmitted edge. The capacitor serves to eliminate the DC power loss, remove an unwanted bias voltage, and differentiate the incoming test pulse. The rising edge of this test voltage inserts a negative signal input, while the falling edge inserts a positive one. These pulses can be of a sufficiently constant value to establish a one-point calibration check.

This circuit can be used for one channel, for all 16, or since there is a quad packaging concept used here, for four channels. In any event the coupling diodes must have short leads to the signal lines, since the resulting capacitance degrades the signal. The entire circuit should be compact with leads as short as reasonable, but it is not as critical as the signal side.

Another kind of self-test system, involving shorting out the input to the integrators, is described later. This enables a zero-signal calibration. The test block is shown in Fig. 9.25.

The sections that follow comprise the signal processing system shown in Fig. 9.25.

9.10.6 Wideband Amplifier

There are a number of different wideband amplifiers in this system; to avoid repetition, only one is described. This amplifier is very flexible and variations for different conditions can be easily made, see Section 2.1 on wideband amplifiers.

Figure 9.32 shows the amplifier, which is connected for a gain of 12. The gain–bandwidth product of the amplifier is 12(0.18) = 2.16 GHz, which is reasonably constant over a limited range of gain. Obviously, the gain cannot exceed the open-loop value.

The magnitude of the feedback resistor, R_f, required to obtain a desired gain is a matter of trial and error, as it is driving a complex impedance. This amplifier develops proper drive only for a negative output pulse. Changing the output transistor to an NPN would produce an amplifier with a positive-pulse drive capability. The polarity choice of the first two transistors represents a series of compromises, and could be either NPNs, PNPs, or one of each depending upon the emphasis desired. An NPN–PNP combination would provide a temperature compensation of the base to emitter junctions, but with a 470 Ω resistor in the second-stage emitter and capacitive coupling between the second and third stages drift is no problem. In the case at hand two transistors of the same polarity set the second emitter at +1.2 V and allows a larger collector voltage swing. The 2N4261 PNP transistor has a better frequency response than its counterpart the NPN 2N3960, and that was the reason for this choice. It is possible that the MMT3960A would reverse this decision to an NPN with possibly a lower quiescent current drain. When both a positive and negative drive are required, the output stage must employ a complementary arrangement, as used in the buffer amplifier previously described.

A feedback amplifier of this type must be inverting with one gain stage, as shown, and with no more than one blocking capacitor. If this is not the case, the stabilization of the amplifier becomes a problem and the complexities increase rapidly. It is well to point out that the time constant involved with the blocking capacitor is large enough so that the short, low-repetition rate pulses defined in this system are not "averaged," that is, the true positive and negative peaks are maintained for the signal processor. The size of the load resistor, R_L, controls the maximum gain (open loop) and the frequency response by means of its time constant with the capacitance of that circuit node. Feedback then reduces the gain and increases the bandwidth. The size of the collector inductance, as well as the Q reducing resistor in parallel, is determined empirically. As a starter, though, it should be set for resonance, with the estimated node capacitance at the maximum frequency. A TO-18 socket adds about 0.9 pF capacitance and is not used.

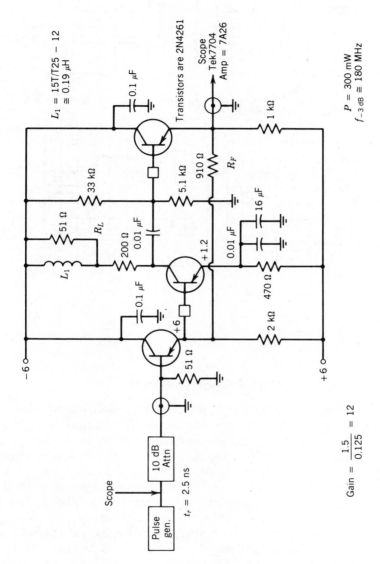

$L_1 = 15T/T25 - 12 \cong 0.19 \ \mu H$

0.1 μF

Transistors are 2N4261

Scope
Tek7704
Amp = 7A26

1 kΩ

910 Ω

R_F

33 kΩ

5.1 kΩ

16 μF

51 Ω

R_L

200 Ω

0.01 μF

+1.2

0.01 μF

L_1

0.1 μF

+6

470 Ω

2 kΩ

−6

51 Ω

+6

$P = 300 \ mW$
$f_{-3 \ dB} \cong 180 \ MHz$

Scope

10 dB
Attn

$t_r = 2.5$ ns

Pulse
gen.

Gain $= \dfrac{1.5}{0.125} = 12$

FIGURE 9.32 (*a*) Wideband amplifier and (*b*) response. (*Figure continues on p. 291.*)

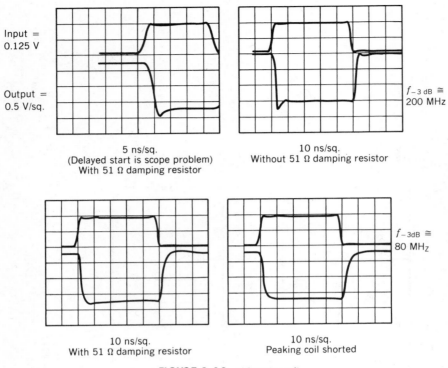

Input =
0.125 V

Output =
0.5 V/sq.

$f_{-3\,dB} \cong$
200 MHz

5 ns/sq.
(Delayed start is scope problem)
With 51 Ω damping resistor

10 ns/sq.
Without 51 Ω damping resistor

$f_{-3dB} \cong$
80 MHz

10 ns/sq.
With 51 Ω damping resistor

10 ns/sq.
Peaking coil shorted

FIGURE 9.32   (*Continued*)

9.10.7 Peak Detector

As shown in Fig. 9.25, the signal processor contains a positive and a negative peak detector. These are identical circuits, recording a positive peak, except that one has an extra inverter in the signal line so that it in effect records the negative part of the incoming signal.

The basic circuit is also the same as the signal latch shown in Fig. 9.28. There are 10 levels of each polarity which use the same building block of four circuits per quad comparator packages. This makes 20/4 = 5 packages.

To make a peak detector the reference voltages are staggered in an increasing series so that the stage with the highest latched condition represents the resolved peak. This flexibility is very convenient, since any spread of sensitivity can be selected. In this instance the factor

of $R = \sqrt[9]{\dfrac{E_{max}}{E_{min}}} = \sqrt[9]{\dfrac{4000}{20}} = 1.8$ was used. Table 9.3 shows the resulting levels.

The peak detectors also enable a 10:1 attenuator in the integrator circuits; thus, the limited dynamic range of this device can be increased to a satisfactory level. There are separate attenuators for each of the integrators, as both polarities can occur in one signal train. One of the polarities is generally an overshoot of the other and accordingly smaller.

9.10.8 Signal Integrator

An early attempt was made to design an integrator from available discrete components, but the resulting complexity, power consumption, and speed limitations dictated by component and wiring capacitance did not allow an acceptable result.

A monolithic design is feasible, but the market for such a product is so limited that a very expensive custom circuit would have been required. A product search, however, revealed that two devices manufactured by Le Croy Research Systems would result in an integrator closely approaching the requirements of this system.

Figure 9.33 shows how the MQT200F charge to time, C/T converter, and the SC100 sealer are combined to perform the integration. The SC100 is a dual unit which works out just fine for this application. Figure 9.34 shows how the C/T converter is connected.

The input is a direct coupled virtual ground (low-impedance) circuit that accepts fast $0--30$ mA current pulses. A 50 Ω resistor is used in series with the input to provide a termination for a coaxial line.

A necessary part of all integrators is a clamp to prevent charge accumulation during nonsignal periods. This is especially true for fast integrators where the storage capacitor is necessarily small. Accordingly, the C/T converter has a gate that must precede the input signal. In this system a signal delay line of 30 ns provides this function.

TABLE 9.3
Peak Detector Trip Levels

4.0 V
2.2 V
1.22 V
680 mV
210 mV 10:1 attn signal
117 mV
65 mV
36 mV
20 mV

A more conventional method of integration would use a high-impedance buffer to connect the storage capacitor to a fast A/D converter which would transmit the data to the microprocessor. However, practical difficulties rapidly emerge. A fast sample and hold circuit would be required between the charge capacitor and the A/D to allow the output voltage to be transferred to a larger holding capacitor so that the A/D would have time for the conversion. These functions take more power than this system would allow.

It should be pointed out that this device is being used at its maximum capabilities to obtain the integrating speeds required, and accordingly, the setup and initial calibration are very important. This should not be taken as a criticism of the device because no other system could be developed at this time that could perform this function with the limits on power and complexity set forth in this system. With slower rise times, the C/T converter becomes much more tolerant of its operating conditions.

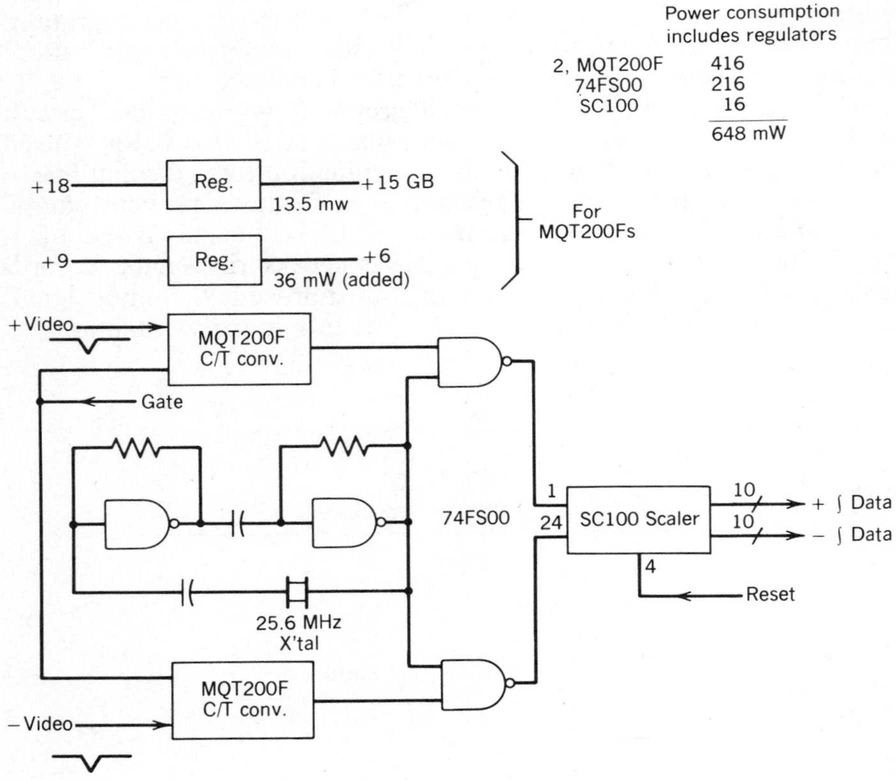

FIGURE 9.33 Integrator subsystem.

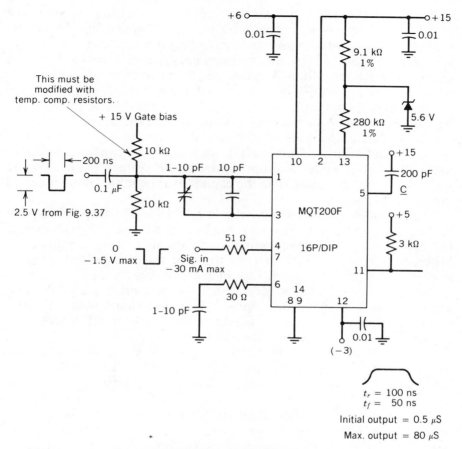

FIGURE 9.34 C/T converter.

Before proceeding with the operational description, a definition should be clarified. This device is called a charge to time converter, but when the source of the charge (e.g., a capacitor) is buffered it becomes a voltage integrator to time converter and is so used in this application. Consider a static charge on a capacitor that is buffered: the C/T converter integrates the voltage produced by the charge at the output of the buffer, but there is no direct determination of the magnitude of the charge.

The operational description follows: The C/T converter must be enabled at least 20 ns prior to the arrival of the signal and remain enabled for its duration. In this system there are 30 ns of lead time and a pulse duration of 200 ns, amplitude of 2.5 V, and a bias level of +7.5 V, all of which must be tightly controlled. Due to coupling of this pulse as well as various leakage currents within the structure of the chip, there is an output with no signal input. This cannot be reduced to zero without adversely affecting the operation. There are several ways to minimize this voltage, only one of which has proven useful to this application. A capacitor is placed from pin 1 to pin 3, which injects a canceling charge from the gate signal. Since the charge also controls the initial linearity, both factors must be observed. The *RC* combination from pin 6 to ground is recommended to prevent oscillation, although none was observed.

The output of this circuit is a T^2L logic signal whose time duration, minus the initial value, is proportional to the voltage (or the charge since the capacitor is fixed) on the capacitor. The initial value is called the pedestal.

The beginning of the output pulse is established by the trailing edge of the gate enable. A program current is applied to pin 13 to discharge the capacitor, whose level is measured by an internal comparator. When the capacitor is discharged to zero, the comparator changes state and the output pulse is terminated (see Fig. 9.35).

This program current is very critical to the calibration of the unit and therefore a 5.6 V zener (a very stable zener value) with a 1% carbon film resistor of 280 kΩ is used to establish $I_P = 5.6$ V$/280$ K $= 20$ μA. The integrating capacitor is 200 pF.

Figure 9.36 shows results of tests made on the C/T converter. The shape of the minimum signal (min. sig.) is defined. In some forms of terminology this would be called a 2 ns pulse (half-voltage points); at any rate, it is very short.

Three temperature conditions are shown. The photos on the left show the no signal output, while those on the right side shows the output with the minimum signal required to produce lift-off. Lift-off is defined by Fig. 9.37, which shows that as the min. sig. amplitude

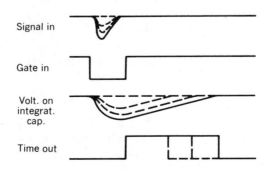

FIGURE 9.35 Timing relationship of the C/T converter.

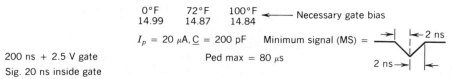

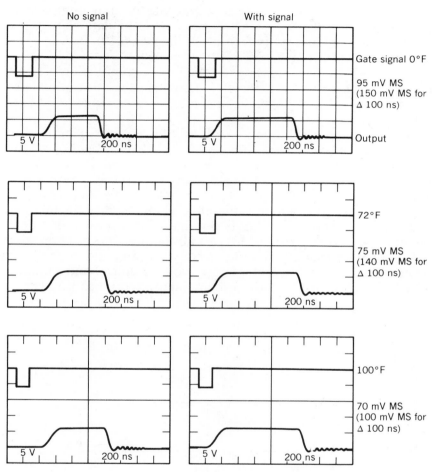

FIGURE 9.36 Lift-off characteristics.

is increased a ''bump'' appears before the main output and increases in size with the increasing amplitude of signal until it suddenly reaches full amplitude with an expansion of the pulse.

Observing the 72°F condition in Fig. 9.36, it is seen that the pulse length has expanded from 640 to 1000 ns, a very substantial increase. The amplitude of the min. sig. required for this transition was 75 mV.

To gain an additional 100 ns an increase of $140 - 75 = 65$ mV is required.

The dynamic range of the integrator can be expressed in several ways. The shortest output at 72°F is 1 μs. If the minimum change is 100 ns, with an 80 μs max., the dynamic range is 79 μs/100 ns = 790.

Considering the area of the input signal, the minimum size is 65 mV (4)ns/2 = $1.30(10)^{-10}$ V·s, whereas from the data shown in Fig. 9.37, the maximum area is 600 mV(100)ns = $6(10)^{-8}$ V·s. The dynamic range is thus $6(10)^{-8}/1.3(10)^{-10} = 460$.

However, the dynamic range of the voltage input is only 1.5 V/75 mV = 20, which is not sufficient; therefore, the 10:1 attenuator is added, bringing the voltage dynamic range to 200, equal to that of the peak detector.

The maximum resolution is set by the 80 μs max. length and the 11-bit output of the scaler. This requires a clock period of $80(10)^{-6}/2$ in. = 39 ns or $f = 25.6$ MHz. The guaranteed operating frequency of the scaler is 25 MHz, typically 30 MHz. The clock will not be synchronized and accordingly the 11th bit is discarded, resulting in a 10-bit readout. Resolution is therefore about 0.1% of the max. area: $6(10)^{-8}/10^3 = 6(10)^{-11}$. This is one half of the previously defined minimum area of 1.3 $(10)^{-10}$ V·s, so all the numbers balance nicely.

Accuracy or stability is another consideration and depends upon the combined factors of temperature, voltage, noise, and calibration. An overall evaluation of these combined effects has not yet been

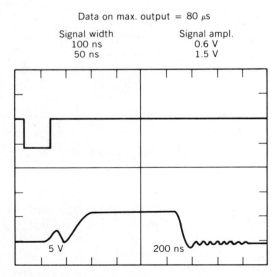

Data on max. output = 80 μs

Signal width	Signal ampl.
100 ns	0.6 V
50 ns	1.5 V

5 V   200 ns

FIGURE 9.37   Transition stage of pedestal showing lift-off.

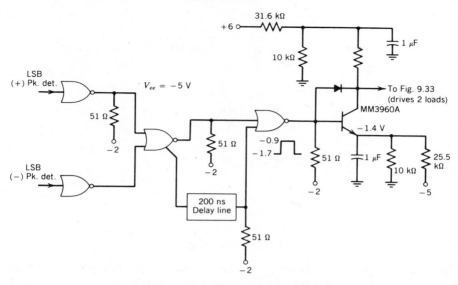

FIGURE 9.38   OR one shot (200 ns).

made, but based on the data it appears that the stability is suitable for the project at hand.

If there is a criticism to be made of the C/T converter it would be that the 100 ns rise time and 50 ns fall time of the output pulse is far too slow for the resolution the device is capable of producing.

The SC100 dual scaler, shown in Fig. 9.33, converts the time duration output of the C/T converter to a latched 10-bit output to be recorded by the microprocessor, which then resets the scaler for the next event. The scaler is turned on by the output of the C/T converter. This is the enable signal for the NAND gates which connect the oscillator to the scaler.

The data transmitted contains the zero signal which is subtracted out at the ground station. Considering that zero-signal calibrations are periodically made on the system, this method of data recording is preferred.

In another application a monostable calibrated for the zero-signal duration and triggered by the trailing edge of the converter enable signal could be used on a third input to the NAND gates. The output would then be directly proportional to the integral.

Considerations for the 30 ns delay line are discussed in Section 8.7.

The two remaining processing blocks are the OR one shot (OR-OS), shown in Fig. 9.38, and the crystal oscillator, shown in Fig. 9.33. These circuits are described in Chapter 4.

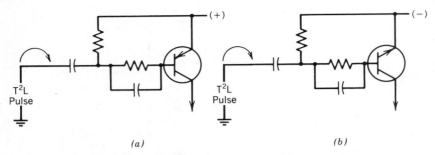

(a)   *(b)*

FIGURE 9.39   Power strobing.

9.10.9 Power Strobing

In circuits such as this, where the signal can be delayed or where there is other information as to when the signal to be processed will arrive, power strobing can be very useful. Figure 9.39 demonstrates the use of a PNP transistor for positive supplies and an NPN transistor for negative supplies. These circuits can deliver 0.4 A in 10 ns. The base drive must be tailored for the required load. Schottky T^{2}L is a logical choice; Fairchilds FACT family of CMOS logic is another possibility.

Most high-speed circuits can be turned on in a time comparable to their rise times providing there is no capacitance beyond the intrinsic capacitance of the chip. Some decoupling capacitance is always required and the limiting value determined by the relation

$$It = CE$$

As an example for a 15 V supply, 0.4 A of charging current and a 60 ns rise time, we have

$$C = \frac{0.4(10)^{-8}}{15} = 260 \text{ pF}$$

9.11 A HIGH-EFFICIENCY SWITCHING REGULATOR

There are a great variety of power supplies ranging from a rectifier and capacitor to complex switching and flyback schemes. There is also an overabundance of suppliers for all types, so generally a purchased supply can be found suitable for almost any application.

Over the past 10 years or so a great number of one-chip regulators have become available both with fixed and adjustable voltage outputs. These come in a variety of power levels depending upon the package style. Silicon General and Unitrode are among the many good sources for these chips.

Nevertheless there are times when a custom power supply is desirable and accordingly a design discussion is presented. The power supply shown in Fig. 9.40 is a good working design but it is described to show design decisions rather than laborious arithmetic details. This circuit, which has a +28 V input and multiple DC outputs, employs a Silicon General SC1524 regulator chip.

This type of design, a high-efficiency switching circuit, has many subtle considerations and is well worth a review for this purpose alone.

9.11.1 The Switching Stage

The regulating technique is pulsewidth modulation (PWM). The power transistors driving the primary of the output transformer are switched from the full on condition to total cutoff as rapidly as possible.

There are no losses that are of concern in the transistor off state, but there are in the finite switching times and in the conduction stage. Therefore, a figure of merit would be fast switching and low on resistance.

In a circuit where a large amount of power is controlled with small losses, minor glitches, spikes, or other forms of circuit misbehavior can result in very large increases of power dissipation and consequently device failure. Based on this concern large geometry devices are desired but this increases the capacitance, thereby increasing the switching times, which, in turn, decreases efficiency and raises the operating temperature.

The Solitron STD8304 transistor used in this design is far from ideal, but it is rugged and, most importantly for this application, was space approved. The original design used an IRF150 FET which produced an efficiency of 85%, about 5% higher than the present design, but was eventually ruled out because of lack of qualification data (see Section 1.3.5).

The operating frequency of this circuit is 50 kHz and, since each half of the circuit alternates with the other half, the transistors are switched at a 25 kHz rate (see Fig. 9.41). The data is shown for 24 V and 32 V, the expected variation of the input voltage. There is a substantial "guardband" where no current is flowing through either transistor. As the input voltage is lowered, the current pulse becomes

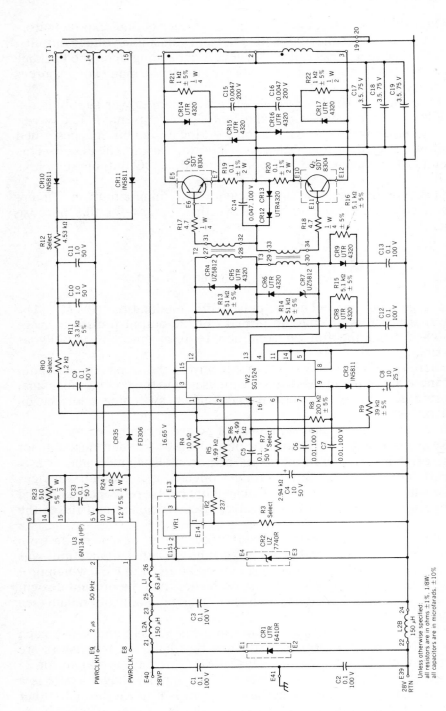

FIGURE 9.40 Switching power supply: (*a*) primary circuit.

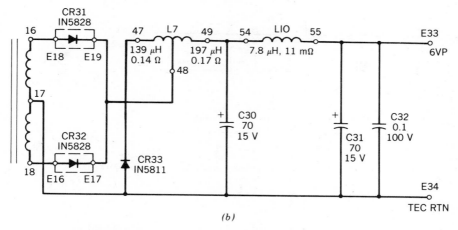

FIGURE 9.40 Switching power supply: (*b*) secondary circuit.

wider until the guardband reaches a minimum, at which time regulation safely ceases.

Under no possible circumstance should there ever be simultaneous conduction of the two transistors. In this condition the magnetizing ampere turns of the two halves of the transformer winding cancel and the transistors have no inductive protection against a destructive current flow. It is up to the chip manufacturer to build this safeguard into the regulating chip and up to the circuit designer to follow the application information carefully.

Simultaneous conduction is one of the two critical destructive mechanisms in this kind of circuit. This conduction can occur for a great variety of reasons, most of which are beyond reasonable design calculations. Instead, a code of good design conduct must be strictly adhered to and backed up by keen observation under all possible operational conditions.

The two principal culprits involved with simultaneous conduction are unwanted feedback and spurious oscillations. Because there are very large switching currents passing through the input filter capacitors (C17–19), care must be taken so that these currents do not couple with the control lines. To avoid this the heavy input ground line should take a short and direct connection to the common mode choke, L2B, and then to the ground of the input filter capacitor. Another short, heavy wire then connects the emitter side of the switching transistors to the other side of capacitors. From here a small wire, or in difficult cases, a 1 or 2 Ω resistor, connects to the remainder of the input ground system.

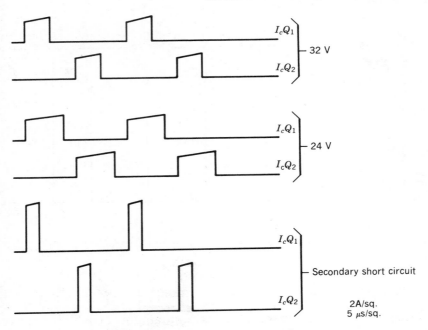

FIGURE 9.41   Normal current waveforms.

Spurious oscillations are brought about by many reasons; again, good housekeeping should be exercised to prevent this. The transformers should be wound for a minimum of leakage reactance and positioned with the switching transistors so that the leads are as short as possible.

Q spoiling resistors (R17 and R18) or ferrite beads should be used if sensitivity to hand motion or other symptoms indicate parasitic instabilities. In this circuit, collector to ground reverse voltage diodes (CR15 and CR16) are used to clamp any possible negative-going transients.

The snubber circuits employing the diodes CR14 and CR17 are used to clamp any possible positive transients that might rise above the average maximum positive voltage at the transistor collectors. There are also snubber circuits and zener–diode combinations employed with the base driving transformer circuits.

After taking the above precautions, no undesirable waveform of any sort could be detected with this regulator. In this regard a comment should be made about measurement techniques used with a circuit of this type, particularly the scope. False waveforms can be picked up through the scope probe, its grounding clip, and other instrumentation connections. This can be very frustrating, but any undesirable or unexplainable waveform must be accounted for. In many cases it is the measuring technique that must be changed.

9.11.2 Magnetic Considerations

The second critical destructive mechanism is magnetic imbalance. Unequal magnetic drives on the two primary halves are equivalent to passing a DC through one half of the winding and can quickly lead to destructive saturation. It is absolutely imperative that the primary of the power transformer be a bifilar winding so that not only are the turns of each half of the primary winding equal in numerical count but also in effectiveness. There are circuits and driving techniques available to correct for the lack of symmetrical on times for the two transistors.

The SG1524 used in this design has since been replaced by the SG1524B, which is a plug-in replacement and should be used instead of the SG1524 in existing older circuits.

For new designs, the SG1526 is an improved regulating chip and the SG1846 (UC1846 by Unitrode) offers additional advantages. In particular, pulsewidth balancing is ensured, which eliminates a major problem with the SG1524.

In the design being reviewed the core was simply made 50% larger than dictated by normal design standards and trouble was averted. This is not recommended procedure, but seemed the best solution at the time. In any event, it is wise to be conservative in setting the maximum flux density in these kinds of designs.

Figure 9.42 shows the waveforms that develop as the imbalance increases. The danger point is reached when even the slightest upward curve in one of the current waveforms is noticed. This means that saturation is being approached on one half of the drive and after this the current increase is extremely rapid and can be caused by a very minor disturbance. Transistor destruction is almost certain.

A necessary and standard test for any magnetic circuit is to lower the frequency carefully while observing the current waveforms. In

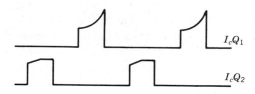

FIGURE 9.42   Current waveforms showing saturation due to magnetic imbalance.

this kind of balanced push–pull drive, collector current from both transistors should show the upward curve at the same time and at a frequency considered by the designer to offer the intended safety margin.

In this circuit, regulation is provided for variations in the input voltage alone and there is no feedback information for regulation due to load variation of the secondary. When this condition is acceptable the efficiency is higher because the secondary control losses have been eliminated.

9.11.3 Regulation and Loop Stability

The necessary sensing information comes from a winding dedicated for that purpose alone. This is done so that the requirements for loop stability and input frequency rejection can be separated from the requirements of proper filtering for the secondary. If there is only one secondary voltage these functions can sometimes be combined, thus furnishing load as well as input regulation. This circuit, however, has multiple secondaries and the added complication is not worthwhile.

The technique for designing loop stability is deliberately not covered because it is complex and initial guidelines are included in the manufacturer's application notes. The basic principles, as described in Chapter 3 on op-amps, can only be applied as a rough guide because these techniques do not include such effects as direct delays, storage, and nonlinear capacitance and inductance. Testing for loop stability and the required experimental adjustment, however, is relatively easy. Figure 9.43 shows two test circuits, one for applying a sine or square wave to the input and the second for applying the same signals as a load disturbance. The technique of observing the damping or ringing characteristics of a square wave input and the peaking and roll-off of a sinusoidal response apply whether or not the circuit is linear or of the linear phase classification (see Chapter 3).

9.11.4 Parameter Selection

The selection of the operating frequency depends on a number of different factors. Foremost is the transistor switching speed. Bipolar transistors have a storage delay, while the FET does not, and this is a major limiting factor. Schottky clamps to limit the saturation level and hence the delay are not practical because the on-condition losses are too great. Chapter 1 on FETs includes a side-by-side comparison of FET and comparable bipolar switching speeds and drive requirements.

The maximum frequency of operation of the SG1524 is 300 kHz. If one presumes that the switching rate is independent of frequency,

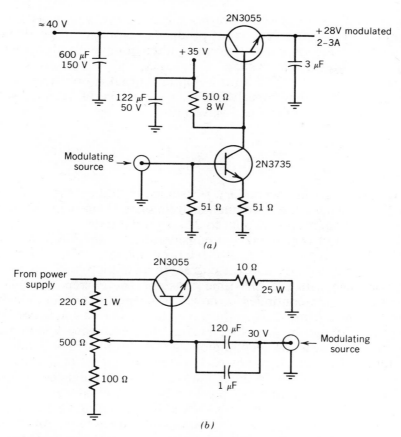

FIGURE 9.43 Test circuits: (*a*) modulated power source; (*b*) modulated load.

the transistor switching losses increase directly with the switching frequency.

The input capacitor has an effective series resistance (ESR) and the losses here also increase directly with the switching frequency. The inductance of the capacitor must also be considered at the higher frequencies. In a general sense the physical size of the capacitor must be increased to lower the losses. Conversely, the electrical size is decreased by increasing frequency. Appendix IV contains information on capacitors in general and also information relating specifically to switched regulator applications.

9.11.5 Rectification and Filtering

A PWM regulating system requires that the filter circuit on the secondaries have a choke input because the choke input filter produces an output proportional to the average input voltage, whereas the more commonly used capacitive input produces a voltage proportional to the peak voltage. A capacitive input filter completely destroys the regulation of the PWM system.

For a choke input filter to develop an output proportional to the average voltage input properly, it must be above certain critical value. For a full wave rectifier this is given by

$$L_C = \frac{R}{6\pi f} \text{ H}$$

where R is the total secondary resistance including the choke and transformer and f the fundamental frequency. Common practice is to make the input choke equal to $2L_C$ as a minimum.

A second and very important consideration in the PWM regulator comes about because the input drive is completely shut off for a portion of each cycle. Because the current in an inductive circuit decays in accordance with the L/R time constant, the current through the conducting diode continues to flow during the off period. This half of the secondary now acts as the magnetizing source and accordingly induces a voltage in the other half of the secondary winding in a direction that turns the second diode on. Both diodes are conducting simultaneously, which produces two undesirable effects. First, the currents through the two diodes are not always balanced so that a net DC, which is capable of putting the core in saturation, can be produced. Second, if both diodes are still conducting when the other transistor is turned on it will be looking into a short circuit that will cause dangerous current spikes.

This situation can be neutralized nicely by a third diode, CR33, and by overwinding the input choke as shown in Fig. 9.43b. The overwind back-biases the two rectifying diodes, forcing the current to flow through the third diode CR33 and through the load. Reference [2] in Chapter 5 contains design equations for calculating the amount of overwind that is needed. However, it is generally easier to determine the correct number of turns empirically. The overwind should first be made about equal to the filter winding and the current going through the two rectifying diodes observed as the turns are reduced. A few extra turns beyond that required to reduce the currents to zero is the proper value.

9.11.6 Miscellaneous Considerations

To complete this discussion the purpose of the remaining components in the circuit is described. The diodes CR1 and CR2 are high-current devices to protect against reverse voltage and excessive voltage spikes, respectively.

In this application there are long cables to the primary power supply so that common mode voltages become a problem. The choke L2A–L2B has two bifilar windings on the same core and is connected such that the normal input and return currents produce opposing ampere turns; hence, there is no net inductance. A common mode voltage, however, sees both chokes in series and presents a substantial impedance.

The input choke L1 and the input capacitors C17–19 are compromise values, since a number of conflicting conditions must be met. First, any noise on the input line should be reduced as much as possible, which calls for a large L and C. However, many power supplies have maximum current turn-on limits which call for a small C and large L. Often there is also a maximum time period for the in-rush current, which dictates a small L and small C. Finally, to contain the large primary switching currents, the capacitance should be as large as possible.

In such circuits, heating of the input capacitors can be a significant problem. In this case, a special clamp was machined so that good thermal contact could be made with the capacitors. Without these clamps, a safe design would not have been possible. For this application wet slug tantalum capacitors were used. This type of capacitor is more reliable than the normal dry forms but has a substantial loss of capacitance at low temperatures. Polycarbonate capacitors were too large for the allowable space of this design.

A small series regulator VR1 was necessary to produce a stable supply for the switching regulator chip U2.

The frequency of oscillation is set by the resistor and capacitor from pins 6 and 7, respectively. Very often it is desired to synchronize the switching frequency with an external clock to lock the effects of any switching frequency pickup in a definite pattern. This makes computer correction easier and is also less distracting in visual displays. In this case the synchronizing frequency is isolated by an opto-isolator U3 to avoid ground-loop problems. The synchronizing signal is applied to pin 3 of U2.

Short-circuit protection is an absolute must for any power supply and it is provided in this circuit by applying a sensing voltage from R19 and R20 to pins 4 of U2. The short circuit current through the switching transistors is shown in Fig. 9.41. Good judgment and solid testing are required for short-circuit protection because it is the input current that is limited and the short circuits generally occur across the secondaries. The secondary components are protected only by suitable design margins.

TABLE 9.4
Transformer Winding Data

T1 Core:	Magnetics, Inc. ZJ4813 ferrite
Primary wdg:	1–2 and 2–3 are bifilar wound 16 turns each with 3 #22 gauge formivar insulated wires each; they are connected start to finish as indicated by the polarity dots in Fig. 9.40.
Shield:	A Faraday shield of a 1-layer copper strip overlapping but not shorting is placed between the primary and secondary windings and this shield grounded
Secondary wdg feedback:	13–14 and 14–15 are bifilar wound with 7 turns each of #33 guage formivar insulated wire
T2 and T3 core:	Magnetics, Inc. J41506 ferrite
Primary wdg:	97 turns #31 wire
Secondary wdg:	16 turns #26 wire

There is a problem with starting transients using this regulator and the manufacturer recommends the "soft start" time-delay circuit attached to pin 9 of U2 to avoid undesired transient conditions.

The regulator contains an internal +5 V reference available at pin 16. This is divided down to +2.5 V, which is applied to pin 2, one input to an internal comparator. The feedback voltage is applied to pin 1 and the other comparator input to develop the control voltage for the circuit.

The feedback voltage from pins 13, 14, and 15 of T1 are conditioned by a carefully selected filter system. The component values are first set up in accordance with the manufacturer's suggestions and then fine tuned empirically for the desired results. These components are a factor in controlling the input regulation and also which of four different secondary loads of this design receive the best regulation. They are also a factor in controlling the transient response of input disturbances. A pure analytic analysis of these multiple effects is extremely difficult. The best approach is a combination of sensible preliminary calculations followed by careful testing and adjustments for both square wave and sinusoidal signals applied to the +28 V input line. Experience reduces this task to a reasonable procedure.

The transformers T2 and T3 are again the result of preliminary calculations and empirical adjustment to match the complex load of the transistor inputs. Winding data for these transformers and that of the output transformer are given in Table 9.4.

The last part of the circuit to be discussed is the self-biasing network of CR12, CR13, and C14. These components produce a common negative voltage to both transistors to ensure that they do not conduct in an undesired manner. This bias is in addition to the natural reverse swing produced by the transformer coupling.

9.12 A ROM-CONTROLLED CIRCUIT

Figure 9.44 shows how a ROM can be used to implement a hardware function. In Fig. 9.45, a truth table is shown for a particular function, as an example, but this is where the designer places his own program.

This system is designed with high-speed CMOS and therefore uses very little power. The standby dissipation is approximately 1.3 mW and operation at 1 MHz consumes about 60 mW.

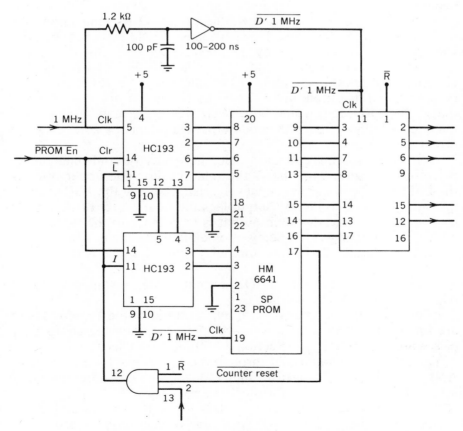

FIGURE 9.44 PROM-controlled circuit.

Not used							Program data (Hex)	
Q_7	Q_6	Q_5	Q_4	Q_3 Q_2 Q_1 Q_0			Adr	Data
1	0	0	0				0 1	0 8
1	0	0	1				0 2	0 9
1	1	1	1				0 3	0 B
1	1	1	1				0 4	0 F
1	1	1	0				0 5	0 E
1	1	0	0				0 6	0 C
1	0	0	0				0 7	0 8
0	0	0	0				0 8	0 0

FIGURE 9.45 Truth table for 3 ϕ clock.

The ROM used in this circuit is a programmable device and thereby becomes a PROM. It is manufactured by Harris and is 512 bits × 8 channels. Accordingly, there are 9 address lines. This application uses 6; the other 3 are grounded. This particular PROM has exceptionally bad transition transients; they are beyond the "glitch" definition, since they are about 50 ns wide. The SN74HC273 latch is used to eliminate the undesired outputs. The latch does have an additional benefit in that its output drive capability is considerably greater than that of the PROM. It would have been nice if the manufacturer had included a proper latch with good output characteristics, but they did not choose to do so.

As in the case of all sequential logic, there must be controlled timing waveforms. Figure 9.46 shows the relationship. The upper trace is the LSB of the counter which lags the rising edge of the 1 MHz clock by about 20 ns. The PROM output lags the falling edge of D' 1 MHz by about 80 ns, and the latch output is very close to the rising edge of D' 1 MHz. The overall delay of clock input to latch output is 600 ns, which is not the minimum delay but was adequate in this application.

The second signal in the PROM output is the unwanted transient which is eliminated by the latch.

In this case the counter is reset by an output of the PROM. There are times when a quicker reset is required and then the complexity of a word recognizer (see Section 4.3.3) must be used.

The reset is accomplished through the load input by means of an AND gate. This allows a reset signal for the initial condition and for a PROM disable by some form of external logic.

D' 1 MHz is developed from 1 MHz by an RC circuit and an inverter. As explained in Section 4.3.4, this is an acceptable procedure only with CMOS and even then certain precautions must be taken.

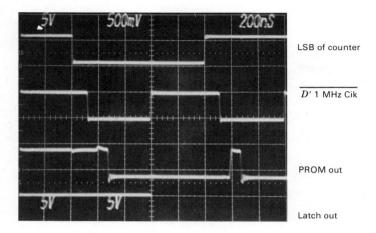

FIGURE 9.46   PROM timing characteristics.

9.13 AN ELECTRO-OPTICAL TACHOMETER

Rate feedback is important in stabilizing many servomotor drive systems. A DC generator has been the conventional manner of developing this voltage, but optical encoders and the associated electronics have so advanced that they are preferred under certain conditions. These conditions include low shaft speed, where it is not desirable to add a gear train, and where low inertia and friction are important.

The optical encoder used in this application is a HEDS-5000 made by Hewlett-Packard. This encoder produces two outputs phased 90° apart with 1024 cycles/revolution.

Figure 9.47*a* includes a unique circuit suggested by Hewlett-Packard. The two quadrature channels, *A* and *B*, are processed by U1 and U2 to produce the waveforms shown in Fig. 9.48. It is seen that both the clock and U/D signal are at twice the input frequency and that when the rotation is changed the ⌐ clock edge is shifted from one polarity of the U/D signal to the other. When these two signals go to the *D* f/f, as shown, the *Q* output switches polarities, depending upon the direction of rotation. A note of caution here: It is necessary that the square waves driving any circuit that responds to both edges be symmetrical, otherwise the timing periods produced by the doubler will have alternate durations, which frequently cause problems. Fortunately, the accuracy of the quadrature relation is not very critical.

Figure 9.47*b* shows the use of the AD650 *f*/V converter made by Analog Devices. The doublted frequency from U2-6 drives this circuit through a differentiating *RC* circuit. The negative spike from this input

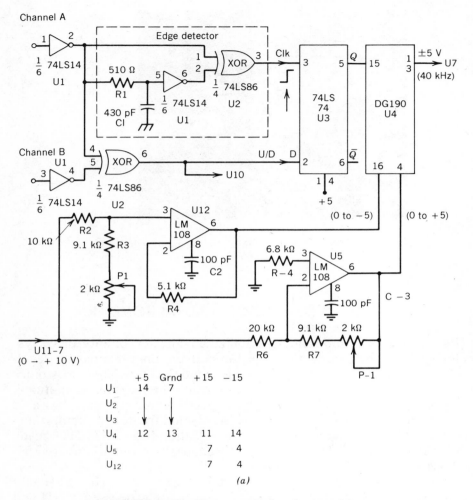

FIGURE 9.47　Electro-optical tachometer (a).

triggers an internal monostable where duration is controlled by the capacitor on pin 6. The monostable in turns develops a series of constant current pulses to produce a voltage across the *RC* connected to pins 1 and 3. These are all components that must be adjusted in terms of the frequency range that is being accommodated.

At the lower frequencies, the *RC* droop at the output of the *f*/V converter often becomes a problem, which is nicely solved by the S/ H. This chip, the Harris HA2425, samples the output with a delayed pulse developed by the monostables of U10. The duration of the delay and sampling pulse width is tailored for the problem at hand.

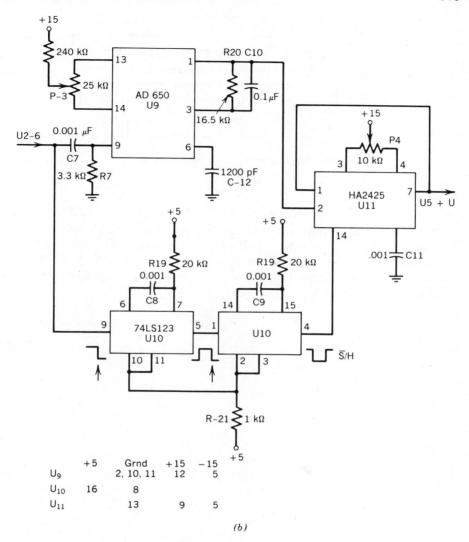

(b)

FIGURE 9.47   Electro-optical tachometer (*b*).

All rate signals, no matter how they are generated, eventually reach a high-frequency roll-off, after which they are no longer a rate signal or a lead network. It is important that this time constant be substantially smaller than the limiting system lag (30 ms in this application). $\frac{1}{10}$ the time is a good number. With the S/H technique, careful control of the sampling pulse permits the use of a very fast time con-

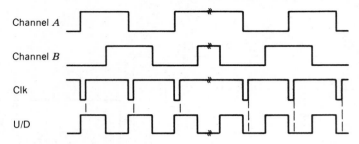

FIGURE 9.48   Encoder waveforms.

stant in the f/V converter ($RC = 1.65(10)^4(10)^{-7} = 1.65$ ms) and consequently good performance for the servoloop.

From this we go back to Fig. 9.47a, where the $+10$ V max. output is divided down to $+5$ and an inversion stage is added. Now, by means of the analog switch, this is a ± 5 V output that denotes direction as well as shaft velocity.

TEN

Laboratory Procedures

The term laboratory procedures covers more than just electronic wiring techniques. If an afternoon is wasted, it does not make much difference whether there was a design error or the technician could not find his tools. The point is that if an area plans to establish an electronic activity, be it big or small, the area must be organized and maintained in a manner suitable for electronic design, construction, and testing. Much too often an engineer designs a circuit and then naively turns it over to the construction area to be completed. The engineer and technician must have a good mutual understanding of how different circuits are to be constructed. This takes time on the part of the engineer. It is important that the engineer work with a limited number of technicians so that this mutual understanding can develop. The technician must have the tools of the trade and a good collection of the commonly used hardware items.

Any area involved in electronic circuit design must have ready access to an up-to-date set of catalogs from all the major manufacturers. In addition, the use of such general catalogs as *Electronic Engineers Masters* (EEM), *Electronic Designs Gold Book*, and *Electronics Buyers Guide* are required for locating specialty manufacturers.

A current list of local sales representatives and distributors should be maintained to ensure access to the latest products and information about them.

The ability to handle small purchase orders directly is crucial to the operation of a development laboratory. Even in the best-planned program there are always last-minute changes and corrections. If the project is delayed for a lot of paperwork and a signature routine, the abilities of a competent designer are vastly diluted.

The testing technique can often be as important and challenging as the original design. Proper high-frequency measurement and noise interference are the most common problems.

When the circuit board allows, there is a simple technique for eliminating many of the problems with high-frequency analog measurements. The first is to determine where a 10 MΩ, 10 pF oscilloscope probe can be placed without disturbing the circuit. If necessary, a built-in test buffer should be provided for this purpose. Second, a flange-mounted BNC connector should be soldered to the ground plane so that a BNC probe adapter can be used. This allows the probe to be grounded directly by its grounding ring and avoids the use of the ground wire. There are also miniaturized probe adapters that are smaller than the BNC combination described. The test outputs must be planned in the original layout. It is important that the test connector be so placed that the scope probe points away from the circuit. The body of the probe often couples two parts of the circuit together, causing serious difficulties. The flange-mounted BNC connector is also used for any input and output signals.

Coping with the noise problem can be difficult. If the BNC adapters just described and a good ground plane with proper decoupling are used, part of the problem is under control. If the problem is the power-line frequency, a number of things should be checked:

1. There may be an instrument with a defective power supply that is allowing the noise to enter.

2. All of the instruments may not be grounded to the same line. For example, adjacent benches may have a potential between their two ground straps. This is a common form of interference.

3. One of the instruments or an adjacent piece of equipment may be producing an electromagnetic field that is causing the problem. A soldering iron is often an offender.

4. At times one or more of the test instruments must operate ungrounded. Accordingly, an interconnecting power-line plug that breaks the ground line is used.

5. If a nonpolarized two-wire power line is used, reversing the plug can sometimes help.

6. Local shielding should be used, that is, the circuit being tested should be placed in a box. Sometimes a steel box is more effective than a nonmagnetic structure.

7. Batteries in place of the regular power supply can help. With this it may be possible to operate with only one instrument energized by the power line. For example, a simple on-board oscillator powered by the battery could be the input signal. This leaves the scope as the only instrument connected to the power line.

8. Occasionally, special instruments are needed, some of which may have to be built. These include filters. Often use of a fre-

quency-sensitive voltmeter (a wave analyzer) is the only way in which some measurements can be made.

Other forms of interference must first be defined to know how to deal with them. Radio transmitters can be a problem. Even low-frequency circuits can rectify the *RF* signal, resulting in a very confusing and erratic modulating voltage. Any device that produces sparks can, and usually does, give trouble. Chapter 6 contains additional information on this subject.

10.1 HIGH-FREQUENCY WIRING TECHNIQUES

Most high-frequency and fast-pulse circuits perform better on a plated board where a good ground plane can be established. A solid board is best, but sometimes the prepunched vector-type board is satisfactory. The use of an insulated board with discrete ground leads requires much care and planning. The problem with the prepunched board is that the ground plane is perforated and therefore not as effective. Cutting around the holes to allow the use of noninsulated standoffs is a bad practice, since this further reduces the effectiveness of the ground plane and with carelessness may actually sever it. Insulated standoffs should be used.

One problem with the plated board is that the capacitance from components to ground is increased. Accordingly, good judgment is required in establishing how far from the board the components should be placed and which components are sensitive to this added capacitance. A counter consideration is the fact that circuits tending to be unstable may sometimes be stabilized by placing them close to the ground plane to minimize the spread of their radiating fields. In general, sensitive parts should be about $\frac{1}{4}$ in. off the ground plane.

In Fig. 10.1 the critical line to ground is that from the collector of Q_1, Q_{1c} to the base of Q_2, Q_{2b}. In the normal circuit the capacitor C_4 does not exist "electrically" at high frequencies. C_4 is, however, a serious problem because of its capacitance to the ground plane, and also because of inductive reactance and the resonance that can occur.

It is important to note that the collector–base line consists of all conducting parts that are attached to the wire between the two points, such as socket, terminals, coupling capacitor, the side of the load, and bias resistors that are attached to the wire. The use of terminals for mechanical support is minimized by employing the transistor socket as a wiring post when practical. If a load resistor must span a distance considerably greater than its length, the distance should be covered by extending the cold lead of the resistor, for example, the end opposite to that attached to the collector-to-base line. Figures

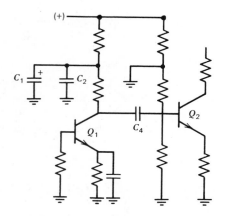

FIGURE 10.1   Basic high-frequency circuit.

10.2 and 10.3 show the correct and incorrect wiring techniques, respectively.

Referring back to Fig. 10.1, there are two coupling capacitors, C_1, a large tantalytic, and C_2, a small ceramic one. The small capacitor is there because the larger one may have too much inductance to be a good filter at high frequencies. It is therefore permissible to move the larger capacitor a bit from the crowded transistor area. The smaller one, however, should be kept close.

Figure 10.4 is a more explicit form of Fig. 10.1, showing that the emitter bypass capacitor should be connected to the same point on the ground plane as the input resistor. This is to prevent ground currents from injecting an input voltage between the base and emitter. If there is no bypass capacitor, the emitter resistor should be connected at the same spot as the input resistor. In some cases there may

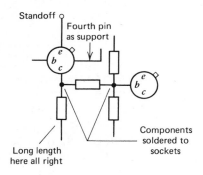

FIGURE 10.2   Correct parts layout.

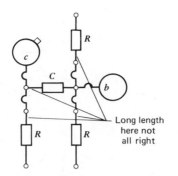

FIGURE 10.3 Incorrect parts layout.

be multiple bypass capacitors for the emitter. In this case the smallest (highest-frequency) gets preferred positions, but the large capacitor should still be positioned so that a feedback voltage cannot be developed between the base and emitter. The signal current passing through a transistor does not have to pass through the power supply, and in fact a determined effort should be made to prevent this from happening. Figure 10.5 shows the correct and incorrect way of placing the capacitor of a tuned circuit.

The point of concern here is that the signal current flowing in either leg of the tank circuit is Q times the current entering the tank and is accordingly just that much harder to contain properly. Despite this,

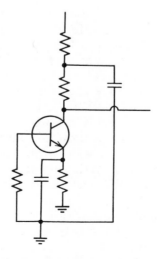

FIGURE 10.4 Bypass details.

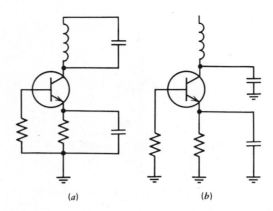

(a)   (b)

FIGURE 10.5   (*a*) Correct tuned circuit; (*b*) incorrect tuned circuit.

the connection of Fig. 10.5*b* is sometimes used because of other layout conflicts, including the fact that the resonating capacitor may be a variable type with a nut for grounding to an easy access plate. When it is necessary to use an insulated board with discrete ground leads, great care must be taken to ensure that the large output signal currents do not couple with the sensitive input leads.

10.2 DIGITAL WIRING TECHNIQUES

In digital circuits grounding is equally important, but the effect of poor grounding is somewhat different. The principal danger is that ground voltages may overcome the input thresholds, causing improper logic inputs to the system. In pure 5 V T^2L systems it is very often convenient to have a second copper plating, or a division of the first, to form a low-inductance path for the $+5$ V line. In any case, it is worthwhile to place a 0.01–0.1 μF high-frequency ceramic capacitor at the $+5$ V pin of each package.

Large digital systems are general laid out on a special board and the connections made with a wire wrap tool. The ground and $B+$ lines are plated on the boards. If there is more than one supply voltage, the connections are generally made by wire wrap and the decoupling becomes more critical.

When analog and digital circuits are on the same board, the analog circuits can seldom be wired the same way. This decision must always be made on an individual basis, of course. In general, however, the danger of the analog circuits being affected by digital noise is very great.

The analog and digital grounds should always be isolated from each other. Separate ground leads should be used to connect to their respective power supplies. Reference between the analog and digital sections is then maintained by connecting the grounds together with a suitable resistor. That is, a value much larger than the resistance of the grounds leads but small enough to minimize pickup between the two grounds. This resistor should be placed such that its value can be changed when system tests are underway.

Cradles are available to hold the passive parts required by the analog circuits (and occasionally by the digital blocks) when it is decided that wire wrap is satisfactory. If it is not practical to put the analog circuits on a separate board, they can be mounted on a designated copper clad board and hand wired. This board is then mounted to the larger wire wrap board at a suitable spot.

When the dual-in-line packages (DIP) were first introduced, having a 14-pin and a 16-pin package seemed like a good idea. This has, however, become a headache for wire wrap boards. There are, of course, other DIP packages: 8P, 10P, 18P, 20P, 22P, 24P, 28P, and larger assorted sizes. The 18P and 20P have the same pin-spacing as the 14-pin and 16-pin devices. The 22-pin is an oddball, having a 0.4 in. space between the pin rows instead of the 0.3 in. in smaller sockets. The 24-pin and 28-pin sockets are double the pin spacing of the small sockets, so that this works out all right.

Many of the integrated circuits are now being placed in 8-pin dip package as an alternative to the round 8-pin T05 package. This is very handy because the integrated circuit and a 4-pin component holder can both be plugged into one 16-pin dip socket. If $\frac{1}{8}$ W resistors are used, they will fit nicely in this header and make a package that is more compact and better looking than the T05 construction will allow. In addition, the T05 sockets are very expensive, often several times the cost of the integrated circuit.

Most of the packages on a digital board have 14 and 16 pins, and many costly mistakes are made by getting the pin numbers mixed up. There are several kinds of digital boards. One has holes for a socket as an integral part of the board. In the latter case the sockets are generally for 16-pin devices. When 14-pin packages are used, two of the pins are empty. Looking at the pin side of the sockets, we have Fig. 10.6.

Some schematics relabel the 14-pin sockets, as shown in Fig. 10.6a. For development boards, lines should be drawn and the sockets labeled so that each device is clearly identified from the back. 14- and 16-pin sockets should be coded by different colors. From the back of a wire wrap board everything looks the same, and without an obvious means of identification errors occur.

A third, and very popular, type of board simply has columns of individual pin sockets at 0.3 in. spacings, so that the dual in-line pack-

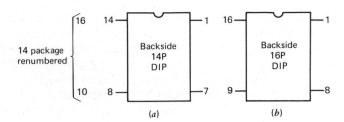

FIGURE 10.6 DIP socket designations.

ages can be directly plugged in. Here the columns are labeled as letters and the rows as numbers. Larger boards are made in groups of these rows and columns and are also labeled in letters. Each pin is accordingly designated by group, column, and row; for example, pin AC41. These pin designations are then placed on the schematic and the wire wrap connections made directly.

It is more difficult to isolate errors on a wire wrap board than it is with conventional analog wiring. Even simple changes or corrections can become very complex if the wires being changed have other wires laid on top of them. To minimize the difficulty of making changes with wire wrap boards, it is important to organize the sequence of wiring so that the most likely lines for change are the last to be put in.

Some sockets have a built-in capacitor between the standard power and ground pins; the use of such sockets is strongly recommended. If standard sockets are used, the capacitor should be soldered between the power and ground pin. This operation is second only to placing the identification tape between the pin rows. This soldering must be done very carefully, with Teflon tubing used to insulate the leads. Solderable ground tabs are also recommended for the power ground pin, but not other grounds.

Having a capacitor between the power and ground lead of a digital IC merits further discussion. T^2L and CMOS ICs both have a period of high current conduction during the transition time. (ECL, being a linear logic family, does not have this problem, but still requires signal containment.) With a proper value (0.1 F is a good average choice) wired directly between the power and ground pin, this current spike does not travel to other parts of the board.

This should be an *absolute requirement* for all digital boards, but unfortunately it is a very neglected and abused procedure. For instance, monostable pulse generators containing an *RC* time constant are often shunned because of their sensitivity to accidental triggering. While it is true that they are more sensitive to noise spikes than the straight logical gates, in many, if not most, cases the problem is really poor board construction, specifically, the lack of individual capacitors for each IC.

With monostables, it is also very important that the timing resistor and capacitor be soldered directly to the wire wrap pins. This is extra work and somewhat sloppy in appearance, but it allows proper operation, whereas the normal wire wrap and cradle construction can be extremely unreliable.

Signal containment is discussed in Chapter 6 and also in the analog section of this chapter. The case for individual capacitors for signal containment in analog circuits is more widely accepted because often these circuits oscillate without the capacitors giving an instant warning. The dangers with digital circuits, not always so obvious, are equally dangerous.

A drill motor, with a well-sparking commutator, can be used as a noise source. The circuit performance should be monitored as the drill motor is moved in the vicinity of the circuit. The degree of noise interference can be varied by changing the distance between the motor and the circuit board. Although this gives no quantitative measure of noise tolerance, it is a fairly tough test. A circuit that remains undisturbed is probably in satisfactory shape.

10.3 A CONTINUITY METER

A very common and necessary procedure in the laboratory is checking for continuity, that is, making certain that leads go where they are supposed to when visual observation is unclear. Semiconductors are often involved in the circuit, and care must be taken that damage does not occur to them as a result of these tests. The normal ohmmeter has 3 and 15 V batteries in series, with varying amounts of resistance. Electronic meters also apply voltage, the amount varying with the manufacturer.

Figure 10.7 shows a circuit where the maximum applied voltage is 0.2 V, which is not capable of breaking down a junction, either silicon or germanium. This meter draws about 1 mA of current when the switch is closed; hence it should be turned off when not in use. With reasonable care and use a battery lasts several years. A minor convenience is that this meter also acts as a crude ohmmeter where 100 $\Omega = 96$, 1 k$\Omega = 66$, and 10 k$\Omega = 18$.

Other types of measuring devices can also produce output voltages. Specifically, the digital voltmeter often injects a small voltage into the circuit while in use. Although this voltage is seldom large enough to cause damage, disturbances can be created if the meter is used for monitoring during operation. All DVMs and ohmmeters should have their inputs checked by a scope and labeled accordingly so that this problem can be properly judged.

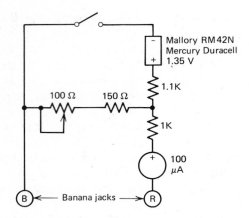

FIGURE 10.7 Continuity meter.

10.4 CONNECTORS AND CABLES

This section may seem trivial to those who have not been exposed to the disaster of intermittent, broken, and shorted cable connections, but unless the cable is properly constructed, much difficulty is encountered. This is especially true of cables that must be repeatedly connected and disconnected.

Connectors can be divided into two broad groups. In one a wire is soldered to a pin; in the other a crimping or piercing action is accomplished by special tools or jigs furnished by the manufacturer. In the latter case the range of quality and reliability is so great that it becomes a matter of individual judgment for each product and application. A word of caution, though: There is some very poor merchandise around.

To judge connectors with a solder connection, refer to the section that follows.

1. A connector *must* come with a good strain relief clamp for the cable. There are two types: one that clamps directly behind the connector and one that clamps off to the side. The choice depends largely on where the cable is going and how the available space is distributed. More care is required with the right-angle strain relief because there is a considerable difference in the length of the conductors from the pin to the clamp. The individual wires must all be properly bent and strain-free before the clamp is tightened. The clamp must *never* be used to force the wires in place.

The selection of the wire size in a cable is made first by the *mechanical* considerations and then by the electrical requirements. Generally, the signal currents in the cable wires are small and require only a very fine wire that would be quite fragile. If more current is required, parallel wires should be used.

Before the wires are soldered to the connector, it is a good idea to bunch them together and try to judge their fit in the cable clamp. This is particularly true for the right-angle clamp. Most cables have a connector on both ends. The cable clamp for the first connector is relatively easy to install because all the irregularities in the cable length can be passed down the cable. If possible, at least one of the cable clamps should be straight and, with its connector, should be attached last.

After the first connector and clamp have been attached, the cable should be laced to its proper shape and length to keep the wires even and free of strains and bulges.

2. The soldering of the wires to the connectors is an orderly and precise procedure. Of great importance is a soldering iron of the correct size and temperature with a clean and well-tinned tip. A wet sponge is needed for tip maintenance.

   a. With the socket firmly secured in a vise, each connector pin receptacle is filled with solder by first touching the solder-wetted tip to the pin and then properly placing the solder wire for a quick melt.

   b. The wires are then carefully stripped to a length that is just enclosed by the pin receptable. This requires that a mechanical stop of some sort be attached to the wire stripper.

   c. The wire insulation *must* be of the nonmeltable type, such as Teflon.

   d. If the wire is stranded (which is preferred), the exposed wire is lightly finger-twisted in the direction of the natural twist to ensure that no strands protrude.

   e. The wire, now held steady by a clamp, is lightly solder-wetted.

   f. A piece of properly sized shrink tubing, perhaps $\frac{1}{2}$ in. long, is placed over the wire. This tubing must be cut by a jig that gives a square cut if the proper protection is to be obtained.

   g. The wire can be quickly soldered by placing it next to the receptacle opening and touching the pin with a solder-wetted iron. At the instant of the melt the wire is pushed to its full depth.

   h. When the soldering is finished, a second knowledgeable person should inspect the workmanship. Even a very competent technician can become bored and careless on a job of this kind.

i. The shrink tubing is now carefully pressed into place and heat is applied to finish the process.

A few extra comments are in order at this time. Connectors with internal pins, which become inaccessible after all connections have been made, should be avoided if at all possible. When trouble develops, they cannot be visually inspected without a major disturbance. It is much better to use multiple connectors with accessible pins than one larger connector. Furthermore, the strain relief problem is generally more reliable with the smaller connectors.

The repair of a cable and connector is a messy and unreliable process. A connector and cable are meant to be attached once, and that is the end of it.

10.5 SCHEMATIC DRAWINGS

Drawing a schematic for constructing a circuit or for recording and reporting requires considerable forethought and good judgment. No single procedure serves all purposes, but the rules and ideas given below can help in making useable and understandable schematics.

1. Decide whether the sketch is large or small. My own definition of a small sketch is one that can fit on a standard $8\frac{1}{2} \times 11$ in. sheet of paper. These sketches need not have the organization required of a more complex circuit.

2. If the schematic is larger, arrange the semiconductor parts carefully in the manner of the natural signal flow. Perhaps first a block diagram is necessary to achieve a good result. Sometimes it helps to make paper cutouts and arrange them in the most suitable manner. Always keep in mind the critical leads and those parts that are connected with a great number of leads. This part of the project will take some time, so admit it and do a good job.

3. Power-supply leads, standard decoupling capacitors, socket descriptions, and even part numbers need not be on the main schematic. A separate list conveys such information equally well. (This list also assists in the proper procedure of wiring the power pins and their decouplers first.)

The main schematic components generally need only their circuit numbers—U1, U2, and so on—and a short descriptive abbreviation if the symbol is not self-explanatory. For example, a NAND gate, a transistor, and op-amp, or a FET need not be described. A counter, D/A, one-shot, or other special functions are generally drawn simply as a box and need a short label.

4. Some connections take up a great deal of room on a schematic. For example, four 4-bit counters driving a 16-bit D/A can be shown on the schematic as one counter with the main control lines, clock, load, and enable and a single connection to the D/A. Figure 10.8a illustrates this point.

Even in the "detail sketch," obvious groups of wires are kept together. For example, each counter has a group of four wires, which can be combined as a cable with 16 lines. Section 9.2 describes the identification technique.

Figure 10.8b shows another common building block: delayed one-shot. Here one IC contains two one-shots which are connected and require two resistors, two capacitors, and two potentiometers as external passive parts.

All connections are defined by the combination of the main schematic, the power table, and the detail sketches.

Relays deserve a special mention. Until the early 1960s, they were widely used in many forms of logic circuits, and an improperly drawn schematic made a circuit almost impossible to follow and understand.

Except in very simple cases, it does not make any sense to show the contacts of a relay next to the relay coil. Relay R1 operates contacts C1, and the contacts are placed where they belong in the circuit, shown as required, in their NO or NC positions. Wiring pins can be assigned and, if suitable, subdesignations such as C1a and C1b can be used. Automobile manufacturers have never gotten this straight, and with the advent of electronic switching it will be interesting to see how the new circuits will be illustrated.

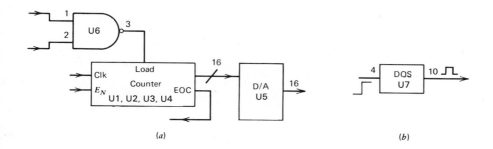

FIGURE 10.8 Abbreviated circuits.

10.6 RAPID BREADBOARD CONSTRUCTION

After all the somber warnings about the effects of poor workmanship, a word must be said about trade-offs of time and the proper procedures in electronic construction. Many circuits are built purely to obtain some specific information that will be used in the final design. The bench efforts then may be largely empirical, involving much soldering and unsoldering. Intelligence can still be used in the construction, but high reliability and good looks are a waste of time. The proverbial "rat's nest" does indeed have a solid place in good engineering.

ELEVEN

Design Projects

In line with the intent of this book, the usual form of problems has been changed to design projects. These projects are based on the contents of the book and are defined on a chapter-by-chapter basis. Many of them, however, require extra references for satisfactory solutions.

It is suggested that when this book is used as a classroom text that the larger projects be undertaken by groups and that the results of the design efforts of each group be compared and debated. A design problem often has many different but equally satisfactory solutions. After all, the purpose of this book is to enable the student to develop practical techniques of electronic circuit design and not to stuff numbers in mathematical expressions.

It is also important that the designs be built and test results compared with the design calculations and with other design approaches. This may mean that the designs might have to be altered to be compatible with available laboratory equipment and supplies. This is not at all unusual; successful electronic circuit design is a very practical profession.

It would be well to review Chapter 10, Laboratory Procedures at this time because construction techniques are vital to a successful project.

11.1 CHAPTER 1

This chapter is a preparation for Chapter 2, and consequently all of the relationships discussed in this chapter are used in the succeeding chapter. Accordingly, there are no design projects for this chapter.

11.2 CHAPTER 2

2.1. Design an amplifier with discrete transistors to operate from a record pickup head to a 10 W load. The load is to consist of two speakers, a high-frequency tweeter and a low-frequency woofer. Amplitude and phase response should be good from 20 Hz to 20 kHz, and distortion should be low over this spectrum.

This design project can have a wide range of variations involving increasing amounts of difficulty. The basic design of the amplifier is very straightforward, but if the acoustics are considered, it is a different matter. First, the impedance of the speakers is not constant with frequency; second, the electrical to acoustic transfer is very complex and depends upon the baffling, the room structure, and, most of all, upon the preferences and needs of the listener. This is the reason for the various forms of frequency emphasis in hifi systems.

2.2. Design a broadband amplifier DC to 100 MHz, a gain of 100 and an output of 20 V_{PP}. Use any form of frequency emphasis suitable to assist in obtaining this response. If the goals are too difficult, cut back a bit on the gain or frequency response. For more of a challenge try a push–pull output with 50 V_{PP}.

Although it is not fair for this project, Harris makes a unity gain buffer, the HA5002, that provides ±200 mA of output current and an $f_{-3\,dB}$ of 110 MHz.

If available, a spectrum analyzer should be used to examine distortion.

2.3. Design a low-noise amplifier with a gain of 10,000 and a bandwidth of 20 Hz to 1 MHz. The output should drive a 50 Ω load. Use an RMS meter to measure the noise and, if possible, a spectrum analyzer for a detailed examination of the noise structure. In particular, watch for pickup (60 Hz line) and oscillations. There should be a $1/f$ corner where the noise rises as the frequency is lowered. Look for a high-frequency noise corner as well, but it should not occur before 1 MHz.

11.3 CHAPTER 3

3.1. Design a lead–lag network using an op-amp with a straight 6 dB/octave roll-off. This would be a relatively slow amplifier and makes measurements easier. (See Section 3.1.5.)

Determine, by plotting the $1/\beta$ response on the open-loop gain curve in the data manual, where the frequency of instability will occur. Determine a suitable high-frequency lag corner that will give stability. Test this with a square wave and observe the ringing as the lag corner is moved in the vicinity of the intersection.

Apply a low-frequency corner. Check observed data against calculated performance.

3.2. The AD538 analog multifunction chip, by Analog Devices, performs the operation $Y(Z/X)^M$.

Using the data sheets and application notes, choose a useful circuit and test the performance against calculations. As a classroom project, all applications should be different and the results discussed and compared.

3.3. Set up a circuit to solve the equation $E_o = E_{in^2} - 6E_{in} - 5$. Apply both square waves and sinusoidal inputs, with variable amplitudes, and check the results for possible applications.

11.4 CHAPTER 4

4.1. Design and build a discrete pulse amplifier on the order of Fig. 4.29. Examine the output response with and without the diodes and the speed-up RC network. Distinguish between initial delay, rise time, storage time, and fall time.

Compare different transistors and check against data book specifications. Also note that most test circuits in the data books have a negative return (NPN) for the base resistor, which is very helpful when such a supply is available.

As a sound test procedure, use a BNC connector on the output with a BNC to scope probe adapter. This is to assure a good ground to the probe to avoid ringing due to the inductance in the probe ground lead. Try the same measurement with a typical ground lead on the scope probe.

4.2. Set up a circuit to "power-strobe" various integrated circuits in the manner shown in Fig. 9.39. Read the section regarding this illustration before proceeding. Power strobing is often a useful technique and some experience with this procedure is very valuable.

4.3. This is a very large effort and is intended as a class project where subsections of the system can be developed separately by individual groups.

With reference to Fig. 4.27, design a system as indicated by the block diagram of Fig. 11.1. This processor has a D/A converter controlled by an 8-bit hexadecimal thumbwheel switch. This D/A should have 2 bits greater resolution than the A/D that it is driving. By using the top 8 bits of the D/A, a stable analog source to the A/D should be assured.

The serial output of the A/D goes to the serial-to-parallel converter whose output goes to both the address and data inputs of the RAM. The control lines with the required time displacements and durations are developed by the timing control subsystem. The Read or Write function is controlled by a toggle switch.

Since the data is a constant, all of the addresses have the same data which is an 8-bit word. This word, selected (and equal to the setting) by the thumbwheel switch, is displayed on the scope. The data should be the same in Read or Write. A close examination, perhaps with the lights out, should show no ghost images on the scope for either Read or Write. This indicates that all of the addresses have the same data.

In a practical application the thumbwheel switches and the D/A would be replaced by the appropriate analog signal source. However, the purpose of this design study is to decipher and apply the manufacturer's timing instructions properly and to understand the operations of these components better.

11.5 CHAPTER 5

5.1. Design a transformer to reflect a 200 Ω load in the secondary to a 50 Ω load in the primary. This will allow it to be driven by a 50 Ω signal generator with a proper termination. Two transformers should be constructed, the first with a trifilar winding. This allows the secondary to use two of the windings in series for the necessary turns

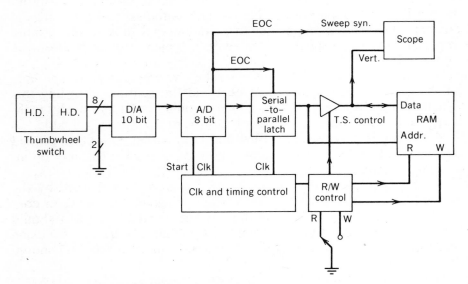

FIGURE 11.1   Experimental data system.

ratio. The second transformer should have the secondary wound on top of the primary. Compare the results.

The transformer should be designed for the desired low frequency and a specified amplitude. The core-material selection should be made on the basis of the tolerable high-frequency losses.

The transformer should be checked first for the low-frequency transmission. The primary current should be observed for saturation as the frequency is lowered.

This should be done with both a sine wave and a square wave input. Next, the high-frequency response should be checked with both a square wave and the sinusoidal input. Watch for ringing and frequency peaking with the respective inputs.

The power level and the bandwidth are the designer's choice.

5.2. Design a transmission line transformer as indicated by Fig. 5.9. Measure the bandwidth with a grounded input source, first with one secondary grounded and then with the other secondary grounded. Compare the data with the design calculations.

Connect the transformer in a step-up and step-down configuration and as an in-phase combiner as shown in Fig. 5.11.

Build a second, identical transformer and measure the transmission properties as illustrated in Fig. 5.11*d* and *e*.

11.6 CHAPTERS 6, 9, and 10

These chapters do not lend themselves directly to the type of projects presented in this text. However, as a practical matter, the contents of Chapter 6, Interfacing and Interference, and especially those of Chapter 10, Laboratory Procedures, apply to all of the projects.

In that regard, it would be well to compare the construction techniques used by different student groups and see if any correlation can be made to properly functioning circuits and to those that are not working as planned.

Chapter 9 lends itself to the projects of the other chapters in the role of an experience background. This should assist in using good judgment for some of the design decisions required in these projects.

11.7 CHAPTER 7 and APPENDIX III

Chapter 7 and the corresponding design tables in Appendix III are a plentiful source of design projects. For class assignments, different types of filters should be assigned to the various groups. The results should then be discussed and compared.

Specifically, pulse and sinusoidal response data should be taken on all filters. The pulse inputs will show the variations of phase response. For example, compare a low-pass linear phase design with an elliptic function design using the same corner frequency and an equal number of poles. Then try the same filters when the 30 dB attenuation frequencies are set equal.

Digital filters and normal active filters should also be added to the list, and of course, band-pass and high-pass transformation should also be a part of this project.

It is very convenient to use the same frequency for most of the tests; 1 MHz for the passive filters and say 10 kHz for the active filters are good choices. The reason for this is that at 1 MHz the passive components are easy to obtain and measurements more reliable. 1 MHz is on the high side for many active filters, and since no inductors are involved, 10 kHz is a more certain frequency for these applications.

With regard to the passive filters, it is important to use only inductors having a closed magnetic field. Torroids are best at higher frequencies, while laminated cores are more suitable for lower frequencies. Inductors in which part or all of the flux has an air path have an inductance that is very unstable with position and in addition will couple very easily with each other.

Commercial types of tuned circuits that employ nonmagnetic paths for the flux are entirely different. They are largely an empirical design, rigidly held in place, generally shielded, and the existing magnetic coupling is included in the design. These types of circuits are not covered in this text.

It is valuable to include a few designs in the 50–100 MHz range. This now becomes a filter design with additional important considerations in layout and measurement technique. The considerable amount of extra effort that these designs require is very rewarding in good practical experience.

11.8 CHAPTER 8

This chapter is similar to Chapter 7 in that there is abundant material for short, direct projects. As demonstrated in Chapter 7, the choice of design frequency can significantly affect design construction and the measurement of its properties. 1 MHz is again a good choice, since becoming familiar with the basic design and the frequency range of 50–100 MHz will add to experience in the construction and measurement techniques required in this frequency range.

A method of selecting projects is simply to go through the table of contents.

Parallel resonant circuits are not difficult, but extremely low or high frequencies can cause problems. A poor choice of L to C ratios results in either impossible designs or at least one in which the resonance is seriously affected by the stray parameters. Do not forget that the source impedance affects the Q by being effectively in parallel with the tank circuit.

Series and loaded resonant circuits offer additional worthwhile experience.

Various forms of coupling add additional requirements and should follow the basic resonance projects. Coupled resonators are a further complication that add to practical design experience.

Matching networks are not specifically resonant circuits, but they do employ inductive and capacitive reactances, and in this sense are similar. The assigned projects should proceed from the simple L to the π and T, and finally to the multiple L networks.

Basic Information

The information in this appendix is intended as background material for the design procedures given in the text. In-depth treatments or proofs are not intended.

I.1 TRANSISTOR FORMULAS

Table I.1 defines the amplifier performance of the common emitter, common base, and emitter follower amplifiers for low-frequency applications. The accurate equations assume that β is high (25 or over), while the approximate equations carry their own restrictions.

These expressions are for the intrinsic transistor only. However, the external resistors R_E and R_B can be added directly to the respective transistor values r_e and r_b in all cases. The external load resistor R_L is contained in the equations.

Figures I.1 through I.4 are essentially plots of the transistor relations shown in Table I.1 as a function of some outside parameters. They illustrate how the three basic connections are modified by these parameters.

The desired **T** parameters [2] can be obtained from the grounded emitter **h** parameters by the following relations:

$$r_e = \frac{\mathbf{h}_{12e}}{\mathbf{h}_{22e}}$$

$$\text{where } \Delta\mathbf{h}_e = \mathbf{h}_{11e}\mathbf{h}_{22e} - \mathbf{h}_{21e}\mathbf{h}_{12e}$$

$$r_b = \frac{\Delta\mathbf{h}_e - \mathbf{h}_{12e}}{\mathbf{h}_{22e}}$$

$$r_c = \frac{1 + \mathbf{h}_{21e}}{\mathbf{h}_{22e}}$$

$$\beta = \mathbf{h}_{21e}$$

TABLE I. 1

TABLE I. 1
Transistor Parameter Relations[a,b]

Accurate	Approximate

Common Emitter

$$r_i = r_b + r_e \left[\frac{r_c + R_L}{r_c/\beta + r_e + R_L} \right] \qquad r_b + \beta r_e \text{ if } \frac{r_c}{\beta} \gg R_L \text{ and } r_e$$

$$r_o = \frac{r_c}{\beta} + r_e \left[\frac{r_b + r_c}{r_b + r_e} \right] \qquad \frac{r_c}{\beta} + \frac{r_c}{1 + r_b/r_e} \text{ if } r_c \gg r_b$$

$$V_{\text{gain}} = \frac{(r_c - r_e)R_L}{r_b(r_c/\beta + r_e + R_L) + r_e(r_c + R_L)} \qquad \frac{R_L}{r_e + r_b/\beta} \text{ if } \frac{r_c}{\beta} \gg r_e \text{ and } R_L$$

$$I_{\text{gain}} = \frac{r_c - r_e}{r_c/\beta + r_e + R_L} \qquad \beta$$

$$\frac{r_c}{\beta} \gg r_e \text{ and } R_L$$

Emitter Follower

$$r_i = r_b + r_c \left[\frac{r_e + R_L}{r_c/\beta + r_e + R_L} \right] \qquad r_b + \left[\frac{r_c\beta R_L}{r_c + \beta R_L} \right]$$

$$\text{if } R_L \gg r_e$$

$$r_b + \beta R_L \text{ if } r_c \gg \beta R_L$$

$$r_o = r_e + \frac{r_c}{\beta} \left[\frac{r_b}{(r_b + r_c)} \right] \qquad r_e + \frac{r_b}{\beta} \text{ if } r_c \gg r_b$$

$$V_{\text{gain}} = \frac{r_c R_L}{r_b(r_c/\beta + r_e + R_L) + r_c(r_e + R_L)} \qquad \frac{R_L}{r_b/\beta + r_e + R_L}$$

$$I_{\text{gain}} = \frac{r_c}{r_c/\beta + r_e + R_L} \qquad \beta$$

$$\frac{r_c}{\beta} \gg r_e \text{ and } R_L$$

Common Base

$$r_i = r_e + r_b \left[\frac{r_c/\beta + R_L}{r_b + r_c + R_L} \right] \qquad r_e + \frac{r_b}{\beta} \text{ if } \frac{r_c}{\beta} \gg R_L$$

$$R_L \gg r_b$$

$$r_o = r_c - r_b \left[\frac{(r_c - r_e)}{(r_e + r_b)} \right] \qquad r_c \text{ if } r_b \text{ is small}$$

TABLE I. 1 (*Continued*)

Accurate	Approximate
$V_{gain} = \dfrac{(r_c + r_b)R_L}{r_b(r_c/\beta + r_e + R_L) + r_e(r_c + R_L)}$	$\dfrac{R_L}{r_e + r_b/\beta}$ if $\dfrac{r_c}{\beta} \gg r_e, r_b$ and R_L
$I_{gain} = \dfrac{r_c + r_b}{r_c + r_b + R_L}$	1 $r_c \gg R_L$

[a] From Ref. [1].
[b] *Symbols*:

r_e = transistor emitter resistance
r_b = transistor base resistance
r_c = transistor collector resistance
r_i = transistor input resistance
r_o = transistor output resistance
R_E = external emitter resistance
R_B = external base resistance
R_L = external load resistance

From Fig. IV.1, curve 1 at 5 mA, we have

$$\mathbf{h}_{11e} \text{ or } \mathbf{h}_{ie} = 1.15(10)^3$$

$$\mathbf{h}_{21e} \text{ or } \mathbf{h}_{re} = 1.6(10)^{-4}$$

$$\mathbf{h}_{21e} \text{ or } \mathbf{h}_{fe} = 210$$

$$\mathbf{h}_{22e} \text{ or } \mathbf{h}_{oe} = 32(10)^{-6}$$

$$\Delta\mathbf{h} = \mathbf{h}_{11}\mathbf{h}_{22} - \mathbf{h}_{21}\mathbf{h}_{12} = 1.15(10)^3(32)(10)^{-6} - 210(1.6)10^{-4}$$

$$= 36.8(10)^{-3} - 33.6(10)^{-3} = 3.2(10)^{-3}$$

$$r_e = \frac{\mathbf{h}_{12e}}{\mathbf{h}_{22e}} = \frac{1.6(10)^{-4}}{32(10)^{-6}} = 5\ \Omega$$

$$r_b = \frac{\Delta\mathbf{h}_e - \mathbf{h}_{12e}}{\mathbf{h}_{22e}} = \frac{3.2(10)^{-3} - 1.6(10)^{-4}}{32(10)^{-6}} = 95\ \Omega$$

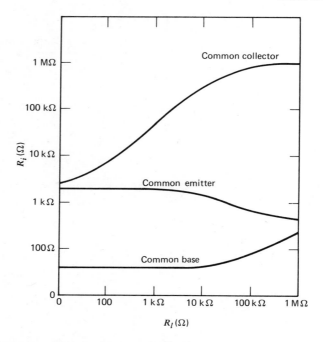

FIGURE I.1 Input resistance vs. load resistance. (Reprinted with permission from *Radio Engineers Handbook*, by F. E. Terman. Copyright © 1943 McGraw-Hill Book Company.)

$$r_c = \frac{1 + \mathbf{h}_{21e}}{\mathbf{h}_{22e}} = \frac{1 + 210}{32(10)^{-6}} = 6.6(10)^6 \ \Omega$$

The output resistance r_o is obtained from the equation in Table I.1:

$$r_o = \frac{r_c}{\beta} + \frac{r_c}{1 + r_b/r_e}$$

$$= \frac{6.6(10)^6}{210} + \frac{6.6(10)^6}{1 + 95/5}$$

$$= 31.4(10)^3 + 330(10)^3$$

$$= 361.4(10)^3 \ \Omega$$

REFERENCES

[1] R. F. Shea, *Principles of Transistor Circuits*, Wiley, New York, 1955.
[2] R. F. Shea, *Transistor Circuit Engineering*, Wiley, New York, 1957.

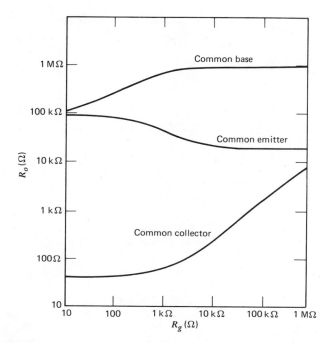

FIGURE I.2 Output resistance vs. generator resistance. (Reprinted with permission from *Radio Engineers Handbook* by F. E. Terman. Copyright © 1943 McGraw-Hill Book Company.)

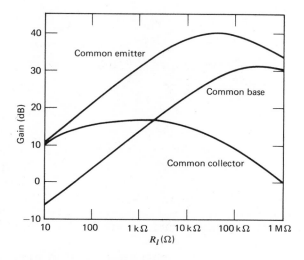

FIGURE I.3 Power gain vs. load resistance. (Reprinted with permission from *Radio Engineers Handbook* by F. E. Terman. Copyright © 1943 McGraw-Hill Book Company.)

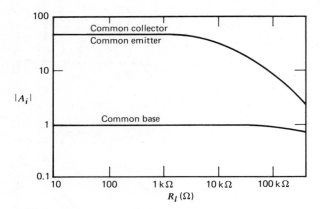

FIGURE I.4 Current amplification vs. load resistance. (Reprinted with permission from *Radio Engineers Handbook* by F. E. Terman. Copyright © 1943 McGraw-Hill Book Company.)

I.2 DECIBELS

A decibel is defined for power ratios. 10 log P_1/P_2 = the number of the decibel gain (or dB as it is called). Since $P = E^2/R$, we can also write

$$\text{dB} = 10 \log \frac{E_1^2}{R_1} \Big/ \frac{E_2^2}{R_2}$$

If $R_1 = R_2$,

$$\text{dB} = 10 \log \left(\frac{E_1}{E_2}\right)^2$$

which is the same as

$$\text{dB} = 20 \log \left(\frac{E_1}{E_2}\right)$$

Now, expressing gain ratios in the decibel system is very convenient for electronic calculations. This is because adding the logarithms of two numbers is the same as multiplying the two numbers. Likewise, subtracting the logarithms is equivalent to division. A convenient graph of voltage ratios and decibel are plotted in Fig. I.5.

20 dB = a power ratio of 100 and a voltage ratio of 10. However, as long as we are not trying to convert voltage gain to the equivalent

power gain, there is no need to have $R_1 = R_2$. For example, the decibel gain of a FET amplifier may be 20, which is a voltage gain of 10, but because of the very high input resistance, the power gain is far better than 100.

Figure I.6 shows a multistage amplifier. The gain of this amplifier is $10 + 6 - 5 = 11$ dB. The buffers are inserted only to clarify the fact that the stages are not loading each other and thereby changing the gain in that manner. Expressing voltage gain in decibel without regard to the resistance levels is common practice and is so used in this text. Again the voltage gain of a system in decibel cannot be

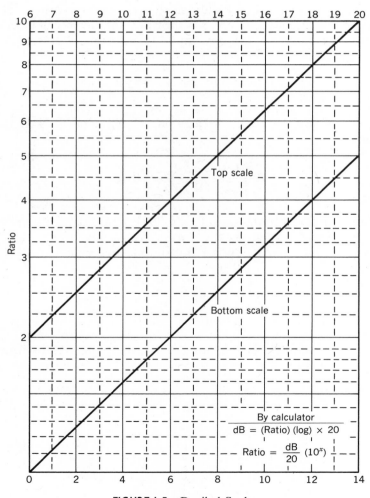

FIGURE I.5   Decibel Scale.

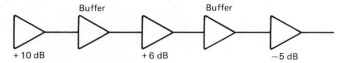

FIGURE I.6   Combining decibels.

converted to power without first going back and taking into account the resistance levels.

Gains less than unity are expressed as $-$dB. For example, if a two-stage amplifier has a gain of $(0.1)(10) = 1$, this is expressed as -10 dB $+ 10$ dB $= 0$ dB.

The dB system is very handy in describing networks that are a function of frequency. Figure I.7 shows a simple RC network. The response of this network is developed in Section I.8 and shows that

$$\frac{E_o}{E_{in}} = \frac{1}{\sqrt{1 + (\omega RC)^2}}$$

At the frequency where $X_C = R$, $1/\omega C = R$, or $\omega RC = 1$, the gain becomes

$$\frac{1}{\sqrt{1 + 1}} = \frac{1}{\sqrt{2}} = 0.707$$

The gain expressed in dB is $20 \log (0.707) = -3$ dB. This frequency is commonly referred to as the corner frequency or $f_{-3\,dB}$. As the frequency is increased beyond this point, the gain expression approaches the value

$$\frac{E_o}{E_{in}} = \frac{1}{\omega RC} = \frac{1}{(2\pi RC)f}$$

The gain is inversely proportional to the frequency. If the frequency doubles, the gain is cut in half ($0.5 = -6$ dB). We therefore can say

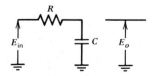

FIGURE I.7   The RC lag network.

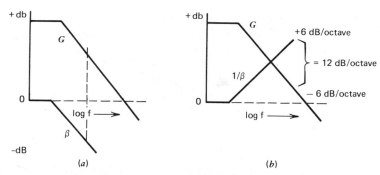

FIGURE I.8   Plotting with the decibel.

that after $f_{-3\,\text{dB}}$ the gain approaches a roll-off of 6 dB/octave. An equivalent statement that is commonly used is 20 dB/decade.

If the resistance is replaced by an inductance, there is an asymptotic condition after resonance. In this case X_L increases at the same rate as X_C decreases and the roll-off is twice as great or 12 dB/octave.

When the reciprocal of a function is plotted, the result is a mirror image of the original function. For example, $1/g$ of the RC gain function has a rise in gain of $\sqrt{2}$ at $f_{-3\,\text{dB}}$ and then continues to increase at 6 dB/octave.

An application of this is helpful in analyzing feedback amplifiers. If it is desired to multiply two functions, β and G, their graphs in decibels can be added. The same result is obtained if one of the functions is plotted as a reciprocal and then subtracted from the other function. The latter results in a considerable convenience, as illustrated by Fig. I.8.

The figure shows dB plots of the two functions. It is desired to know the slope where the product is unity (dB = 0). As can be seen in Fig. I.8a this is a trial-and-error procedure. Once this point has been determined, the two slopes must be measured and then added. Finally, the graph area had to be extended to include the negative dB range. In Fig. I.8b the unity gain frequency is the intersection of the two plots. The slope of the product of the functions is measured directly as shown and no added graph area is required.

I.3   WAVEFORM ANALYSIS

The material in this section is based on information selected from *Reference Data for Radio Engineers* [1].

The most commonly used nonsinusoidal waveform is the rectangular wave shown in Fig. I.9. The amplitudes of the harmonics in this waveform are given by

$$C_n = 2A_{av} \left| \frac{\sin(n\pi t_0/T)}{n\pi t_0/T} \right|$$

$$A_{av} = \frac{At_0}{T}$$

(I.2)

where A = peak-to-peak amplitude, n = the harmonic to be evaluated, and C_n = the coefficient or peak value of that harmonic. The most common form of this waveshape is that of the square wave where $t_0/T = \frac{1}{2}$. Under these conditions we have

$$C_n = \frac{2A}{n\pi} \left| \sin\left(n\frac{\pi}{2}\right) \right|$$

(I.2)

Here we see that the sine term has an absolute value of 1 for odd values of n and 0 for the even numbers. To clarify, a square wave has no even harmonics; in fact, any repetitive symmetrical waveform consists only of odd harmonics. Furthermore, since $2A/\pi$ is a constant, the harmonic amplitudes are inversely proportional to the frequency.

This waveform is drawn above ground, hence has a DC component that is equal to A_{av} or for the square wave $A/2$. If the DC is blocked by a capacitor, this term disappears, but the remainder of the equation remains the same. The power developed by the waveform is, however, reduced as shown below:

With DC component: $P = \frac{A^2}{R}\left(\frac{1}{2}\right) = \frac{A^2}{2R}$

Without DC component: $P = \frac{(A/2)^2}{R} = \frac{A^2}{4R}$

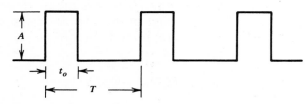

FIGURE I.9 Rectangular wave. $A_{av} = A(t_0/T)$; $A(t_0/T)^2$. (From *Reference Data for Radio Engineers*, 6th Edition, Copyright © 1977; Indianapolis, IN 46268.)

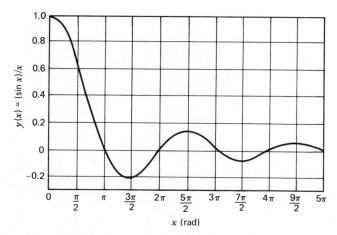

FIGURE I.10 Sin x/x. (From *Reference Data for Radio Engineers*, 6th Edition, Copyright © 1977; Indianapolis, IN 46268.)

Referring back to the general case in Eq. I.1, it is noticed that the expression between the vertical bars (which means absolute value, e.g., not a function of time) is of the form sin x/x. Figure I.10 shows a plot of this function which is convenient for evaluation of the harmonic values. The curve is used by sampling at $n\pi(t_0/T)$ and multiplying by $2A(t_0/T)$. For example, if $t_0/T = \frac{1}{4}$,

$$C_1 = \left(\frac{2A}{4}\right)(0.9) = 0.45A$$

= peak value of first harmonic

$$C_2 = \left(\frac{2A}{4}\right)(0.6) = 0.3A$$

= peak value of second harmonic

$$C_3 = \left(\frac{2A}{4}\right)(0.3) = 0.15A$$

= peak value of third harmonic

To avoid confusion, it should be stated that the first harmonic is often called the fundamental frequency.

A second group of related waveforms which are of importance is the sawtooth family. The basic sawtooth is shown in Fig. I.11, where the two sweep directions are unbalanced. Figure I.12 shows the special case where the flyback time is negligible, and finally Fig. I.13 describes the balanced relation or triangular waveform.

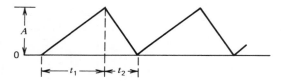

FIGURE I.11   General sawtooth wave. $C_n = A(T^2/\pi^2 n^2 t_1 t_3)$ [sin $n\pi(t_1/T)$]; $t_1 + t_2 = T$; $A_{av} = A/2$; $A_{rms} = A/\sqrt{3}$. (From *Reference Data for Radio Engineers*, 6th Edition, Copyright © 1977, Indianapolis, IN 46268.)

Two remaining common waveforms are shown. Figure I.14 is the half-wave rectified sine wave and Fig. I.15 is the full-wave rectified sine wave.

For the half-wave rectified sine wave, the harmonic amplitudes are expressed by three equations. $C(2n + 1) = 0$ states that there are no odd harmonics but has the qualifying statement that there is a first harmonic whose value is $A/2$. The remaining even harmonics have amplitudes designated by $2A/\pi(4n^2 - 1)$. The expression C_{2n} means that $n = 1$ gives the coefficient C_2, and accordingly only *even* harmonics are allowed.

The full-wave rectified sine wave can cause some confusion if not clearly defined. At first it is better to consider only the waveform as shown with no reference to its origin. This waveform has a period of T. Then for C_1 we have

$$\frac{4A}{\pi(4 - 1)} = \frac{4A}{3\pi}$$

This is the *fundamental* for the waveform shown, but if we relate it to the original waveform, it is the *second harmonic* of *that* waveform. The original waveform has a period of $2T$ and is *entirely* eliminated by the full-wave rectification process. This double-reference possibility does not exist for the half-wave rectifier.

In the practical world, however, the original waveform does come through because of various imbalances. This is particularly bothersome for the filter systems of polyphase rectifiers.

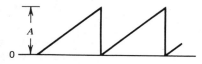

FIGURE I.12   Flyback sawtooth wave. $C_n = A/\pi n$; $A_{av} = A/2$; $A_{rms} = A/\sqrt{3}$. (From *Reference Data for Radio Engineers*, 6th Edition, Copyright © 1977, Indianapolis, IN 46268.)

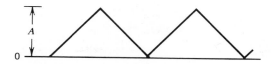

FIGURE I.13 Triangular wave. $C_n = 4A(\pi^2 n^2/\sin n\pi/2)$; $A_{av} = A/2$; $A_{rms} = A/\sqrt{3}$. (From *Reference Data for Radio Engineers*, 6th Edition, Copyright © 1977, Indianapolis, IN 46268.)

FIGURE I.14 Half-wave rectified sine wave. $C_{2n+1} = 0$ except for $C_1 = A/2$; $C_{2n} = 2A/\pi(4_n^2 - 1)$; $A_{av} = A/\pi$; $A_{rms} = A/2$. (From *Reference Data for Radio Engineers*, 6th Edition, Indianapolis, IN 46268.)

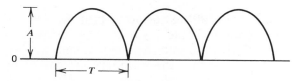

FIGURE I.15 Full-wave rectified sine wave. $C_n = 4A/\pi(4_n^2 - 1)$; $A_{av} = 2A/\pi$; $A_{rms} = A/\sqrt{2}$. (From *Reference Data for Radio Engineers*, 6th Edition, Indianapolis, IN 46268.)

TABLE I.2
C_n Relative to A^a

Waveform Harmonic	Square	Flyback	Triangle	Half-Wave
1	0.64	0.318	0.405	0.5
2	—	0.159	—	0.212
3	0.21	0.106	0.045	—
4	—	0.079	—	0.042
5	0.127	0.064	0.0162	—
6	—	0.053	—	0.018
7	0.09	0.045	0.008	—
8	—	0.04	—	0.01
9	0.07	0.035	0.005	—
10	—	0.032	—	0.006
11	0.058	0.029	0.003	—
12	—	0.026	—	0.0045

^{a} A = peak-to-peak of original wave; C_n = peak of harmonic sine wave.

TABLE I.3
C_n Relative to A

Fundamental Harmonic	Full-Wave Rectified Sine Wave Harmonics Relative to Original Sine Wave
2nd	0.424
4th	0.085
6th	0.036
8th	0.02
10th	0.013
12th	0.009

Table I.2 shows values of the harmonics for the definite waveforms described in this section. Table I.3 takes the harmonics of the full-wave rectifier and relates them to the original sine wave that was full-wave rectified. It is seen that the numbers are the same if they are related to two times the harmonic frequency of Table I.2. The values in Table I.3 should be used to design a filter when it is necessary to remove the harmonics of a full-wave rectifier.

REFERENCES

[1] *Reference Data for Radio Engineers*, 6th ed., ITT, Indianapolis, IN 46268, 1977.

GENERAL REFERENCES

F. E. Terman, *Radio Engineers Handbook*, McGraw-Hill, New York, 1943.

I.4 MILLER EFFECT

The Miller effect is a relation between a feedback impedance and the gain of an amplifier. Figure I.16 shows how this develops.

If e_s is placed across an impedance Z_F, a current $i = e_s/Z_F$ flows through Z_F. If the connection in Fig. I.21 is used, the voltage across Z_F is $(1 + G)e_s$ and a current of $(1 + G)(e_s/Z_F)$ flows through Z_F. To the signal e_s it appears as through Z_F has been changed to $Z_F/(1 + G)$.

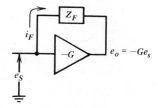

FIGURE I.16 Miller effect.

In a transistor the collector-to-base capacitance C_{cb} is accordingly multiplied by $(1 + G)$ and can cause a serious loss of high-frequency response in the previous stage. For this reason a gain stage is generally driven by an emitter follower. The low output resistance of the emitter follower then generally moves the roll-off past the signal band.

I.5 THÉVENIN'S THEOREM

Thévenin's theorem states that "any two terminal linear networks may be replaced by a voltage source equal to the open circuit output voltage in series with the output impedance." Figure I.17 shows a simple resistor network. Accordingly, the Thévenin equivalent circuit is as shown in Fig. I.18a. Figure I.18b can be transformed into the circuit of Fig. I.19. This is known as Norton's theorem.

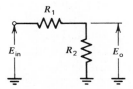

FIGURE I.17 Simple resistor network. $E_o = R_2 E_1/(R_1 + R_2)$, $R_o = R_1 R_2/(R_1 + R_2)$.

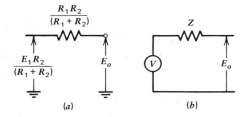

FIGURE I.18 Thévenin's equivalent circuit.

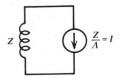

FIGURE I.19   Norton's equivalent circuit.

I.6 TRANSMISSION LINES

A transmission line can be defined as a pair of wires connecting a source and a load that have a defined geometry with respect to each other and are positioned or arranged so that their fields are not modified by other factors. Practical transmission lines can be coaxial, twisted pair, or twin lead and are limited to relatively small geometries, say 1 in. maximum in diameter. Coaxial lines are the most self-contained, while twin leads have the largest external fields.

These lines have what are called distributed parameters, that is, their basic resistance, inductance, and capacitance are evenly distributed per unit length. A transmission line can also be made of lumped parameters, that is, the inductance and capacitance are discrete parts connected together. The resistance, which is normally undesirable, comes as a by-product of the inductance. These lumped parameter lines only approximate the characteristics of the distributed line and do so over a limited frequency range. Their usefulness lies in their small size at the lower frequencies.

The transmission lines discussed in this section are considered lossless, which is a very good assumption for the short runs used in most circuit applications. Long runs such as outdoor transmissions require some modification, the principal consideration being repeater stages to regain the loss of amplitude. Within these bounds the discussion that follows applies to all types of lines.

I.6.1 Matched Terminations

A transmission line has a characteristic impedance which is controlled by its geometry and the dielectric constant of the surrounding material. This is given as

$$Z = \sqrt{\frac{L}{C}} \tag{I.3}$$

where L is the inductance per unit length of line in henries and C is the capacitance per unit length in farads. Although the term impedance is commonly used, it is really a nondissipating resistance (for the defined lossless line) because of the manner in which L and C interact.

When a pulse is applied to a transmission line, say 50 Ω, the pulse proceeds down the line as though it were looking at 50 Ω. The pulse does not recognize the length of the line, nor what is there, until that point is reached. The speed of the wave varies with the type of line, but 1.5 ns/ft is typical (light $\cong$ 1 ns/ft).

If the line is terminated by its characteristic impedance, the applied input voltage appears across the load and dissipates as E^2/R. When the line is not matched, some of the energy is absorbed and the remainder is reflected back to the source, depending on the degree of mismatch. The subject of mismatch is covered in the next section, so at this point we proceed with the matched condition. Figure I.20 shows a typical transmission line.

It is often desirable but not essential that $R_S = Z_0$. In fact, R_S can be any value at all and e_o will simply be $e_s R_L/(R_S + R_L)$. However, perfect matching by R_L is not always possible. There is usually some capacitance and inductance associated with the load, which means that part of the signal energy is reflected back to the source. If the source now represents a perfect Z_0, all of this energy is absorbed and no more reflections occur. In general, a complete absorption of the signal energy at the load is not possible. For a pulse or square wave this results in ringing and multiple pulse shapes, while a sine wave develops a standing wave. The standing wave is discussed in the next section.

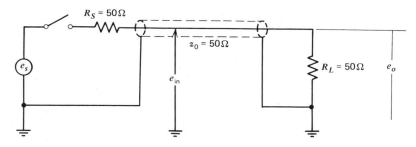

FIGURE I.20   Matched transmission line.

A second mode of transmission is possible where $R_S = Z_0$ and R_L is a high impedance. Figure I.21 shows the waveforms that are associated with this form of transmission and the application of a step function.

Figure I.20 shows a switch in series with e_s. When the switch is closed, e_{in} goes from 0 to $e_s/2$ as shown in Fig. I.21. This is because the signal entering the transmission line sees 50 Ω and is accordingly $e_s(50)/(50 + 50)$. At the end of the line, t_D, the signal now sees an open circuit and regains its initial value of e_s by means of the reflected wave. At the time $2t_D$, the reflected wave has reached the source and the signal on the line has stabilized to e_s. Although this discussion is based on a step function, other waveforms act in a similar manner.

The source termination method has several important advantages:

1. A low power driver can be used because the output voltage develops across a high impedance. In this case, however, the driving *impedance must still be low* so that an accurate termination can be set by the source resistor.
2. The voltage gain is twice that of the two-termination system.
3. The high impedance load has a smaller signal current, hence feedback troubles are less likely because of the ground return path.

1.6.2 Unmatched Terminations

The unmatched terminations are first considered for a quarter wavelength line with an open circuit and a short circuit. A sine wave signal is used because mismatched terminations result in tuned circuits and a square wave produces a very complex result. Mismatched termi-

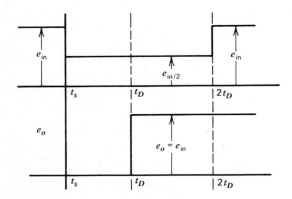

FIGURE I.21 Source termination waveforms.

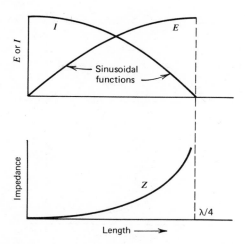

FIGURE I.22 $\frac{1}{4}\lambda$ Line with open-circuited output.

nations for sine wave applications can result in very useable connections as coupling networks. Their use with square waves would probably be limited to a specific filtering application. Figure I.22 shows the waveforms of a $\frac{1}{4}\lambda$ transmission line with the output open.

An open circuit states that E is a maximum, I is 0, and Z is ∞. This condition is established at $\lambda/4$; accordingly, the start of the signal is the value of the sine wave at $0°$, which is I = maximum and $E = 0$. This represents a short-circuit condition at the input of the line.

Figure I.22 shows the $\lambda/4$ transmission line with the output shorted. This, as might be suspected, is the same as Fig. I.22 with the E and I curves interchanged. We now have a parallel resonant circuit. At this frequency the line acts like a lumped L and C in resonance, but as the frequency changes the resemblance disappears. The transmission line alternates between series and parallel resonance every quarter-cycle and will repeat itself every half-cycle. It can be observed that when a $\lambda/2$ line is used, Figs. 1.22 and I.23 have a mirror image response to the left and are noninverting; that is, the condition at the load is the condition at the source.

Another application of the $\lambda/4$ line is that of an impedance matcher or transformer. This is defined by

$$Z_0 = \sqrt{Z_{in}Z_0} \qquad (I.4)$$

For example, if it were desired to match a 600 Ω line to a 50 Ω line, we would have $Z_0 = \sqrt{(50)(600)} = 173$ Ω. At times it may not be possible to find an available transmission line of the correct impedance. But if the application is important, a line of the correct imped-

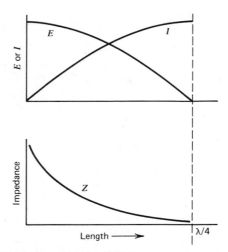

FIGURE I.23 $\frac{1}{4}\lambda$ Line with short-circuited output.

ance can usually be constructed by referring to one of the many radio handbooks. If the physical length of the cable is a problem, a lumped parameter line can sometimes be used.

Both the voltage and current magnitude represent standing waves and are generated in the same manner. Since the voltage wave is easier to understand, however, we limit our discussion to the voltage.

It should be pointed out that the voltage plotted in Fig. I.30 represents the peak voltage of the sine wave that is going from $(+)$ peak through zero to $(-)$ peak and so forth as a repetitive sine wave. The nodes or zero points are the only places on the line that are steady and even these are seldom pure nodes, having some residual value.

The standing wave is a vector addition of the transmitted wave and the reflected wave. If the source impedance is exactly Z_0, there are only two waves to add. If it is not, there are repeated reflections, all of which must be added to produce the final result. And, again, if the terminating load is exactly Z_0, there are no standing waves at all, regardless of the source impedance.

Mismatched transmission lines are generally used for a single frequency and are conveniently measured in wavelengths at that frequency. An electromagnetic wave (which includes visible light) travels at $300(10)^6$ m/s or $983.7(10)^6$ ft/s in free space. Through a cable, however, the speed is reduced, and this reduction is called the velocity factor V. As an example, $V = 0.66$ for the popular 50 Ω cable, RG-58. Accordingly, for an RG-58 coaxial line at 10 MHz.

$$\lambda = \frac{984(10)^6}{f} V = \frac{984(10)^6}{10(10)^6} (0.66) = 65 \text{ ft}$$

and

$$\frac{\lambda}{4} = 16.2 \text{ ft}$$

By operating transmission lines off resonance, they can be made to look inductive or capacitive and can have a step-up or step-down ratio as desired. This does, however, require more detail than is suitable for a book of this type and two excellent references are recommended.

GENERAL REFERENCES

Milton S. Kiver, *UHF Radio Simplified*, D. Van Nostrand, New York, 1945.
The ARRL Antenna Book, American Radio Relay League, Newington, CT, 1986.

I.7 TRANSFORMER ANALYSIS

Figure I.24 shows a fairly complete model of a transformer. Despite the complexity, this is still a lumped parameter equivalent of a component that is essentially of a distributed nature and limited in the amount of detailed performance that can be predicted with its use. The capacitors that are connected to undefined taps of R_P and R_S are an attempt to recognize this factor. It is very important in trying to analyze the performance of a transformer to approximate the model with regard to the parameter being investigated or the analysis rapidly gets out of hand.

Figure I.24 shows the term M which is the mutual inductance. If the coupling between the primary and secondary is perfect, k becomes

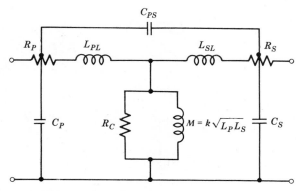

FIGURE I.24   Transformer equivalent circuit.

unity, which will make the leakage reactances L_{PL} and L_{SL} disappear, and the ability to predict and understand the transformer performance is greatly improved.

In Chapter 5 it is stated that an impedance Z connected across the secondary of an ideal transformer would be equivalent to $Z(N_P/N_S)^2$ connected across the primary. This was put forth on a more or less intuitive basis.

To establish this property in an analytical manner we assume that k = unity and eliminate all the transformer resistance and capacitance. This leads to Fig. I.25 and the set of equations below:

$$E_{in} - I_1X_P + I_2X_m = 0 \qquad (I.5)$$

$$I_1X_m - I_2X_S - I_2R = 0 \qquad (I.6)$$

Solving Eq. I.6 for I_2, we have

$$I_2 = \frac{I_1X_m}{R + X_S}$$

Substituting in Eq. I.5,

$$\frac{E_{in}}{I_{in}} = X_P - \frac{(X_m)^2}{R + X_S}$$

but since $X_m = \sqrt{X_PX_S}$,

$$\frac{E_{in}}{I_{in}} = X_P - \frac{(X_PX_S)}{R + X_S} \qquad (I.7)$$

With unity coupling, the inductance is proportional to the square of the turns. If $N = N_P/N_S$, we have $X_P = N^2X_S$, and

$$\frac{E_{in}}{I_{in}} = X_P - \frac{X_P^2/N^2}{R + X_P/N^2} = X_P - \frac{X_P^2}{N^2R + X_P}$$

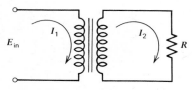

FIGURE I.25   Ideal transformer equivalent circuit. $X_m = \sqrt{X_PX_S}$.

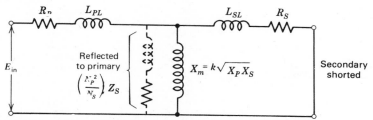

FIGURE I.26 Model for determining leakage reactance.

$$= \frac{X_P N^2 R + X_P^2 - X_P^2}{N^2 R + X_P} = \frac{X_P(N^2 R)}{N^2 R + X_P} \qquad (I.8)$$

This is recognized as X_P in parallel with $N^2 R$.

Figure I.26 shows the transformer model used to determine leakage reactance. In using this model it should be pointed out that the coupling is defined so that X_m is represented by turns of the primary and secondary that are 100% coupled and the leakage reactance is defined as turns with zero coupling.

With the secondary shorted, L_{SL} and R_S become the secondary impedance Z_S and are reflected to the primary as shown. E_{in} must be carefully adjusted to the value that produces the normal full-load current or damage may result. E_{in}/I_{in} then produces Z_{in}, and the combined leakage reactances are calculated by $Z = \sqrt{R^2 + X^2}$ or by measuring the phase angle between E_{in} and I_{in} and proceeding in that manner.

I.8 COMPLEX ALGEBRA

This section is not an overall treatment of complex algebra, but is intended to show how complex algebra is applied in this book.

Impedances are represented by vectors as shown in Fig. I.27. j is called an operator, and when it multiplies a vector, it advances the phase $+90°$. Two multiplications would advance the phase $180°$, and so on. However, since $180°$ is the negative of $0°$, $j^2 = -1$ or $j = \sqrt{-1}$. The symbol i is generally used in mathematical texts in place of j where it is called the imaginary term. $I = E/Z$, and if $Z =$ an inductance, we have $I = E/jX_L$. For clarity, the j is never left in the denominator; hence we have $I = jE/j^2 X_L = -jE/X_L$.

This states that the current in an inductor lags the voltage by $90°$, which is correct, and verifies that the multiplication of the inductive reactance by the operator j is correct. Likewise, $I = E/-jX = jE/$

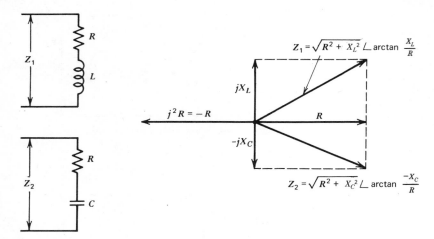

FIGURE I.27   Vector relations.

X, stating that the current leads the voltage by 90° for a capacitive load.

Let us consider some basic circuits. First, from Fig. I.28a, $E_o/E_{in} = -jX_C/(R - jX_C)$. To remove the j term from the denominator, it is multiplied by the complex conjugate:

$$\frac{E_o}{E_{in}} = \frac{-jX_C(R + jX_C)}{(R - jX_C)(R + jX_C)}$$

$$= \frac{X_C(X_C - jR)}{(R^2 + X_C^2)}$$

(I.9)

The denominator is equal to

$$R^2 + \cancel{jX_C R} - \cancel{jX_C R} - jX_C(jX_C)$$

Since $j^2 = -1$, we have the term $(R^2 + X_C^2)$.

Referring to Fig. I.27, it is seen that since the j term is 90° out of phase with the non-j term their sum is the hypotenuse of a right triangle. It thus has the value $\sqrt{R^2 + X_C^2}$, and this vector is at an angle with respect to the non-j term. This angle has a tangent of the j term/non-j term. Equation I.9 can now be written as

$$\frac{E_o}{E_{in}} = \frac{X_C(R^2 + X_C^2)^{1/2}}{(R^2 + X_C^2)} \angle \varphi = \frac{X_C}{(R^2 + X_C^2)^{1/2}} \angle \arctan \frac{-R}{X_C} \quad (I.10)$$

At low frequencies, where $R \ll X_C$, this equation becomes

$$\frac{E_o}{E_{in}} = \frac{X_C}{X_C} \angle 0°$$ (I.11)

or unity gain with no phase shift. At high frequencies, where $R \gg X_C$, we have

$$\frac{E_o}{E_{in}} = \frac{X_C}{R} \angle -90°$$ (I.12)

Since $X_C = \frac{1}{2}\pi f C$, Eq. I.10 is the same as $E_o/E_{in} = \frac{1}{2}\pi f C R \angle -90°$ and the gain is seen to be inversely proportional to the frequency. In decibel terms, the gain is falling at 6 dB/octave.

If we take the special case where $R = X_C$, Eq. I.10 becomes

$$\frac{E_o}{E_{in}} = \frac{X_C}{(2X_C^2)^{1/2}} \angle \arctan \frac{X_C}{X_C} = \frac{1}{\sqrt{2}} \angle -45$$ (I.13)

$1/\sqrt{2}$ in decibel form is -3 dB.

The case of Fig. I.28b is very similar.

$$\frac{E_o}{E_{in}} = \frac{R}{(R - jX_C)} = \frac{R}{(R^2 + X_C^2)^{1/2}} \angle \arctan \frac{X_C}{R}$$ (I.14)

This is the same as Fig. I.28a except that frequency has the opposite effect, that is, unity gain at frequencies much higher than the breakpoint and a 6 dB/octave loss as the frequency is lowered below the breakpoint.

Figure I.28c is slightly more complicated. This is the commonly used lag circuit for the op-amp. The gain is given by $E_o/E_{in} = -Z_F/Z_{in}$. The first step here is to evaluate the parallel circuit, Z_F.

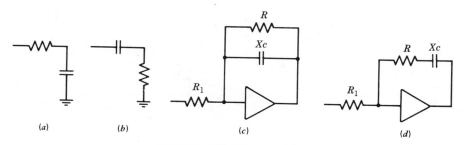

(a) (b) (c) (d)

FIGURE I.28 Basic circuits.

$$Z_F = \frac{-jX_CR}{(R - jX_C)} = \frac{-jX_CR(R + jX_C)}{(R^2 + X_C^2)} = \frac{X_CR(X_C - jR)}{(R^2 + X_C^2)} \quad \text{(I.15)}$$

$$\text{Gain} = \frac{-Z_F}{Z_{in}} = \frac{-X_CR(X_C - jR)}{R_1(R^2 + X_C^2)}$$

and in polar form we have

$$\text{Gain} = \frac{-X_CR(R^2 + X_C^2)^{1/2}}{R_1(R^2 + X_C^2)} \angle \varphi$$

$$= \frac{-X_CR}{R_1(R^2 + X_C^2)^{1/2}} \angle \arctan \frac{-R}{X_C} \quad \text{(I.16)}$$

This is seen to be identical to the *RC* network of Fig. I.28a except for the gain factor R/R_1 and a phase inversion.

Figure I.28d can be analyzed in the same manner as Fig. I.28c, and it will be seen that the response is entirely different.

The complex algebraic techniques have been demonstrated to show how to arrive at an analytical expression for a given circuit. However, even with slightly complex circuits, this analysis can be very laborious. Under these conditions an intuitive approach using the breakpoint techniques demonstrated in Chapter 3 are of great value. The derivation of the analytical expression for Fig. I.28d is quite simple, but the intuitive approach is used to demonstrate the process.

The response of this circuit to a steady-state sine wave is shown in Fig. I.29a, which is sometimes referred to as the frequency domain. In Fig. I.29b the response to a step function is shown, and this is referred to as the time domain. For high frequencies, the capacitor of Fig. I.28d can be considered a short circuit. At very low frequencies, *R* can be ignored and the response to Fig. I.29a is easily understood.

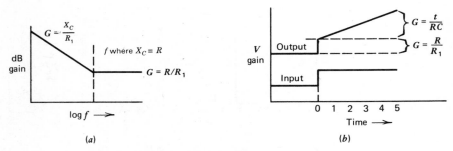

FIGURE I.29   Response of Fig. I.28d.

The beginning of a step function is a high-frequency region where the capacitor offers no appreciable impedance and the immediate gain is R/R_1. After this, the constant current flowing through R charges the capacitor in a linear manner, producing the ramp as shown.

For the frequency domain a log plot is used, that is, a log scale for frequency against decibels, which is a logarithm of the gain. In the time domain both scales are linear. This is not a mathematical necessity, but is very convenient.

APPENDIX
II

Digital Relations

II.1 NUMBER SYSTEMS

Our normal number system is based on 10 specific digits, 0 to 9, and any number outside this range is some sequential arrangement of these 10 digits. The binary system is based on 2 digits, 0 and 1, and also forms numbers outside this range by sequential arrangements. For example, the decimal number 3192 means $2 \times 1 + 9 \times 10 + 1 \times 100 + 3 \times 1000$. The binary number 10110 means $0 \times 1 + 1 \times 2 + 1 \times 4 + 0 \times 8 + 1 \times 16$ and equals the decimal number 22. This shows the conversion of a binary number to a decimal number.

The conversion of decimal number to its binary equivalent is not as obvious but still very straightforward. This is performed by successive division as follows. Take the decimal number 229, divide by a succession of 2's, and tabulate the remainders:

$$\frac{229}{2} = 114 + 1 \qquad \frac{14}{2} = 7 + 0$$

$$\frac{114}{2} = 57 + 0 \qquad \frac{7}{2} = 3 + 1$$

$$\frac{57}{2} = 28 + 1 \qquad \frac{3}{2} = 1 + 1$$

$$\frac{28}{2} = 14 + 0 \qquad \frac{1}{2} = 0 + 1$$

The binary equivalent of the decimal 229 is now 11100101. Converting back, we have $(1 + 4 + 32 + 64 + 128) = 229$.

Binary numbers are put into various codes to suit one purpose or another. Most of these codes are used in detailed digital processing techniques that are not within the scope of this text. The two codes that are described are the binary coded decimal, BCD, and the hexadecimal code.

Four binary digits can represent 16 numbers, 0 to 15. This is generally referred to as binary. In BCD 4 bits are used to equate to the decimal system, that is, 0 to 9. The numbers 10 to 15 are not allowed in one manner or another. A group of 4 binary bits is used to represent each decimal number. For example, 287 = 0010 1000 0111. The binary number is separated here for clarity. It is generally grouped together, 001010000111, and it is up to the individual to make the separation. It is necessary that the BCD be identified in some manner because it is not the same as straight binary. The number above in straight binary is 647. BCD is less efficient than straight binary and therefore is not preferred for large calculations. Its usefulness lies in interfacing with the decimal system.

The hexadecimal code is simply a way of compactly representing a large binary number. The code is shown in Table II.1.

For example, a 16-bit binary word

$$\underset{\displaystyle D7F3}{\underbrace{1101 \quad 0111 \quad 1111 \quad 0011}} \quad \text{is represented as}$$

Prior to the advent of the hexadecimal code the octal code was widely used to condense a binary number. The representation is as follows:

$$\underset{\displaystyle 4573_8}{\underbrace{100 \quad 101 \quad 111 \quad 011}}$$

The octal system is still used, but it has several disadvantages in comparison with the hexadecimal system:

1. Although it has no 8's or 9's, it is easily confused with the decimal system. The occasional presence of a letter in the hexadecimal will usually wake up a sleepy operator.

2. It is less efficient than the hexadecimal system.

3. Most digital blocks are multiples of 4 rather than three (e.g., 4-bit shift registers and counters) and accordingly there is not a fit with the hardware.

II.2 ARITHMETIC OPERATIONS

II.2.1 Binary Addition

Addition in binary form is the same as in decimal form. It is simple because there are only two digits. The possible combinations are illustrated below:

```
                                        Carry 1
    0  1  0  1                                1
    0  0  1  1                                1
    0  1  1  0 + a carry of 1            1 + a carry of 1
```

Let us now consider two examples:

```
                                        1  1
                           Carry        1  1  1
    Carry  1  1  1                0  1  1  1 = 7
           0  1  1  0  =  6       0  1  1  1 = 7
           1  0  1  1  = 11       0  0  1  1 = 3
        1  0  0  0  1  = 17    1  0  0  0  1 = 17
```

Adding two numbers is straightforward, since there is never a double carry, and this is the manner in which the addition is generally done. If three numbers are to be added, the third number is simply added to the sum of the first two in a separate step. In the three-row example the second column from the right develops a double carry, which means that a carry must be placed one column further to the left. In this example there are two carries in the two left columns. However, as the number of rows increase, the number of possible carries in a given column also increases, resulting in a very clumsy system.

II.2.2 Binary Subtraction and Complementary Numbers

Manual subtraction of binary numbers can be done in a manner similar to addition by substituting borrows for carries. Some examples are shown:

```
         →   →                  →  →  →                    →        →
       1  1  0 1   13        1  0  0  0   8        1  0 1  0 1      21
   (−)    1  1 1   −7           1  1  1  −7        0  1 0  1 0     −10
       1  1 0  =   6        0  0  0  1  =   1          1 0  1 1  =    11
```

When no borrowing is necessary,

$$
\begin{array}{ccc}
1 & 1 & 0 \\
0 & 1 & 0 \\
\hline
1 & 0 & 0
\end{array}
$$

When borrowing is necessary,

$$
\begin{array}{ccc}
0 & \text{becomes} & 1 \\
\underline{1} & & \underline{1} \\
& & 1
\end{array}
$$

and the 1 that was borrowed becomes a 0. This is because the borrowed 1 of the number to the left is twice as large, and so after the $\dfrac{1}{1}$ operation, there is still a 1 left, making the net result $\dfrac{1}{1}$ for the borrow
$$\frac{1}{0} \qquad \qquad \frac{1}{1}$$
condition. When multiple borrows are required as in 8 minus 7, the rules are the same, but somewhat more confusing. Here the MSB where the 1 was finally borrowed becomes a 0 and all the other bits are 1's.

This system of subtractions, however, is not as well adapted to computer processing as the complementary techniques described in the following section.

The complement of a digital number is obtained by interchanging the 1's and 0's. This is also called the ones complement. The twos complement is obtained by adding 1 to the ones complement:

Binary number	1010
Ones complement	0101
Add 1	1
Twos complement	0110

To perform the subtraction $A - B$, either the ones or twos complement can be used.

In ones complement subtraction, the number to be subtracted is put in complementary form and added to the first number. If there is an overflow, it is added to the LSB of the answer or, as it is called, "an end around carry" is performed. For a positive result the answer is correct. If the answer is negative, the result must be complemented. It is seen from this that there is no direct way of knowing whether the answer is positive or negative and that a separate accounting must be kept. The procedure is illustrated as follows:

```
    27        1 1 0 1 1                      1 1 0 1 1
  - 12 (-) 0 1 1 0 0           =            1 0 0 1 1
  + 15                                  ① 0 1 1 1 0
                         Overflow    └──────────→1
                                        0  0 1 1 1 1 = + 15

    12        0 1 1 0 0                        0 1 1 0 0
  - 27 (-) 1 1 0 1 1           = (+) 0 0 1 0 0
  - 15                                    0  1 0 0 0 0
                         Complement  =   0 1 1 1 1
                                              = - 15
```

In twos complement subtraction the number to be subtracted is put in twos complement form and added to the first number. If the result is positive there is a carry of 1. If the result is negative there is no carry. The carry bit depicts the sign of the answer. It is not part of the numerical answer, and in computing circuits this must be recognized. A negative difference requires an extra step because the answer is in twos complement form. This requires that the twos complement be taken of a negative difference to get the correct answer. The process is illustrated as follows:

```
 A = 0 1 1 0 1 = 13      A - B = 13 - 4 = +9
 B = 0 0 1 0 0 = 4                  1  1
 B̄ = 1 1 0 1 1                A =      0 1  1 0 1
   Add 1         1      1 + B̄ =      1 1  1 0 0
1 + B̄   1 1 1 0 0       ①    0 1  0 0 1  = +9
                                    ╲Sign bit

  For B - A we have,

 Ā =   1 0 0 1 0            B =      0 0 1 0 0
   Add 1         1      1 + Ā =      1 0 0 1 1
       1 0 0 1 1       ⓪ 1 0 1 1 1
                                    ╲ Sign bit
```

Since the result is a negative number, we must take the twos complement to get the correct answer:

```
                          10111
   Ones complement        01000
   Add one                    1
   Twos complement        01001  =  - 9
```

II.2.3 Binary Multiplication

Manual binary multiplication is very easy because each partial product is either 0 or the multiplied number. An example is shown:

$$
\begin{array}{rr}
6 & 0\ 1\ 1\ 0 \\
\times\ 5 & (\times)\ \underline{0\ 1\ 0\ 1} \\
\overline{30} & 0\ 1\ 1\ 0 \\
& 0\ 0\ 0\ 0 \\
& 0\ 1\ 1\ 0 \\
& \underline{0\ 0\ 0\ 0} \\
& 1\ 1\ 1\ 1\ 0 = 30
\end{array}
$$

Many types of multiplier chips and assemblies are available, depending on the desired speed and the acceptable complexity and power. The manual process illustrated lends itself to a shift-and-add technique, which is popular and relatively simple.

For small numbers successive addition is often convenient. For example, 4×4 is $4 + 4 + 4 + 4$.

II.2.4 Binary Division

Manual binary division is very similar to decimal division. It uses the subtraction process with the borrow and in that regard can sometimes be confusing. An example is

$$
\begin{array}{r}
23 \\
5\,\overline{\big)\,117} \\
\underline{10} \\
17 \\
\underline{15} \\
2 \\
\overline{5}
\end{array}
\qquad
\begin{array}{r}
10111 = 23\tfrac{2}{5} \\
101\,\overline{\big)\,1110101} \\
\underline{101} \\
1001 \\
\underline{101} \\
1000 \\
\underline{101} \\
111 \\
\underline{101} \\
10 \\
\underline{101}
\end{array}
$$

TABLE II.1
Decimal/Hexadecimal Code

Decimal	Hexa-D	Decimal	Hexa-D	Decimal	Hexa-D	Decimal	Hexa-D	Decimal	Hexa-D	Decimal	Hexa-D	Decimal	Hexa-D	Decimal	Hexa-D	Decimal	Hexa-D
000	00	30	1E	60	3C	90	5A	120	78	150	96	180	B4	210	D2	240	F0
1	01	1	1F	1	3D	1	5B	1	79	1	97	1	B5	1	D3	1	F1
2	02	2	20	2	3E	2	5C	2	7A	2	98	2	B6	2	D4	2	F2
3	03	3	21	3	3F	3	5D	3	7B	3	99	3	B7	3	D5	3	F3
4	04	4	22	4	40	4	5E	4	7C	4	9A	4	B8	4	D6	4	F4
5	05	5	23	5	41	5	5F	5	7D	5	9B	5	B9	5	D7	5	F5
6	06	6	24	6	42	6	60	6	7E	6	9C	6	BA	6	D8	6	F6
7	07	7	25	7	43	7	61	7	7F	7	9D	7	BB	7	D9	7	F7
8	08	8	26	8	44	8	62	8	80	8	9E	8	BC	8	DA	8	F8
9	09	9	27	9	45	9	63	9	81	9	9F	9	BD	9	DB	9	F9

Decimal	Hexa-D	Decimal	Hexa-D	Decimal	Hexa-D	Decimal	Hexa-D	Decimal	Hexa-D	Decimal	Hexa-D	Decimal	Hexa-D	Decimal	Hexa-D	Decimal	Hexa-D
10	0A	40	28	70	46	100	64	130	82	160	A0	190	BE	220	DC	250	FA
1	0B	1	29	1	47	1	65	1	83	1	A1	1	BF	1	DD	1	FB
2	0C	2	2A	2	48	2	66	2	84	2	A2	2	C0	2	DE	2	FC
3	0D	3	2B	3	49	3	67	3	85	3	A3	3	C1	3	DF	3	FD
4	0E	4	2C	4	4A	4	68	4	86	4	A4	4	C2	4	E0	4	FE
5	0F	5	2D	5	4B	5	69	5	87	5	A5	5	C3	5	E1	5	FF
6	10	6	2E	6	4C	6	6A	6	88	6	A6	6	C4	6	E2		
7	11	7	2F	7	4D	7	6B	7	89	7	A7	7	C5	7	E3		
8	12	8	30	8	4E	8	6C	8	8A	8	A8	8	C6	8	E4		
9	13	9	31	9	4F	9	6D	9	8B	9	A9	9	C7	9	E5		

Decimal	Hexa-D	Decimal	Hexa-D	Decimal	Hexa-D	Decimal	Hexa-D	Decimal	Hexa-D	Decimal	Hexa-D	Decimal	Hexa-D	Decimal	Hexa-D
20	14	50	32	80	50	110	6E	140	8C	170	AA	200	C8	230	E6
1	15	1	33	1	51	1	6F	1	8D	1	AB	1	C9	1	E7
2	16	2	34	2	52	2	70	2	8E	2	AC	2	CA	2	E8
3	17	3	35	3	53	3	71	3	8F	3	AD	3	CB	3	E9
4	18	4	36	4	54	4	72	4	90	4	AE	4	CC	4	EA
5	19	5	37	5	55	5	73	5	91	5	AF	5	CD	5	EB
6	1A	6	38	6	56	6	74	6	92	6	B0	6	CE	6	EC
7	1B	7	39	7	57	7	75	7	93	7	B1	7	CF	7	ED
8	1C	8	3A	8	58	8	76	8	94	8	B2	8	D0	8	EE
9	1D	9	3B	9	59	9	77	9	95	9	B3	9	D1	9	EF

Filter Tables

The filter tables in this Appendix relate directly to Chapter 7. As stated in Chapter 7, all the tables are for low-pass filters.

III. 1 PASSIVE LOSSLESS FILTERS

These tables assume that the Q of the elements is high enough so that there is no need to compensate for their losses. Just how high the Q must be to make this assumption valid is variable and difficult to prejudge.

When the Q's are too low, there is an overall degradation of the filter. This is a gradual process and adjustments must be made when the element Q's are not sufficient, such as added gain, additional poles, and a possible change of the cutoff frequency. Table III.1 has been suggested as a guide.

The filters designated in Tables III.2 through III.5 have their elements organized as shown in Fig. III.1.

In some cases the signal source may be a very high impedance or, as it is commonly called, a current source. The source resistance R_S becomes a shunt resistor and the design remains valid. If the source resistance is not high enough to be neglected, a shunt resistor should be selected that will equal the designated R_S when placed in parallel with the signal source.

It should be noted that in the top-row designations, R_S is equal or higher than the normalized 1 Ω load resistor.

In the bottom-row designations, $1/R_S$ is used so that the source resistance R_S is equal or lower than the load resistor.

Tables III.2 through III.5 are for a normalized load of 1 Ω. Very often a filter can be terminated in a high-impedance device such as a FET. These devices, however, frequently have a capacitive input of concern.

TABLE III. 1
Filter Element Q Requirements

Filter Type	Minimum Element Q Required
Bessel	3
Butterworth	15
0.01 dB Chebyshev	24
0.1 dB Chebyshev	39
0.5 dB Chebyshev	57
1 dB Chebyshev	75

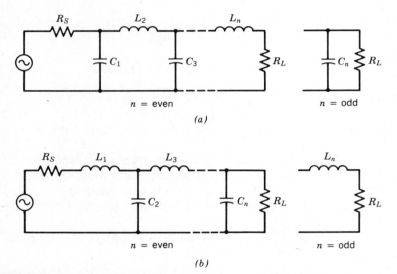

FIGURE III. 1   Filter element designations for Tables III.2 through III.5: (*a*) top-row element designations; (*b*) bottom-row element designations.

TABLE III.2
Butterworth Lossless Filters

N	R_S	C_1	L_2	C_3	L_4	C_5	L_6	C_7	L_8	C_9	L_{10}
2	1.0000	1.4142	1.4142								
	1.1111	1.0353	1.8352								
	1.2500	0.8485	2.1213								
	1.4286	0.6971	2.4387								
	1.6667	0.5657	2.8284								
	2.0000	0.4481	3.3461								
	2.5000	0.3419	4.0951								
	3.3333	0.2447	5.3126								
	5.0000	0.1557	7.7067								
	10.0000	0.0743	14.8138								
	Inf.	1.4142	0.7071								
3	1.0000	1.0000	2.0000	1.0000							
	0.9000	0.8082	1.6332	1.5994							
	0.8000	0.8442	1.3840	1.9259							
	0.7000	0.9152	1.1652	2.2774							
	0.6000	1.0225	0.9650	2.7024							
	0.5000	1.1811	0.7789	3.2612							
	0.4000	1.4254	0.6042	4.0642							
	0.3000	1.8380	0.4396	5.3634							
	0.2000	2.6687	0.2842	7.9102							
	0.1000	5.1672	0.1377	15.4554							
	Inf.	1.5000	1.3333	0.5000							
4	1.1000	0.7654	1.8478	1.8478	0.7654						
	1.1111	0.4657	1.5924	1.7439	1.4690						
	1.2500	0.3882	1.6946	1.5110	1.8109						
	1.4286	0.3251	1.8618	1.2913	2.1752						
	1.6667	0.2690	2.1029	1.0824	2.6131						
	2.0000	0.2175	2.4524	0.8826	3.1868						
	2.5000	0.1692	2.9858	0.6911	4.0094						
	3.3333	0.1237	3.8826	0.5072	5.3381						
	5.0000	0.0804	5.6835	0.3307	7.9397						
	10.0000	0.0392	11.0942	0.1616	15.6421						
	Inf.	1.5307	1.5772	1.0824	0.3827						
5	1.0000	0.6180	1.6180	2.0000	1.6180	0.6180					
	0.9000	0.4416	1.0265	1.9095	1.7562	1.3887					
	0.8000	0.4698	0.8660	2.0605	1.5443	1.7380					
	0.7000	0.5173	0.7313	2.2849	1.3326	2.1083					
	0.6000	0.5860	0.6094	2.5998	1.1255	2.5524					
	0.5000	0.6857	0.4955	3.0510	0.9237	3.1331					
	0.4000	0.8378	0.3877	3.7357	0.7274	3.9648					
	0.3000	1.0937	0.2848	4.8835	0.5367	5.3073					
	0.2000	1.6077	0.1861	7.1849	0.3518	7.9345					
	0.1000	3.1522	0.0912	14.0945	0.1727	15.7103					
	Inf.	1.5451	1.6944	1.3820	0.8944	0.3090					

(Table continues on p. 378.)

TABLE III.2 (*Continued*)

N	R_S	C_1	L_2	C_3	L_4	C_5	L_6	C_7	L_8	C_9	L_{10}
	1.0000	0.5176	1.4142	1.9319	1.9319	1.4142	0.5176				
	1.1111	0.2890	1.0403	1.3217	2.0539	1.7443	1.3347				
	1.2500	0.2445	1.1163	1.1257	2.2389	1.5498	1.6881				
	1.4286	0.2072	1.2363	0.9567	2.4991	1.3464	2.0618				
	1.6667	0.1732	1.4071	0.8011	2.8580	1.1431	2.5092				
6	2.0000	0.1412	1.6531	0.6542	3.3687	0.9423	3.0938				
	2.5000	0.1108	2.0275	0.5139	4.1408	0.7450	3.9305				
	3.3333	0.0816	2.6559	0.3788	5.4325	0.5517	5.2804				
	5.0000	0.0535	3.9170	0.2484	8.0201	0.3628	7.9216				
	10.0000	0.0263	7.7053	0.1222	15.7855	0.1788	15.7375				
	Inf.	1.5529	1.7593	1.5529	1.2016	0.7579	0.2588				
	1.0000	0.4450	1.2470	1.8019	2.0000	1.8019	1.2470	0.4450			
	0.9000	0.2985	0.7111	1.4043	1.4891	2.1249	1.7268	1.2961			
	0.8000	0.3215	0.6057	1.5174	1.2777	2.3338	1.5461	1.6520			
	0.7000	0.3571	0.5154	1.6883	1.0910	2.6177	1.3498	2.0277			
	0.6000	0.4075	0.4322	1.9284	0.9170	3.0050	1.1503	2.4771			
7	0.5000	0.4799	0.3536	2.2726	0.7512	3.5532	0.9513	3.0640			
	0.4000	0.5899	0.2782	2.7950	0.5917	4.3799	0.7542	3.9037			
	0.3000	0.7745	0.2055	3.6706	0.4373	5.7612	0.5600	5.2583			
	0.2000	1.1448	0.1350	5.4267	0.2874	8.5263	0.3692	7.9079			
	0.1000	2.2571	0.0665	10.7004	0.1417	16.8222	0.1823	15.7480			
	Inf.	1.5576	1.7988	1.6588	1.3972	1.0550	0.6560	0.2225			
	1.0000	0.3902	1.1111	1.6629	1.9616	1.9616	1.6629	1.1111	0.3902		
	1.1111	0.2075	0.7575	0.9925	1.6362	1.5900	2.1612	1.7092	1.2671		
	1.2500	0.1774	0.8199	0.8499	1.7779	1.3721	2.3874	1.5393	1.6246		
	1.4286	0.1513	0.9138	0.7257	1.9852	1.1760	2.6879	1.3490	2.0017		
	1.6667	0.1272	1.0455	0.6102	2.2740	0.9912	3.0945	1.1530	2.4524		
8	2.0000	0.1042	1.2341	0.5003	2.6863	0.8139	3.6678	0.9558	3.0408		
	2.5000	0.0822	1.5201	0.3945	3.3106	0.6424	4.5308	0.7594	3.8825		
	3.3333	0.0608	1.9995	0.2919	4.3563	0.4757	5.9714	0.5650	5.2400		
	5.0000	0.0400	2.9608	0.1921	6.4523	0.3133	8.8538	0.3732	7.8952		
	10.0000	0.0198	5.8479	0.0949	12.7455	0.1547	17.4999	0.1846	15.7510		
	Inf.	1.5607	1.8246	1.7287	1.5283	1.2588	0.9371	0.5776	0.1951		
	1.0000	0.3473	1.0000	1.5321	1.8794	2.0000	1.8794	1.5321	1.0000	0.3473	
	0.9000	0.2242	0.5388	1.0835	1.1859	1.7905	1.6538	2.1796	1.6930	1.2447	
	0.8000	0.2434	0.4623	1.1777	1.0200	1.9542	1.4336	2.4189	1.5318	1.6033	
	0.7000	0.2719	0.3954	1.3162	0.8734	2.1885	1.2323	2.7314	1.3464	1.9812	
	0.6000	0.3117	0.3330	1.5092	0.7361	2.5124	1.0410	3.1516	1.1533	2.4328	
9	0.5000	0.3685	0.2735	1.7846	0.6046	2.9734	0.8565	3.7426	0.9579	3.0223	
	0.4000	0.4545	0.2159	2.2019	0.4775	3.6706	0.6771	4.6310	0.7624	3.8654	
	0.3000	0.5987	0.1600	2.9006	0.3539	4.8373	0.5022	6.1128	0.5680	5.2249	
	0.2000	0.8878	0.1054	4.3014	0.2333	7.1750	0.3312	9.0766	0.3757	7.8838	
	0.1000	1.7558	0.0521	8.5074	0.1153	14.1930	0.1638	17.9654	0.1862	15.7504	
	Inf.	1.5628	1.8424	1.7772	1.6202	1.4037	1.1408	0.8414	0.5155	0.1736	
	1.0000	0.3129	0.9080	1.4142	1.7820	1.9754	1.9754	1.7820	1.4142	0.9080	0.3129
	1.1111	0.1614	0.5924	0.7853	1.3202	1.3230	1.8968	1.6956	2.1883	1.6785	1.2267
	1.2500	0.1388	0.6452	0.6762	1.4400	1.1420	2.0779	1.4754	2.4377	1.5245	1.5861
	1.4286	0.1190	0.7222	0.5797	1.6130	0.9802	2.3324	1.2712	2.7592	1.3431	1.9646
	1.6667	0.1004	0.8292	0.4891	1.8528	0.8275	2.6825	1.0758	3.1895	1.1526	2.4169
10	2.0000	0.0825	0.9818	0.4021	2.1943	0.6808	3.1795	0.8864	3.7934	0.9588	3.0072
	2.5000	0.0652	1.2127	0.3179	2.7108	0.5384	3.9302	0.7018	4.7002	0.7641	3.8512
	3.3333	0.0484	1.5992	0.2358	3.5754	0.3995	5.1858	0.5211	6.2118	0.5700	5.2122
	5.0000	0.0319	2.3740	0.1556	5.3082	0.2636	7.7010	0.3440	9.2343	0.3775	7.8738
	10.0000	0.0158	4.7005	0.0770	10.5104	0.1305	15.2505	0.1704	18.2981	0.1872	15.7481
	Inf.	1.5643	1.8552	1.8121	1.6869	1.5100	1.2921	1.0406	0.7626	0.4654	0.1564
N	$1/R_S$	L_1	C_2	L_3	C_4	L_5	C_6	L_7	C_8	L_9	C_{10}

TABLE III.3
Chebyshev Lossless Filters, Ripple = 0.01 dB

N	R_S	C_1	L_2	C_3	L_4	C_5	L_6	C_7	L_8	C_9	L_{10}
2	1.0007	1.3472	1.4829								
	1.1111	1.2472	1.5947								
	1.2500	0.9434	1.9974								
	1.4286	0.7591	2.3442								
	1.6667	0.6091	2.7496								
	2.0000	0.4791	3.2772								
	2.5000	0.3634	4.0328								
	3.3333	0.2590	5.2546								
	5.0000	0.1642	7.6498								
	10.0000	0.0781	14.7492								
	Inf.	1.4118	0.7415								
3	1.0000	1.1811	1.8214	1.1811							
	0.9000	1.0917	1.6597	1.4802							
	0.8000	1.0969	1.4431	1.8057							
	0.7000	1.1600	1.2283	2.1653							
	0.6000	1.2737	1.0236	2.5984							
	0.5000	1.4521	0.8294	3.1644							
	0.4000	1.7340	0.6452	3.9742							
	0.3000	2.2164	0.4704	5.2800							
	0.2000	3.1934	0.3047	7.8338							
	0.1000	6.1411	0.1479	15.3899							
	Inf.	1.5012	1.4330	0.5905							
4	1.1000	0.9500	1.9382	1.7608	1.0457						
	1.1111	0.8539	1.9460	1.7439	1.1647						
	1.2500	0.6182	2.0749	1.5417	1.6170						
	1.4286	0.4948	2.2787	1.3336	2.0083						
	1.6667	0.3983	2.5709	1.1277	2.4611						
	2.0000	0.3156	2.9943	0.9260	3.0448						
	2.5000	0.2418	3.6406	0.7293	3.8746						
	3.3333	0.1744	4.7274	0.5379	5.2085						
	5.0000	0.1121	6.9102	0.8523	7.8126						
	10.0000	0.0541	13.4690	0.1729	15.5100						
	Inf.	1.5287	1.6939	1.3122	0.5229						
5	1.0000	0.9766	1.6849	2.0366	1.6849	0.9766					
	0.9000	0.8798	1.4558	2.1738	1.6412	1.2739					
	0.8000	0.8769	1.2350	2.3785	1.4991	1.6066					
	0.7000	0.9263	1.0398	2.6582	1.3228	1.9772					
	0.6000	1.0191	0.8626	3.0408	1.1345	2.4244					
	0.5000	1.1658	0.6985	3.5835	0.9421	3.0092					
	0.4000	1.3983	0.5442	4.4027	0.7491	3.8453					
	0.3000	1.7966	0.3982	5.7721	0.5573	5.1925					
	0.2000	2.6039	0.2592	8.5140	0.3679	7.8257					
	0.1000	5.0406	0.1266	16.7406	0.1819	15.6126					
	Inf.	1.5466	1.7950	1.6449	1.2365	0.4883					
6	1.0007	0.8514	1.7956	1.8411	2.0266	1.6312	0.9372				
	1.1111	0.7597	1.7817	1.7752	2.0941	1.6380	1.0533				
	1.2500	0.5445	1.8637	1.4886	2.4025	1.5067	1.5041				
	1.4286	0.4355	2.0383	1.2655	2.7346	1.3318	1.8987				
	1.6667	0.3509	2.2978	1.0607	3.1671	1.1451	2.3568				
	2.0000	0.2786	2.6781	0.8671	3.7683	0.9536	2.9483				
	2.5000	0.2139	3.2614	0.6816	4.6673	0.7606	3.7899				
	3.3333	0.1547	4.2448	0.5028	6.1631	0.5676	5.1430				
	5.0000	0.0997	6.2227	0.3299	9.1507	0.3760	7.7852				
	10.0000	0.0483	12.1707	0.1623	18.1048	0.1865	15.5950				
	Inf.	1.5510	1.8471	1.7897	1.5976	1.1904	0.4686				
7	1.0000	0.9127	1.5947	2.0021	1.8704	2.0021	1.5947	0.9127			
	0.9000	0.8157	1.3619	2.0886	1.7217	2.2017	1.5805	1.2060			
	0.8000	0.8111	1.1504	2.2618	1.5252	2.4647	1.4644	1.5380			
	0.7000	0.8567	0.9673	2.5158	1.3234	2.8018	1.3066	1.9096			
	0.6000	0.9430	0.8025	2.8720	1.1237	3.2496	1.1310	2.3592			
	0.5000	1.0799	0.6502	3.3822	0.9276	3.8750	0.9468	2.9478			
	0.4000	1.2971	0.5072	4.1563	0.7350	4.8115	0.7584	3.7900			
	0.3000	1.6692	0.3716	5.4540	0.5459	6.3703	0.5682	5.1476			
	0.2000	2.4235	0.2423	8.0565	0.3604	9.4844	0.3776	7.8019			
	0.1000	4.7006	0.1186	15.8718	0.1784	18.8179	0.1879	15.6523			
	Inf.	1.5593	1.8671	1.8657	1.7651	1.5633	1.1610	0.4564			

(Table continues on p. 380.)

TABLE III.3 (*Continued*)

N	R_S	C_1	L_2	C_3	L_4	C_5	L_6	C_7	L_8	C_9	L_{10}
	1.0007	0.8145	1.7275	1.7984	2.0579	1.8695	1.9796	1.5694	0.8966		
	1.1111	0.7248	1.7081	1.7239	2.1019	1.8259	2.0595	1.5827	1.0111		
	1.2500	0.5176	1.7772	1.4315	2.3601	1.5855	2.4101	1.4754	1.4597		
	1.4286	0.4138	1.9422	1.2141	2.6686	1.3723	2.7734	1.3142	1.8544		
	1.6667	0.3336	2.1896	1.0169	3.0808	1.1660	3.2393	1.1369	2.3136		
8	2.0000	0.2650	2.5533	0.8313	3.6598	0.9639	3.8820	0.9518	2.9073		
	2.5000	0.2036	3.1118	0.6537	4.5303	0.7653	4.8393	0.7627	3.7524		
	3.3333	0.1474	4.0539	0.4826	5.9828	0.5697	6.4287	0.5718	5.1118		
	5.0000	0.0951	5.9495	0.3170	8.8889	0.3770	9.6002	0.3804	7.7668		
	10.0000	0.0462	11.6509	0.1562	17.6067	0.1870	19.1009	0.1895	15.6158		
	Inf.	1.5588	1.8848	1.8988	1.8556	1.7433	1.5391	1.1412	0.4483		
	1.0000	0.8854	1.5513	1.9614	1.8616	2.0717	1.8616	1.9614	1.5513	0.8854	
	0.9000	0.7886	1.3192	2.0330	1.6941	2.2249	1.7402	2.1774	1.5478	1.1764	
	0.8000	0.7834	1.1127	2.1959	1.4930	2.4614	1.5603	2.4565	1.4423	1.5076	
	0.7000	0.8273	0.9353	2.4404	1.2924	2.7808	1.3662	2.8093	1.2927	1.8793	
	0.6000	0.9109	0.7761	2.7852	1.0962	3.2140	1.1688	3.2747	1.1233	2.3295	
9	0.5000	1.0436	0.6290	3.2805	0.9045	3.8249	0.9710	3.9223	0.9436	2.9193	
	0.4000	1.2542	0.4910	4.0329	0.7167	4.7444	0.7739	4.8900	0.7582	3.7637	
	0.3000	1.6151	0.3599	5.2951	0.5325	6.2792	0.5780	6.4989	0.5697	5.1254	
	0.2000	2.3468	0.2349	7.8274	0.3518	9.3504	0.3835	9.7114	0.3797	7.7882	
	0.1000	4.5556	0.1150	15.4334	0.1743	18.5641	0.1908	19.3382	0.1895	15.6645	
	Inf.	1.5646	1.8884	1.9242	1.8977	1.8425	1.7261	1.5217	1.1273	0.4427	
	1.0007	0.7970	1.6930	1.7690	2.0395	1.8827	2.0724	1.8529	1.9472	1.5380	0.8773
	1.1111	0.7083	1.6714	1.6921	2.0763	1.8281	2.1308	1.8167	2.0310	1.5541	0.9910
	1.2500	0.5049	1.7353	1.4005	2.3184	1.5706	2.4371	1.5953	2.3952	1.4574	1.4381
	1.4286	0.4037	1.8958	1.1871	2.6178	1.3552	2.7830	1.3895	2.7685	1.3027	1.8327
	1.6667	0.3255	2.1375	0.9942	3.0205	1.1497	3.2370	1.1863	3.2448	1.1300	2.2923
10	2.0000	0.2586	2.4932	0.8128	3.5878	0.9497	3.8698	0.9849	3.9004	0.9484	2.8867
	2.5000	0.1988	3.0398	0.6394	4.4418	0.7538	4.8173	0.7849	4.8757	0.7617	3.7333
	3.3333	0.1440	3.9619	0.4723	5.8678	0.5612	6.3951	0.5863	6.4939	0.5722	5.0955
	5.0000	0.0451	5.8175	0.3103	8.7220	0.3715	9.5486	0.3893	9.7217	0.3814	7.7563
	10.0000	0.0451	11.3993	0.1530	17.2866	0.1844	19.0046	0.1938	19.3905	0.1904	15.6234
	Inf.	1.5625	1.8978	1.9323	1.9288	1.8907	1.8309	1.7128	1.5088	1.1173	0.4386
N	$1/R_S$	L_1	C_2	L_3	C_4	L_5	C_6	L_7	C_8	L_9	C_{10}

TABLE III.4
Chebyshev Lossless Filters, Ripple = 0.1 dB

n	R_S	C_1	L_2	C_3	L_4	C_5	L_6	C_7	L_8	C_9	L_{10}
	1.3554	1.2087	1.6382								
	1.4286	0.9771	1.9824								
	1.6661	0.7326	2.4885								
	2.0000	0.5597	3.0538								
2	2.5000	0.4169	3.8265								
	3.3333	0.2933	5.0502								
	5.1000	0.1841	7.4257								
	10.0000	0.0868	14.4332								
	Inf.	1.3911	0.8191								
	1.0000	1.4328	1.5937	1.4328							
	0.9000	1.4258	1.4935	1.6219							
	0.8000	1.4511	1.3557	1.8711							
	0.7000	1.5210	1.1927	2.1901							
	0.6000	1.6475	1.0174	2.6026							
3	0.5000	1.8530	0.8383	3.1594							
	0.4000	2.1857	0.6603	3.9675							
	0.3000	2.7630	0.4860	5.2788							
	0.2000	3.9418	0.3172	7.8503							
	0.1000	7.5121	0.1549	15.4656							
	Inf.	1.5133	1.5090	0.7164							

TABLE III.4 (*Continued*)

N	R_S	C_1	L_2	C_3	L_4	C_5	L_6	C_7	L_8	C_9	L_{10}
4	1.3554	0.9924	2.1476	1.5845	1.3451						
	1.4286	0.7789	2.3480	1.4292	1.7001						
	1.6667	0.5764	2.7304	1.1851	2.2425						
	2.0000	0.4398	3.2269	0.9672	2.8563						
	2.5000	0.3288	3.9605	0.7599	3.6976						
	3.3333	0.2329	5.1777	0.5602	5.0301						
	5.0000	0.1475	7.6072	0.3670	7.6143						
	10.0000	0.0704	14.8873	0.1802	15.2297						
	Inf.	1.5107	1.7682	1.4550	0.6725						
5	1.0000	1.3013	1.5559	2.2411	1.5559	1.3013					
	0.9000	1.2845	1.4329	2.3794	1.4878	1.4883					
	0.8000	1.2998	1.2824	2.5819	1.3815	1.7384					
	0.7000	1.3580	1.1170	2.8679	1.2437	2.0621					
	0.6000	1.4694	0.9469	3.2688	1.0846	2.4835					
	0.5000	1.6535	0.7777	3.8446	0.9126	3.0548					
	0.4000	1.9538	0.6119	4.7193	0.7333	3.8861					
	0.3000	2.4765	0.4509	6.1861	0.5503	5.2373					
	0.2000	3.5457	0.2950	9.1272	0.3659	7.8890					
	0.1000	6.7870	0.1447	17.9569	0.1820	15.7447					
	Inf.	1.5613	1.8069	1.7659	1.4173	0.6507					
6	1.3554	0.9419	2.0797	1.6581	2.2473	1.5344	1.2767				
	1.4286	0.7347	2.2492	1.4537	2.5437	1.4051	1.6293				
	1.6667	0.5422	2.6003	1.1830	3.0641	1.1850	2.1739				
	2.0000	0.4137	3.0679	0.9575	3.7119	0.9794	2.7936				
	2.5000	0.3095	3.7652	0.7492	4.6512	0.7781	3.6453				
	3.333	0.2195	4.9266	0.5514	6.1947	0.5795	4.9962				
	5.0000	0.1393	7.2500	0.3613	9.2605	0.3835	7.6184				
	10.0000	0.0666	14.2200	0.1777	18.4267	0.1901	15.3495				
	Inf.	1.5339	1.8838	1.8306	1.7485	1.3937	0.6383				
7	1.0000	1.2615	1.5196	2.2392	1.6804	2.2392	1.5196	1.2615			
	0.9000	1.2422	1.3946	2.3613	1.5784	2.3966	1.4593	1.4472			
	0.8000	1.2550	1.2449	2.5481	1.4430	2.6242	1.3619	1.6967			
	0.7000	1.3100	1.0826	2.8192	1.2833	2.9422	1.2326	2.0207			
	0.6000	1.4170	0.9169	3.2052	1.1092	3.3841	1.0807	2.4437			
	0.5000	1.5948	0.7529	3.7642	0.9276	4.0150	0.9142	3.0182			
	0.4000	1.8853	0.5926	4.6179	0.7423	4.9702	0.7384	3.8552			
	0.3000	2.3917	0.4369	6.0535	0.5557	6.5685	0.5569	5.2167			
	0.2000	3.4278	0.2862	8.9371	0.3692	9.7697	0.3723	7.8901			
	0.1000	6.5695	0.1405	17.6031	0.1838	19.3760	0.1862	15.8127			
	Inf.	1.5748	1.8577	1.9210	1.8270	1.7340	1.3786	0.6307			
8	1.3554	0.9234	2.0454	1.6453	2.2826	1.6841	2.2300	1.5091	1.2515		
	1.4286	0.7186	2.2054	1.4350	2.5554	1.4974	2.5422	1.3882	1.6029		
	1.6667	0.5298	2.5459	1.1644	3.0567	1.2367	3.0869	1.1769	2.1477		
	2.0000	0.4042	3.0029	0.9415	3.6917	1.0118	3.7619	0.9767	2.7690		
	2.5000	0.3025	3.6859	0.7365	4.6191	0.7990	4.7388	0.7787	3.6240		
	3.3333	0.2147	4.8250	0.5421	6.1483	0.5930	6.3423	0.5820	4.9811		
	5.0000	0.1364	7.1050	0.3554	9.1917	0.3917	9.5260	0.3863	7.6164		
	10.0000	0.0652	13.9469	0.1749	18.3007	0.1942	19.0437	0.1922	15.3880		
	Inf.	1.5422	1.9106	1.9008	1.9252	1.8200	1.7231	1.3683	0.6258		
9	1.0000	1.2446	1.5017	2.2220	1.6829	2.2957	1.6829	2.2220	1.5017	1.2446	
	0.9000	1.2244	1.3765	2.3388	1.5756	2.4400	1.5870	2.3835	1.4444	1.4297	
	0.8000	1.2361	1.2276	2.5201	1.4365	2.6561	1.4572	2.6168	1.3505	1.6788	
	0.7000	1.2898	1.0670	2.7856	1.2751	2.9647	1.3019	2.9422	1.2248	2.0029	
	0.6000	1.3950	0.9035	3.1653	1.1008	3.3992	1.1304	3.3937	1.0761	2.4264	
	0.5000	1.5701	0.7419	3.7166	0.9198	4.0244	0.9494	4.0377	0.9121	3.0020	
	0.4000	1.8566	0.5840	4.5594	0.7359	4.9750	0.7630	5.0118	0.7382	3.8412	
	0.3000	2.3560	0.4307	5.9781	0.5509	6.5700	0.5736	6.6413	0.5579	5.2068	
	0.2000	3.3781	0.2822	8.8291	0.3661	9.7699	0.3827	9.9047	0.3737	7.8891	
	0.1000	6.4777	0.1386	17.3994	0.1823	19.3816	0.1912	19.6976	0.1873	15.8393	
	Inf.	1.5804	1.8727	1.9584	1.9094	1.9229	1.8136	1.7150	1.3611	0.6223	

(*Table continues on p. 382.*)

TABLE III.4 (*Continued*)

N	$1/R_S$	L_1	C_2	L_3	C_4	L_5	C_6	L_7	C_8	L_9	C_{10}
	1.3554	0.9146	2.0279	1.6346	2.2777	1.6963	2.2991	1.6805	2.2155	1.4962	1.2397
	1.4286	0.7110	2.1837	1.4231	2.5425	1.5002	2.5915	1.5000	2.5322	1.3789	1.5903
	1.6667	0.5240	2.5194	1.1536	3.0362	1.2349	3.1229	1.2444	3.0839	1.1717	2.1351
	2.0000	0.3998	2.9713	0.9326	3.6647	1.0089	3.7923	1.0214	3.7669	0.9741	2.7572
10	2.5000	0.2993	3.6476	0.7295	4.5843	0.7962	4.7673	0.8090	4.7547	0.7779	3.6136
	3.3333	0.2124	4.7758	0.5370	6.1022	0.5907	6.3734	0.6020	6.3758	0.5822	4.9735
	5.0000	0.1350	7.0347	0.3522	9.1248	0.3902	9.5681	0.3987	9.5942	0.3871	7.6148
	10.0000	0.0646	13.8141	0.1734	18.1739	0.1935	19.1282	0.1981	19.2158	0.1929	15.4052
	Inf.	1.5460	1.9201	1.9216	1.9700	1.9102	1.9194	1.8083	1.7090	1.3559	0.6198
n	$1/R_S$	L_1	C_2	L_3	C_4	L_5	C_6	L_7	C_8	L_9	C_{10}

TABLE III.5
Linear-Phase Equiripple Filters, Phase Error = 0.05°

n	R_S	C_1	L_2	C_3	L_4	C_5	L_6	C_7	L_8	C_9	L_{10}
	1.0000	0.6480	2.1085								
	1.1111	0.5703	2.2760								
	1.2500	0.4955	2.4817								
	1.4286	0.4235	2.7422								
	1.6667	0.3544	3.0848								
2	2.0000	0.2880	3.5589								
	2.5000	0.2244	4.2630								
	3.3333	0.1637	5.4270								
	5.0000	0.1059	7.7400								
	10.0000	0.0513	14.6480								
	Inf.	1.3783	0.4957								
	1.0000	0.4328	1.0427	2.2542							
	0.9000	0.4745	0.9330	2.4258							
	0.8000	0.5262	0.8238	2.6400							
	0.7000	0.5925	0.7153	2.9146							
	0.6000	0.6805	0.6078	3.2795							
3	0.5000	0.8032	0.5015	3.7884							
	0.4000	0.9865	0.3967	4.5487							
	0.3000	1.2910	0.2938	5.8106							
	0.2000	1.8983	0.1931	8.3253							
	0.1000	3.7161	0.0950	15.8472							
	Inf.	1.5018	0.9328	0.3631							
	1.0000	0.3363	0.7963	1.1428	2.2459						
	1.1111	0.2993	0.8810	1.0212	2.4241						
	1.2500	0.2631	0.9865	0.9012	2.6445						
	1.4286	0.2275	1.1216	0.7826	2.9254						
	1.6667	0.1926	1.3009	0.6657	3.2970						
4	2.0000	0.1584	1.5509	0.5502	3.8138						
	2.5000	0.1250	1.9244	0.4364	4.5844						
	3.3333	0.0923	2.5448	0.3242	5.8626						
	5.0000	0.0606	3.7818	0.2139	8.4091						
	10.0000	0.0298	7.4845	0.1058	16.0266						
	Inf.	1.5211	1.0444	0.7395	0.2925						
	1.0000	0.2751	0.6541	0.8892	1.1034	2.2873					
	0.9000	0.3031	0.5868	0.9841	0.9904	2.4589					
	0.8000	0.3380	0.5197	1.1026	0.8774	2.6733					
	0.7000	0.3827	0.4529	1.2548	0.7648	2.9484					
	0.6000	0.4420	0.3865	1.4575	0.6526	3.3144					
5	0.5000	0.5248	0.3204	1.7408	0.5410	3.8254					
	0.4000	0.6486	0.2549	2.1651	0.4302	4.5896					
	0.3000	0.8544	0.1899	2.8713	0.3205	5.8595					
	0.2000	1.2649	0.1257	4.2817	0.2120	8.3922					
	0.1000	2.4940	0.0624	8.5082	0.1051	15.9739					
	Inf.	1.5144	1.0407	0.8447	0.6177	0.2456					

TABLE III.5 (*Continued*)

n	R_S	C_1	L_2	C_3	L_4	C_5	L_6	C_7	L_8	C_9	L_{10}
	1.0000	0.2374	0.5662	0.7578	0.8760	1.1163	2.2448				
	1.1111	0.2120	0.6272	0.6799	0.9726	0.9977	2.4214				
	1.2500	0.1870	0.7032	0.6023	1.0931	0.8807	2.6396				
	1.4286	0.1622	0.8008	0.5253	1.2475	0.7652	2.9174				
	1.6667	0.1378	0.9306	0.4487	1.4530	0.6512	3.2849				
6	2.0000	0.1138	1.1118	0.3725	1.7401	0.5387	3.7958				
	2.5000	0.0901	1.3830	0.2969	2.1698	0.4277	4.5579				
	3.3333	0.0669	1.8340	0.2217	2.8849	0.3182	5.8220				
	5.0000	0.0441	2.7343	0.1472	4.3129	0.2103	8.3408				
	10.0000	0.0218	5.4312	0.0732	8.5924	0.1041	15.8769				
	Inf.	1.5050	1.0306	0.8554	0.7283	0.5389	0.2147				
	1.0000	0.2085	0.4999	0.6653	0.7521	0.8749	1.0671	2.2845			
	0.9000	0.2302	0.4488	0.7374	0.6768	0.9687	0.9580	2.4538			
	0.8000	0.2573	0.3978	0.8274	0.6013	1.0861	0.8489	2.6655			
	0.7000	0.2919	0.3470	0.9431	0.5258	1.2369	0.7400	2.9375			
	0.6000	0.3380	0.2964	1.0972	0.4503	1.4381	0.6314	3.2996			
7	0.5000	0.4023	0.2461	1.3127	0.3749	1.7196	0.5235	3.8051			
	0.4000	0.4986	0.1960	1.6356	0.2995	2.1416	0.4163	4.5613			
	0.3000	0.6585	0.1463	2.1734	0.2242	2.8445	0.3101	5.8180			
	0.2000	0.9778	0.0970	3.2480	0.1492	4.2496	0.2052	8.3246			
	0.1000	1.9340	0.0482	6.4698	0.0744	8.4623	0.1017	15.8281			
	Inf.	1.4988	1.0071	0.8422	0.7421	0.6441	0.4791	0.1911			
	1.0000	0.1891	0.4543	0.6031	0.6750	0.7590	0.8427	1.0901	2.2415		
	1.1111	0.1691	0.5035	0.5415	0.7500	0.6813	0.9362	0.9735	2.4176		
	1.2500	0.1494	0.5650	0.4802	0.8435	0.6041	1.0527	0.8588	2.6349		
	1.4286	0.1298	0.6438	0.4191	0.9637	0.5272	1.2019	0.7459	2.9113		
	1.6667	0.1105	0.7487	0.3583	1.1237	0.4508	1.4004	0.6345	3.2767		
8	2.0000	0.0914	0.8953	0.2978	1.3475	0.3748	1.6776	0.5247	3.7846		
	2.5000	0.0725	1.1148	0.2376	1.6827	0.2991	2.0927	0.4164	4.5418		
	3.3333	0.0539	1.4801	0.1776	2.2411	0.2237	2.7833	0.3096	5.7978		
	5.0000	0.0356	2.2095	0.1180	3.3568	0.1488	4.1627	0.2046	8.3004		
	10.0000	0.0176	4.3954	0.0588	6.7021	0.0742	8.2969	0.1013	15.7878		
	Inf.	1.4953	1.0018	0.8264	0.7396	0.6688	0.5858	0.4369	0.1743		
	1.0000	0.1718	0.4146	0.5498	0.6132	0.6774	0.7252	0.8450	1.0447	2.2834	
	0.9000	0.1900	0.3724	0.6097	0.5519	0.7513	0.6529	0.9352	0.9382	2.4512	
	0.8000	0.2125	0.3302	0.6846	0.4905	0.8436	0.5805	1.0481	0.8314	2.6613	
	0.7000	0.2415	0.2882	0.7807	0.4291	0.9624	0.5079	1.1933	0.7247	2.9315	
	0.6000	0.2800	0.2463	0.9088	0.3676	1.1207	0.4352	1.3870	0.6184	3.2914	
9	0.5000	0.3337	0.2046	1.0880	0.3062	1.3424	0.3624	1.6581	0.5125	3.7941	
	0.4000	0.4141	0.1631	1.3565	0.2448	1.6749	0.2897	2.0647	0.4075	4.5462	
	0.3000	0.5478	0.1219	1.8038	0.1834	2.2289	0.2170	2.7420	0.3035	5.7860	
	0.2000	0.8148	0.0809	2.6977	0.1222	3.3369	0.1445	4.0960	0.2007	8.2890	
	0.1000	1.6146	0.0403	5.3782	0.0610	6.6602	0.0721	8.1556	0.0995	15.7520	
	Inf.	1.4907	0.9845	0.8116	0.7197	0.6646	0.6089	0.5359	0.4003	0.1598	
	1.0000	0.1601	0.3867	0.5125	0.5702	0.6243	0.6557	0.7319	0.8178	1.0767	2.2387
	1.1111	0.1433	0.4288	0.4604	0.6336	0.5609	0.7290	0.6567	0.9089	0.9608	2.4151
	1.2500	0.1267	0.4812	0.4084	0.7127	0.4977	0.8205	0.5820	1.0221	0.8471	2.6323
	1.4286	0.1102	0.5486	0.3567	0.8143	0.4348	0.9380	0.5079	1.1672	0.7354	2.9082
	1.6667	0.0939	0.6383	0.3051	0.9498	0.3721	1.0944	0.4342	1.3600	0.6254	3.2727
10	2.0000	0.0778	0.7637	0.2537	1.1392	0.3096	1.3131	0.3609	1.6291	0.5170	3.7791
	2.5000	0.0618	0.9515	0.2024	1.4232	0.2473	1.6408	0.2880	2.0320	0.4102	4.5340
	3.3333	0.0460	1.2641	0.1515	1.8961	0.1852	2.1866	0.2154	2.7022	0.3049	5.7860
	5.0000	0.0304	1.8885	0.1007	2.8416	0.1232	3.2775	0.1433	4.0406	0.2014	8.2806
	10.0000	0.0151	3.7600	0.0502	5.6766	0.0615	6.5485	0.0714	8.0520	0.0997	15.7441
	Inf.	1.4905	0.9858	0.8018	0.7123	0.6540	0.6141	0.5669	0.5003	0.3741	0.1494
n	$1/R_S$	L_1	C_2	L_3	C_4	L_5	C_6	L_7	C_8	L_9	C_{10}

Table III.6 is predistorted for a normalized Butterworth filter, with $R_S = 1\ \Omega$ and for $R_L = \infty$. The design is also arranged to have its last element capacitive so that the load capacitance can be absorbed.

Figure III.2 shows the element arrangement for this type of filter.

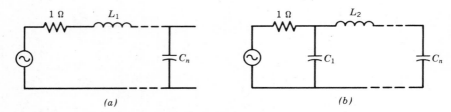

FIGURE III.2 Filter element designations for Table III.6: (*a*) even order; (*b*) odd order.

TABLE III.6
Butterworth Lossless Open-Termination Filters

Poles	L_1	C_2	L_3	C_4	L_5	C_6	L_7	C_8	L_9	C_{10}
2	0.7071	1.414								
4	0.3827	1.082	1.577	1.531						
6	0.2588	0.7579	1.202	1.553	1.759	1.553				
8	0.1951	0.5766	0.9371	1.259	1.528	1.729	1.824	1.561		
10	0.1564	0.4654	0.7626	1.041	1.292	1.510	1.687	1.812	1.855	1.564

	C_1	L_2	C_3	L_4	C_5	L_6	C_7	L_8	C_9
3	0.5000	1.333	1.500						
5	0.3090	0.8944	1.382	1.694	1.545				
7	0.2225	0.6560	1.054	1.397	1.659	1.799	1.588		
9	0.1736	0.5155	0.8414	1.141	1.404	1.620	1.777	1.842	1.563

III.2 UNIFORM DISSIPATION FILTERS

The tables in this section are to be used when a low-pass filter design is to be transformed to a band-pass filter (see Tables III.7 and III.8).

As discussed in Chapter 7, when this transformation is made the Q requirements of the low-pass filter must be multiplied by the Q of the band-pass filter.

The tables in Section III.1 already assume an infinite Q, and although this is not an absolute requirement, these tables are not suitable for high Q bandwidth designs.

The values in the tables of this section have been predistorted to compensate for a low Q. Therefore, a low Q low-pass filter can be designed so that the Q requirements of the band-pass transformation can be realized.

These tables allow for either an open termination with a normalized 1 Ω source resistor or a zero impedance source drive with a 1 Ω normalized termination. Figure III.3 shows the element arrangement.

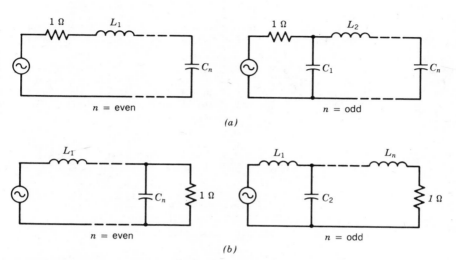

FIGURE III.3 Filter element designations for uniform dissipation filters: (*a*) top-row element designation; (*b*) bottom-row designations.

TABLE III.7
Uniform Dissipation Butterworth Filters

d	L_1	C_2	α_0 dB		d	C_1	L_2	C_3	α_0 dB
0	0.7071	1.414	0		0	0.5000	1.333	1.500	0
0.05	0.7609	1.410	0.614		0.05	0.5405	1.403	1.457	0.868
0.10	0.8236	1.398	1.22		0.10	0.5882	1.481	1.402	1.73
0.15	0.8974	1.374	1.83		0.15	0.6452	1.567	1.334	2.60
0.20	0.9860	1.340	2.42		0.20	0.7143	1.667	1.250	3.45
0.25	1.094	1.290	2.99		0.25	0.8000	1.786	1.149	4.30
0.30	1.228	1.223	3.53		0.30	0.9091	1.939	1.026	5.15
0.35	1.400	1.138	4.05		0.35	1.053	2.164	0.8743	5.98
0.40	1.628	1.034	4.52		0.40	1.250	2.581	0.6798	6.82
0.45	1.944	0.9083	4.94		0.45	1.538	3.806	0.4126	7.66
0.50	2.414	0.7630	5.30						

d	L_3	C_2	L_1	α_0 dB

d	L_1	C_2	α_0 dB
0.55	3.183	0.5989	5.59
0.60	4.669	0.4188	5.82
0.65	8.756	0.2267	5.96

d ;	C_2	L_1	α_0 dB

Three-Pole

Two-Pole

(*Table continues on p. 386.*)

TABLE III.7 (*Continued*)

d	L_1	C_2	L_3	C_4	α_0 dB
0	0.3827	1.082	1.577	1.531	0
0.05	0.4144	1.156	1.636	1.454	1.13
0.10	0.4518	1.240	1.701	1.362	2.27
0.15	0.4967	1.339	1.777	1.250	3.39
0.20	0.5515	1.459	1.879	1.113	4.51
0.25	0.6199	1.609	2.039	0.9400	5.63
0.30	0.7077	1.812	2.384	0.7099	6.73
0.35	0.8243	2.124	3.848	0.3651	7.82
d	C_4	L_3	C_2	L_1	α_0 dB

Four-Pole

d	C_1	L_2	C_3	L_4	C_5	α_0 dB
0	0.3090	0.8944	1.382	1.694	1.545	0
0.02	0.3189	0.9199	1.412	1.712	1.504	0.562
0.04	0.3294	0.9468	1.443	1.730	1.461	1.12
0.06	0.3406	0.9754	1.476	1.750	1.414	1.69
0.08	0.3526	1.006	1.512	1.771	1.364	2.25
0.10	0.3654	1.038	1.549	1.794	1.309	2.81
0.12	0.3794	1.073	1.589	1.822	1.250	3.37
0.14	0.3943	1.111	1.633	1.854	1.184	3.93
0.16	0.4104	1.151	1.681	1.894	1.113	4.48
0.18	0.4281	1.195	1.734	1.946	1.034	5.04
0.20	0.4472	1.243	1.796	2.018	0.9452	5.59
0.22	0.4681	1.296	1.867	2.124	0.8434	6.15
0.24	0.4911	1.354	1.953	2.300	0.7242	6.70
0.26	0.5165	1.419	2.061	2.631	0.5798	7.25
0.28	0.5446	1.493	2.204	3.453	0.3965	7.79
d	L_5	C_4	L_3	C_2	L_1	α_0 dB

Five-Pole

d	L_1	C_2	L_3	C_4	L_5	C_6	α_0 dB
0	0.2588	0.7579	1.202	1.553	1.759	1.553	0
0.02	0.2671	0.7804	1.232	1.581	1.727	1.502	0.671
0.04	0.2760	0.8043	1.264	1.611	1.786	1.446	1.34
0.06	0.2854	0.8297	1.297	1.643	1.802	1.386	2.01
0.08	0.2955	0.8569	1.333	1.679	1.821	1.321	2.68
0.10	0.3064	0.8860	1.372	1.714	1.844	1.250	3.35
0.12	0.3181	0.9172	1.413	1.755	1.874	1.171	4.02
0.14	0.3307	0.9508	1.458	1.802	1.917	1.083	4.69
0.16	0.3443	0.9871	1.508	1.860	1.979	0.9839	5.30
0.18	0.3594	1.027	1.558	1.923	2.080	0.8690	6.00
0.20	0.3754	1.070	1.621	2.008	2.258	0.7313	6.68
0.22	0.3931	1.117	1.690	2.122	2.646	0.5586	7.34
d	C_6	L_5	C_4	L_3	C_2	L_1	α_0 dB

Six-Pole

TABLE III.7 (*Continued*)

d	C_1	L_2	C_3	L_4	C_5	L_6	C_7	α_0 dB
0	0.2225	0.6560	1.054	1.397	1.659	1.799	1.588	0
0.02	0.2297	0.6759	1.084	1.428	1.684	1.808	1.496	0.781
0.04	0.2373	0.6972	1.114	1.461	1.712	1.818	1.428	1.56
0.06	0.2454	0.7198	1.146	1.496	1.742	1.832	1.354	2.34
0.08	0.2542	0.7440	1.180	1.533	1.775	1.851	1.274	3.12
0.10	0.2636	0.7699	1.217	1.573	1.813	1.878	1.184	3.90
0.12	0.2739	0.7980	1.254	1.614	1.860	1.923	1.085	4.68
0.14	0.2846	0.8281	1.294	1.659	1.910	1.992	0.9701	5.45
0.16	0.2966	0.8608	1.344	1.715	1.979	2.111	0.8350	6.23
0.18	0.3091	0.8960	1.394	1.778	2.073	2.356	0.6679	7.00
0.20	0.3232	0.9243	1.453	1.862	2.233	3.177	0.4220	7.77

d	L_7	C_6	L_5	C_4	L_3	C_2	L_1	α_0 dB

Seven-Pole

d	L_1	C_2	L_3	C_4	L_5	C_6	L_7	C_8	α_0 dB
0	0.1951	0.5776	0.9371	1.259	1.528	1.729	1.824	1.561	0
0.02	0.2014	0.5954	0.9636	1.290	1.558	1.752	1.830	1.488	0.890
0.04	0.2081	0.6144	0.9918	1.323	1.590	1.777	1.838	1.409	1.78
0.06	0.2152	0.6347	1.022	1.357	1.624	1.806	1.851	1.321	2.67
0.08	0.2229	0.6564	1.054	1.394	1.622	1.839	1.872	1.224	3.56
0.10	0.2312	0.6796	1.088	1.434	1.703	1.880	1.908	1.114	4.45
0.12	0.2400	0.7046	1.124	1.478	1.750	1.932	1.972	0.9856	5.33
0.14	0.2496	0.7316	1.164	1.526	1.804	2.003	2.101	0.8305	6.22
0.16	0.2600	0.7608	1.208	1.579	1.869	2.110	2.414	0.6307	7.10
0.18	0.2713	0.7926	1.255	1.639	1.951	2.294	3.683	0.3439	7.98

d	C_8	L_7	C_6	L_5	C_4	L_3	C_2	L_1	α_0 dB

Eight-Pole

d	C_1	L_2	C_3	L_4	C_5	L_6	C_7	L_8	C_9	α_0 dB
0	0.1736	0.5155	0.8414	1.141	1.404	1.620	1.777	1.842	1.563	0
0.02	0.1793	0.5316	0.8659	1.171	1.435	1.649	1.798	1.845	1.480	1.00
0.04	0.1852	0.5488	0.8921	1.202	1.469	1.680	1.822	1.851	1.388	2.00
0.06	0.1916	0.5671	0.9199	1.236	1.504	1.713	1.850	1.864	1.286	3.00
0.08	0.1984	0.5867	0.9496	1.272	1.543	1.751	1.884	1.891	1.171	4.00
0.10	0.2058	0.6077	0.9814	1.311	1.584	1.794	1.931	1.942	1.036	5.00
0.12	0.2137	0.6303	1.016	1.353	1.630	1.844	1.997	2.054	0.8735	5.99
0.14	0.2223	0.6547	1.053	1.398	1.682	1.907	2.101	2.340	0.6614	6.99
0.16	0.2315	0.6812	1.093	1.448	1.742	1.991	2.293	3.620	0.3486	7.98

d	L_9	C_8	L_7	C_6	L_5	C_4	L_3	C_2	L_1	α_0 dB

Nine-Pole

(*Table continues on p. 388.*)

TABLE III.7 (*Continued*)

d	L_1	C_2	L_3	C_4	L_5	C_6	L_7	C_8	L_9	C_{10}	α_0 dB
0	0.1564	0.4654	0.7626	1.041	1.292	1.510	1.687	1.812	1.855	1.564	0
0.02	0.1614	0.4800	0.7854	1.069	1.324	1.541	1.714	1.831	1.855	1.471	1.11
0.04	0.1669	0.4956	0.8096	1.099	1.357	1.574	1.744	1.853	1.860	1.367	2.22
0.06	0.1726	0.5123	0.8353	1.132	1.392	1.610	1.777	1.882	1.875	1.249	3.33
0.08	0.1788	0.5301	0.8629	1.166	1.430	1.648	1.814	1.920	1.910	1.114	4.44
0.10	0.1854	0.5493	0.8924	1.203	1.471	1.692	1.860	1.976	1.991	0.9508	5.55
0.12	0.1926	0.5698	0.9242	1.243	1.516	1.741	1.918	2.067	2.201	0.7409	6.65
0.14	0.2003	0.5921	0.9584	1.286	1.566	1.798	1.997	2.239	3.051	0.4349	7.76
d	C_{10}	L_9	C_8	L_7	C_6	L_5	C_4	L_3	C_2	L_1	α_0 dB

Ten-Pole

TABLE III.8
Uniform Dissipation Chebyshev Filters, Ripple = 0.9 dB

d	C_1	L_2	C_3	α_0 dB
0	0.9773	1.332	1.477	0
0.01	1.002	1.332	1.470	0.20
0.02	1.034	1.332	1.464	0.42
0.04	1.102	1.330	1.445	0.87
0.06	1.180	1.328	1.420	1.32
0.08	1.269	1.326	1.394	1.76
0.10	1.376	1.326	1.363	2.24
0.12	1.495	1.326	1.319	2.72
0.14	1.646	1.328	1.269	3.22
0.16	1.828	1.344	1.203	3.76
0.18	2.048	1.382	1.106	4.25
0.19	2.187	1.420	1.043	4.55
0.20	2.337	1.483	0.9670	4.83
0.21	2.513	1.564	0.8847	5.15
0.22	2.721	1.734	0.7609	5.45
0.23	2.959	2.029	0.6158	5.75
0.24	3.248	2.714	0.4367	6.02
0.25	3.600	5.485	0.2023	6.35
d	L_3	C_2	L_1	α_0 dB

Three-Pole

TABLE III.8 (*Continued*)

d	L_1	C_2	L_3	C_4	α_0 dB
0	1.011	1.420	1.879	1.288	0
0.01	1.053	1.422	1.898	1.288	0.2
0.02	1.100	1.426	1.916	1.214	0.5
0.03	1.150	1.433	1.942	1,171	0.7
0.04	1.206	1.439	1.967	1.126	0.9
0.05	1.269	1.445	1.998	1.078	1.1
0.06	1.332	1.457	2.011	1.035	1.3
0.07	1.407	1.470	2.054	0.9701	1.6
0.08	1.495	1.477	2.130	0.9035	1.8
0.09	1.590	1.495	2.204	0.8319	2.0
0.10	1.696	1.514	2.306	0.7502	2.2
0.11	1.822	1.552	2.476	0.6516	2.4
0.12	1.960	1.634	2.777	0.5316	2.6
0.13	2.130	1.696	3.519	0.3739	2.7
0.14	2.331	1.841	7.508	0.1502	2.9

d	C_4	L_3	C_2	L_1	α_0 dB

Four-Pole

d	C_1	L_2	C_3	L_4	C_5	α_0 dB
0	1.029	1.445	1.960	1.602	1.640	0
0.01	1.084	1.458	1.998	1.583	1.608	0.4
0.02	1.147	1.470	2.042	1.558	1.571	0.8
0.03	1.216	1.483	2.086	1.539	1.527	1.2
0.04	1.294	1.495	2.149	1.514	1.477	1.7
0.05	1.382	1.508	2.224	1.496	1.407	2.1
0.06	1.498	1.533	2.324	1.483	1.307	2.5
0.07	1.608	1.558	2.476	1.508	1.156	2.9
0.074	1.659	1.577	2.577	1.546	1.069	3.2
0.078	1.715	1.596	2.664	1.614	0.9594	3.3
0.082	1.778	1.614	2.809	1.759	0.8130	3.5
0.086	1.847	1.640	3.003	2.124	0.6101	3.7
0.088	1.879	1.659	3.135	2.557	0.4769	3.8
0.090	1.916	1.671	3.292	3.651	0.3123	3.9

d	L_5	C_4	L_3	C_2	L_1	α_0 dB

Five-Pole

(*Table continues on p. 390.*)

TABLE III.8 (*Continued*)

d	L_1	C_2	L_3	C_4	L_5	C_6	α_0 dB
0	1.039	1.464	1.992	1.665	2.023	1.357	0
0.010	1.107	1.477	2.048	1.652	2.036	1.288	0.38
0.020	1.186	1.495	2.104	1.634	2.054	1.206	0.75
0.025	1.230	1.502	2.143	1.627	2.067	1.160	0.95
0.030	1.274	1.514	2.180	1.621	2.080	1.110	1.14
0.035	1.326	1.521	2.224	1.624	2.092	1.054	1.33
0.040	1.382	1.533	2.281	1.627	2.117	0.9896	1.51
0.044	1.433	1.546	2.331	1.634	2.143	0.9280	1.66
0.048	1.483	1.558	2.388	1.652	2.193	0.8539	1.80
0.052	1.533	1.571	2.463	1.684	2.274	0.7603	1.94
0.056	1.596	1.590	2.551	1.747	2.463	0.6314	2.08
0.058	1.627	1.596	2.608	1.803	2.664	0.5454	2.14
0.060	1.659	1.608	2.670	1.877	3.079	0.4348	2.21

d	C_6	L_5	C_4	L_3	C_2	L_1	α_0 dB

Six-Pole

d	C_1	L_2	C_3	L_4	C_5	L_6	C_7	α_0 dB
0	1.044	1.473	2.011	1.688	2.091	1.664	1.690	0
0.009	1.118	1.489	2.067	1.678	2.124	1.627	1.633	0.51
0.013	1.154	1.495	2.099	1.672	2.143	1.608	1.609	0.75
0.017	1.193	1.508	2.130	1.671	2.161	1.596	1.571	1.06
0.021	1.233	1.514	2.161	1.666	2.180	1.577	1.534	1.29
0.025	1.275	1.527	2.204	1.665	2.212	1.558	1.489	1.51
0.029	1.326	1.534	2.249	1.666	2.243	1.540	1.426	1.80
0.033	1.376	1.546	2.300	1.678	2.293	1.527	1.351	2.00
0.037	1.432	1.558	2.362	1.696	2.375	1.527	1.230	2.28
0.041	1.491	1.575	2.436	1.730	2.523	1.597	1.032	2.54
0.043	1.523	1.583	2.481	1.759	2.655	1.723	0.8679	2.67
0.045	1.556	1.593	2.532	1.799	2.873	2.138	0.6610	2.80

d	L_7	C_6	L_5	C_4	L_3	C_2	L_1	α_0 dB

Seven-Pole

III.3 ELLIPTIC FUNCTION FILTERS

The characteristics of these filters are described in Chapter 7 and also shown in Figs. III.4 and III.5. Figure III.4 is for a π and its T equivalent and Fig. III.5 is for the double π and its T equivalent. The respective data is given in Tables III.9 and III.10.

Extensive tables are available in the literature for further information on these filters.

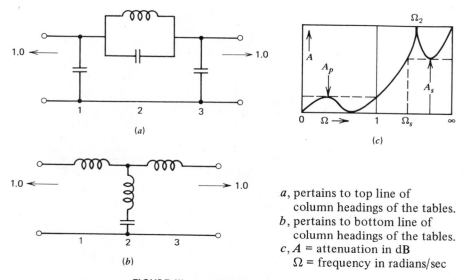

a, pertains to top line of
   column headings of the tables.
b, pertains to bottom line of
   column headings of the tables.
c, *A* = attenuation in dB
   Ω = frequency in radians/sec

FIGURE III.4   Elliptic filter π and T.

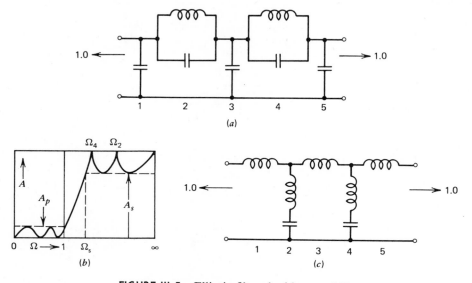

FIGURE III.5   Elliptic filter double π and T.

TABLE III.9
Elliptic Filters π and T

Ω_s	A_s dB	C_1	C_2	L_2	Ω_2	C_3
1.756	20	0.850	0.290	0.871	1.986	0.850
2.082	25	0.902	0.188	0.951	2.362	0.902
2.465	30	0.941	0.125	1.012	2.813	0.941
2.921	35	0.958	0.0837	1.057	3.362	0.958
3.542	40	0.988	0.0570	1.081	4.027	0.988
Ω_s	A_s dB	L_1	L_2	C_2	Ω_2	L_3

$$A_p = 0.1 \text{ dB}$$

Ω_s	A_s dB	C_1	C_2	L_2	Ω_2	C_3
1.416	20	1.267	0.536	0.748	1.578	1.267
1.636	25	1.361	0.344	0.853	1.846	1.361
1.935	30	1.425	0.226	0.924	2.189	1.425
2.283	35	1.479	0.152	0.976	2.600	1.479
2.713	40	1.514	0.102	1.015	3.108	1.514
Ω_s	A_s dB	L_1	L_2	C_2	Ω_2	L_3

$$A_p = 0.5 \text{ dB}$$

Ω_s	A_s dB	C_1	C_2	L_2	Ω_2	C_3
1.295	20	1.570	0.805	0.613	1.424	1.570
1.484	25	1.688	0.497	0.729	1.660	1.688
1.732	30	1.783	0.322	0.812	1.954	1.783
2.048	35	1.852	0.214	0.865	2.324	1.852
2.413	40	1.910	0.145	0.905	2.762	1.910
2.856	45	1.965	0.101	0.929	3.279	1.965
Ω_s	A_s dB	L_1	L_2	C_2	Ω_2	L_3

$$A_p = 1.0 \text{ dB}$$

TABLE III.10
Elliptic Filters Double π and T

Ω_s	A_s dB	C_1	C_2	L_2	Ω_2	C_3	C_4	L_4	Ω_4	C_s
1.309	35	0.977	0.230	1.139	1.954	1.488	0.742	0.740	1.350	0.701
1.414	40	1.010	0.177	1.193	2.176	1.586	0.530	0.875	1.468	0.766
1.540	45	1.032	0.140	1.228	2.412	1.657	0.401	0.968	1.605	0.836
1.690	50	1.044	0.1178	1.180	2.682	1.726	0.283	1.134	1.765	0.885
1.860	55	1.072	0.0880	1.275	2.985	1.761	0.241	1.100	1.942	0.943
2.048	60	1.095	0.0699	1.292	3.328	1.801	0.192	1.148	2.130	0.988
2.262	65	1.108	0.0555	1.308	3.712	1.834	0.151	1.191	2.358	1.022
2.512	70	1.112	0.0440	1.319	4.151	1.858	0.119	1.225	2.619	1.044
Ω_s	A_s dB	L_1	L_2	C_2	Ω_2	L_3	L_4	C_4	Ω_4	L_s

$$A_p = 0.1 \text{ dB}$$

Ω_s	A_s dB	C_1	C_2	L_2	Ω_2	C_3	C_4	L_4	Ω_4	C_s
1.186	35	1.439	0.358	0.967	1.700	1.762	1.116	0.600	1.222	1.026
1.270	40	1.495	0.279	1.016	1.878	1.880	0.840	0.696	1.308	1.114
1.369	45	1.530	0.218	1.063	2.077	1.997	0.627	0.795	1.416	1.241
1.481	50	1.563	0.172	1.099	2.300	2.113	0.482	0.875	1.540	1.320
1.618	55	1.559	0.134	1.140	2.558	2.188	0.369	0.949	1.690	1.342
1.782	60	1.603	0.108	1.143	2.847	2.248	0.291	0.995	1.858	1.449
1.963	65	1.626	0.0860	1.158	3.169	2.306	0.230	1.037	2.048	1.501
2.164	70	1.624	0.0679	1.178	3.536	2.319	0.182	1.078	2.258	1.521
Ω_s	A_s dB	L_1	L_2	C_2	Ω_2	L_3	L_4	C_4	Ω_4	L_s

$$A_p = 0.5 \text{ dB}$$

Ω_s	A_s dB	C_1	C_2	L_2	Ω_2	C_3	C_4	L_4	Ω_4	C_s
1.145	35	1.783	0.474	0.827	1.597	1.978	1.487	0.488	1.174	1.276
1.217	40	1.861	0.372	0.873	1.755	2.142	1.107	0.578	1.250	1.427
1.245	45	1.923	0.293	0.947	1.898	2.296	0.848	0.684	1.313	1.553
1.407	50	1.933	0.223	0.963	2.158	2.392	0.626	0.750	1.459	1.635
1.528	55	1.976	0.178	0.986	2.387	2.519	0.487	0.811	1.591	1.732
1.674	60	2.007	0.141	1.003	2.660	2.620	0.380	0.862	1.747	1.807
1.841	65	2.036	0.113	1.016	2.952	2.703	0.301	0.901	1.920	1.873
2.036	70	2.056	0.0890	1.028	3.306	2.732	0.239	0.934	2.117	1.928
Ω_s	A_s dB	L_1	L_2	C_2	Ω_2	L_3	L_4	C_4	Ω_4	L_s

$$A_p = 1.0 \text{ dB}$$

III.4 ACTIVE FILTERS

These filters and their element designations have been described in Chapter 7. Included here are tables for the Butterworth, Bessel, Chebyshev (0.5, 1.0, 2.0, 3.0 dB ripple), and Butterworth-Thomson filters.

The filter tables are III.11 through III.14. The Butterworth–Thomson characteristics are shown in Fig. III.6. The element values are shown in Table III.11. Inf. in Tables is infinity.

TABLE III.11
Normalized Capacitors for Active Butterworth Filters

n	C_1	C_2	C_3	C_4	C_5	C_6	C_7	C_8	C_9	C_{10}
1	1.00									
2	1.41	0.707								
3	1.39	3.54	0.202							
4	1.08	0.924	2.61	0.383						
5	1.09	1.80	0.509	3.24	0.309					
6	1.41	0.707	1.04	0.966	3.86	0.259				
7	1.38	2.52	0.288	1.11	0.900	4.49	0.223			
8	1.18	0.846	2.05	0.437	0.965	1.04	4.84	0.207		
9	1.36	1.88	0.39	2.00	0.500	1.06	0.940	5.76	0.174	
10	1.12	0.891	1.42	0.706	2.20	0.454	1.01	0.988	6.39	0.156

TABLE III.12
Normalized Capacitors for Active Bessel Filters

n	C_1	C_2	C_3	C_4	C_5	C_6	C_7	C_8	C_9	C_{10}
1	1.00									
2	0.667	0.500								
3	0.565	0.814	0.145							
4	0.345	0.317	0.475	0.183						
5	0.359	0.736	0.0572	0.298	0.235					
6	0.235	0.226	2.268	0.179	0.397	0.0948				
7	0.262	0.735	0.285	0.210	0.185	0.246	0.141			
8	0.179	0.176	0.229	0.114	0.192	0.151	0.352	0.0586		
9	0.235	0.285	0.0729	0.209	0.0927	0.143	0.133	0.337	0.0479	
10	0.187	0.139	0.137	0.147	0.216	0.0778	0.141	0.0963	0.320	0.04

TABLE III.13
Normalized Capacitors for Active Chebyshev Filters

n	C_1	C_2	C_3	C_4	C_5	C_6	C_7	C_8	C_9	C_{10}
1	2.86									
2	1.40	0.470								
3	1.92	0.957	0.762							
4	5.70	0.165	2.36	1.88						
5	3.13	6.46	0.286	8.93	0.108					
6	12.9	0.0759	4.71	0.360	3.45	1.85				
7	4.18	20.6	0.0669	17.5	0.0561	4.33	0.909			
8	22.9	0.0431	8.05	0.168	5.38	0.518	4.56	2.49		
9	5.32	15.9	0.132	29.0	0.0341	10.1	0.126	5.36	1.19	
10	35.8	0.0277	12.4	0.098	7.93	0.237	6.29	0.668	5.68	3.13

0.5 dB Ripple

n	C_1	C_2	C_3	C_4	C_5	C_6	C_7	C_8	C_9	C_{10}
1	1.97									
2	1.82	0.498								
3	2.34	14.8	0.0587							
4	7.17	0.141	2.97	1.21						
5	3.81	8.60	0.246	11.2	0.0905					
6	16.1	0.0628	5.98	0.305	4.31	1.86				
7	5.11	28.6	0.051	21.9	0.046	5.4	0.803			
8	28.6	0.0352	10.0	0.138	6.7	0.438	5.68	2.50		
9	6.52	20.7	0.106	36.1	0.0278	12.6	0.103	6.68	1.05	
10	44.6	0.0225	9.87	0.195	15.4	0.0799	7.83	0.563	7.07	3.15

1.0 dB Ripple

n	C_1	C_2	C_3	C_4	C_5	C_6	C_7	C_8	C_9	C_{10}
1	1.31									
2	2.49	0.631								
3	3.01	26.9	0.0377							
4	9.53	0.113	3.95	1.14						
5	4.90	12.3	0.194	14.8	0.0708					
6	21.3	0.0486	7.79	0.241	5.7	1.75				
7	6.81	14.1	0.315	28.9	0.0355	10.3	0.152			
8	37.7	0.027	13.3	0.106	8.86	0.345	7.51	2.36		
9	8.73	16.9	0.427	47.7	0.0213	16.6	0.0789	10.8	0.219	
10	58.9	0.0172	13.0	0.15	20.3	0.0612	10.3	0.444	9.33	2.96

2.0 dB Ripple

n	C_1	C_2	C_3	C_4	C_5	C_6	C_7	C_8	C_9	C_{10}
1	1.00									
2	3.10	0.455								
3	3.63	43.4	0.0253							
4	11.7	0.0943	4.86	0.05						
5	5.92	15.8	0.160	18.2	0.0586					
6	26.2	0.04	9.57	0.200	7.01	1.61				
7	8.24	17.9	0.262	35.5	0.0291	12.7	0.126			
8	46.3	0.0222	16.3	0.0873	10.9	0.287	9.22	2.16		
9	10.6	21.4	0.356	58.6	0.0174	20.4	0.0647	13.3	0.178	
10	72.3	0.0141	24.9	0.0501	16.0	0.123	12.7	0.368	11.5	2.70

3.0 dB Ripple

TABLE III.14
Normalized Capacitors for Butterworth–Thomson Active Filters

Normalized Capacitor Values Using Unity-Gain Amplifiers

Order	Section	$m = 0.2$			$m = 0.4$			$m = 0.6$			$m = 0.8$		
		C_1	C_2	C_3	C_1	C_2	C_3	C_1	C_2	C_3	C_1	C_2	C_3
2	1	1.3456	0.7431		1.2868	0.7771		1.2361	0.8090		1.1924	0.8387	
3	1	1.3950	3.2775	0.2190	1.3963	3.2851	0.2185	1.3963	3.2853	0.2185	1.3951	3.2779	0.2189
4	1	1.0859	0.9422		1.0900	0.9604		1.0945	0.9785		1.0996	0.9965	
	2	2.2819	0.4283		2.0258	0.4716		1.8224	0.5123		1.6575	0.5506	
5	1	1.3669	1.7467		1.3796	1.7651		1.3922	1.7841		1.4048	1.8036	
	2	2.7449	0.3529	0.4278	2.3795	0.3944	0.4234	2.0976	0.4335	0.4192	1.8742	0.4700	0.4150
6	1	1.0475	0.9835		1.0601	1.0013		1.0729	1.0193		1.0861	1.0374	
	2	1.3741	0.7344		1.3380	0.7611		1.3057	0.7871		1.2766	0.8124	
	3	3.1995	0.3006		2.7211	0.3400		2.3609	0.3769		2.0806	0.4113	

n	i								
7			0.4920		0.4860		0.4799		0.4738
	1	1.3546	1.5423	1.3726	1.5601	1.3909	1.5791	1.4094	1.5992
	2	1.5368	0.6520	1.4755	0.6805	1.4209	0.7081	1.3722	0.7348
	3	3.6458	0.2622	3.0519	0.2995	2.6138	0.3344	2.2782	0.3668
8	1	1.0349	0.9988	1.0505	1.0171	1.0664	1.0356	1.0827	1.0544
	2	1.1962	0.8539	1.1907	0.8762	1.1862	0.8984	1.1827	0.9204
	3	1.7000	0.5856	1.6125	0.6147	1.5353	0.6428	1.4670	0.6698
	4	4.0845	0.2329	3.3733	0.2683	2.8578	0.3012	2.4681	0.3318
9			0.5197		0.5127		0.5056		0.4984
	1	1.3487	1.4715	1.3696	1.4889	1.3908	1.5077	1.4124	1.5279
	2	1.2862	0.7901	1.2690	0.8139	1.2535	0.8373	1.2396	0.8604
	3	1.8660	0.5305	1.7503	0.5598	1.6494	0.5880	1.5610	0.6150
	4	4.5162	0.2907	3.6863	0.2434	3.0941	0.2747	2.6514	0.3036
10	1	1.0293	1.0061	1.0465	1.0249	1.0639	1.0439	1.0818	1.0633
	2	1.1270	0.9118	1.1322	0.9327	1.1379	0.9537	1.1442	0.9747
	3	1.3808	0.7323	1.3506	0.7570	1.3232	0.7814	1.2984	0.8052
	4	2.0324	0.4845	1.8871	0.5138	1.7621	0.5418	1.6534	0.5686
	5	4.9415	0.1910	3.9918	0.2231	3.3235	0.2529	2.8289	0.2804

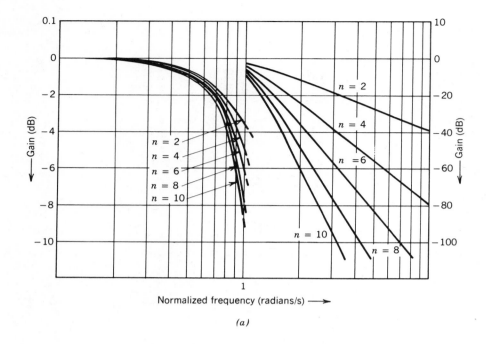

(a)

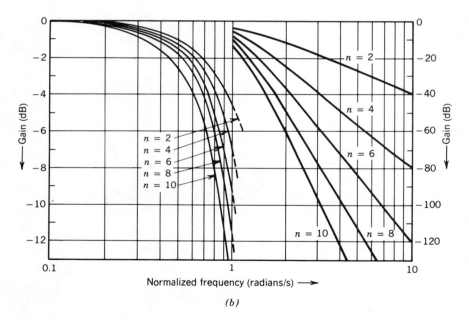

(b)

FIGURE III.6 Butterworth–Thomson characteristics: (a) gain for $m = 0.4$; (b) gain for $m = 0.8$.

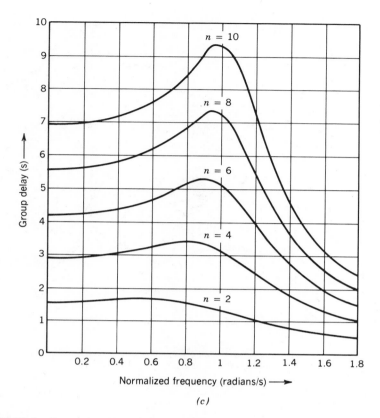

FIGURE III.6   Butterworth–Thomson characteristics: (c) group delay for $m = 0.4$.

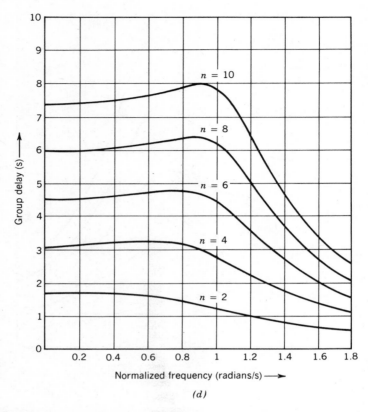

(d)

FIGURE III.6 Butterworth–Thomson characteristics: (*d*) group delay for *m* = 0.8.

APPENDIX
IV

Miscellaneous Data

This appendix contains a collection of data, graphs, and tables that relate directly to the designs in the text. This information is far from complete and, as stated previously, there is no substitute for an up-to-date collection of the manufacturer's data sheets.

IV.1 TRANSISTOR h PARAMETERS

Figures IV.1a through IV.1d are a set of **h** parameters for the 2N2222A transistors. The 1 and 2 curves represent maximum and minimum values, respectively. The values from these graphs are used to obtain the **T** parameters that are applied in the text. The **h** to **T** transformation is given in Section I.1.

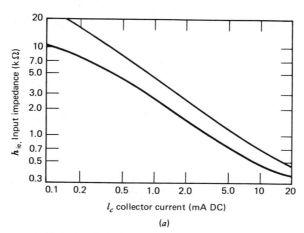

(a)

FIGURE IV.1   **h** Parameters (2N2222A); (a) input impedance (figure continues on page 402).

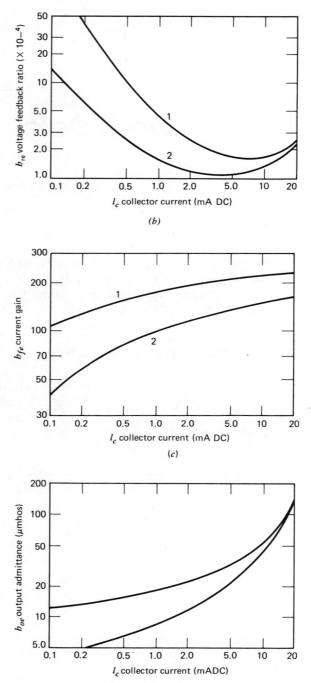

FIGURE IV. 1 (*continued*) (*c*) current gain; (*d*) output admittance. (Courtesy of Motorola.)

IV.2 FERRITE PROPERTIES

Figures IV.2 and IV.3 show the permeability properties versus temperature and frequency, respectively, of the ferrite materials available from Ferroxcube.

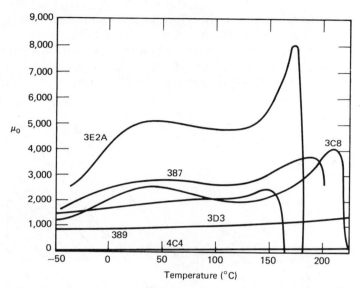

FIGURE IV.2   Initial permeability μ_0 vs. temperature. (Courtesy of Ferroxcube.)

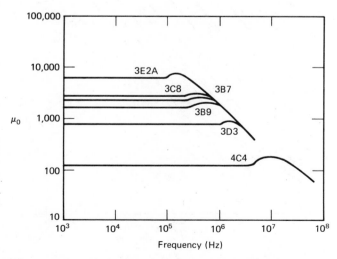

FIGURE IV.3   Initial permeability μ_0 vs. frequency. (Courtesy of Ferroxcube.)

Figure IV.4 shows the core losses of the 3E2A ferrite versus frequency and flux density.

Figure IV.5 is a graph that assists in selecting the proper core size for a given amount of proper output, P_o (W) in watts, for a sign wave application. Figure IV.6 has the same data for a square wave application.

The bottom horizontal designation is $W_a A_c$ $(10)^6$ cir mils cm^2, where W_a is the available core window area and A_c is the affective core cross-sectional area. Both are in circular mils.

The top horizontal line shows the core designation (Magnetics, Inc.) to obtain the $W_a A_c$ shown on the bottom horizontal line. The corresponding Ferroxcube designation is the same, but without the first 4.

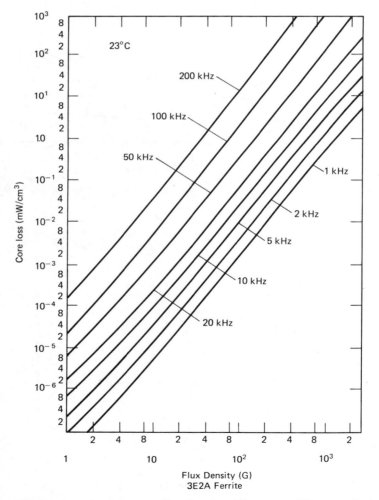

FIGURE IV.4   Core loss vs. flux density. (Courtesy of Ferroxcube.)

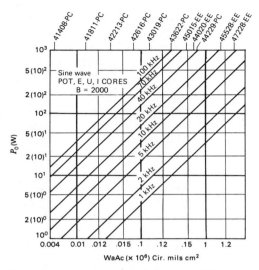

FIGURE IV.5   Core size vs. power and frequency. (Courtesy of Magnetics, Inc.)

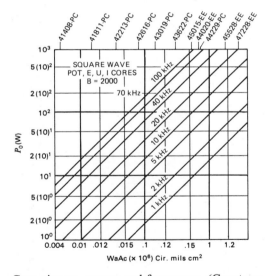

FIGURE IV.6   Core size vs. power and frequency. (Courtesy of Magnetics, Inc.)

IV.3 STANDARD INDUCTORS

The curves shown in Fig. IV.7 are taken from Vangard Electronics
data book and gives the principal properties of their line of miniature
toroidal inductors. More information can be obtained from the complete set of data sheets.

Apparent Inductance (μH)	Min. Q	Test Freq. (MHz)	Min. Self Res. Freq. (MHz)	Max. DC Res. (Ω)	Rated DC Current (mA)
0.01	60	150	1000	0.02	3000
0.012	60	150	1000	0.02	3000
0.015	60	150	1000	0.02	3000
0.018	60	150	1000	0.02	3000
0.022	60	100	900	0.02	3000
0.027	60	100	800	0.02	3000
0.033	60	100	750	0.02	3000
0.039	60	100	700	0.02	3000
0.047	60	100	650	0.02	3000
0.056	60	100	600	0.02	3000
0.068	60	100	550	0.03	2500
0.082	60	100	500	0.04	2200
0.10	80	50	450	0.04	2200
0.12	80	50	400	0.05	2000
0.15	80	50	350	0.06	1800
0.39	80	50	320	0.07	1600
0.22	80	50	300	0.08	1500
0.27	80	50	280	0.10	1400
0.33	80	50	260	0.12	1300
0.39	80	50	240	0.15	1150
0.47	80	50	220	0.20	1000
0.56	70	50	200	0.25	900
0.68	70	50	180	0.30	800
0.82	70	50	160	0.35	750
1.0	70	50	150	0.40	700

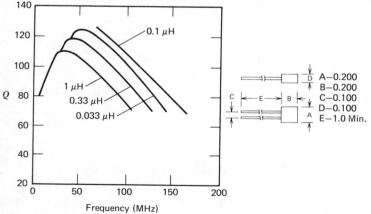

FIGURE IV.7 Miniature toroidal inductors. (Courtesy of Vangard.)

406

Apparent Inductance (μH)	Min. Q	Test Freq. (MHz)	Min. Self Res. Freq. (MHz)	Max. DC Res. (Ω)	Rated DC Current (mA)
10	75	2.5	35	1.1	550
12	75	2.5	31	1.3	500
15	75	2.5	27	1.5	450
18	80	2.5	24	1.9	410
22	80	2.5	22	2.3	380
27	80	2.5	20	2.7	350
33	80	2.5	18	3.3	320
39	80	2.5	16	3.9	290
47	80	2.5	14	4.7	260
56	80	2.5	12	5.6	240
68	80	2.5	11	6.8	220
82	80	2.5	10	8.1	200
100	80	2.5	9.1	9.7	180
120	45	0.79	8.2	12	160
150	45	0.79	7.3	14	150
180	45	0.79	6.4	17	140
220	50	0.79	5.6	20	130
270	55	0.79	5.0	24	120
330	55	0.79	4.4	19	130
390	55	0.79	3.9	22	120
470	55	0.79	3.5	27	110
560	55	0.79	3.1	32	100
680	55	0.79	2.8	19	130
820	50	0.79	2.5	23	120
1000	50	0.79	2.2	27	110

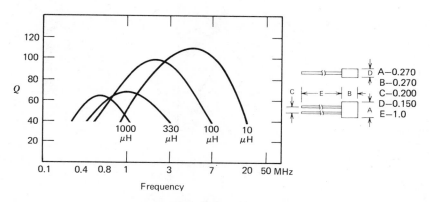

FIGURE IV.7 *(Continued)*

407

Apparent Inductance (μH)	Min. Q	Test Freq. (MHz)	Min. Self Res. Freq. (MHz)	Max. DC Res. (Ω)	Rated DC Current (mA)
0.10	55	25	450	0.04	2200
0.12	60	25	400	0.05	2000
0.15	60	25	350	0.06	1800
0.18	60	25	320	0.07	1600
0.22	65	25	300	0.08	1500
0.27	65	25	280	0.10	1400
0.33	65	25	260	0.11	1300
0.39	65	25	240	0.14	1200
0.47	65	25	220	0.17	1100
0.56	70	25	200	0.22	1000
0.68	70	25	180	0.27	900
0.82	70	25	160	0.30	800
1.0	70	25	150	0.35	750
1.2	60	7.9	130	0.40	700
1.5	60	7.9	120	0.50	630
1.8	60	7.9	110	0.70	530
2.2	60	7.9	100	0.90	470
2.7	60	7.9	90	1.1	420
3.3	60	7.9	70	1.3	390
3.9	60	7.9	60	1.5	360
4.7	60	7.9	50	1.8	330
5.6	60	7.9	45	2.0	310
6.8	60	7.9	40	2.2	300
8.2	60	7.9	37	2.4	290
10	60	7.9	35	2.6	280

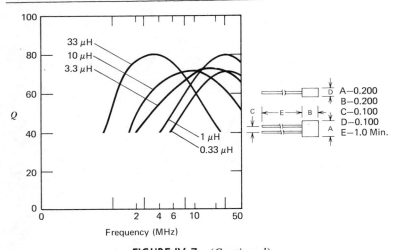

FIGURE IV.7 (*Continued*).

Apparent Inductance (μH)	Min. Q	Test Freq. (KHz)	Min. Self Res. Freq. (MHz)	Max. DC Res. (Ω)	Rated DC Current (mA)
100	75	790	8.4	6	280
120	75	790	7.5	7	260
150	75	790	6.7	8	240
180	75	790	6.0	10	220
220	80	790	5.3	12	200
270	80	790	4.7	14	180
330	80	790	4.2	17	160
390	80	790	3.8	20	150
470	75	790	3.4	24	140
560	75	790	3.1	28	130
680	75	790	2.8	33	120
820	75	790	2.5	39	110
1,000	75	790	2.2	45	100
1,200	45	250	1.9	31	120
1,500	45	250	1.6	37	110
1,800	50	250	1.4	44	100
2,200	50	250	1.3	52	90
2,700	50	250	1.2	61	85
3,300	50	250	1.1	71	80
3,900	50	250	1.0	82	75
4,700	50	250	0.9	93	70
5,600	45	250	0.8	105	65
6,800	40	250	0.7	140	60
8,200	40	250	0.6	160	55
10,000	40	250	0.6	180	50

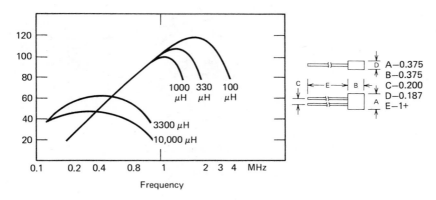

FIGURE IV.7 (*Continued*)

IV.4 CAPACITORS

The curves shown in Fig. IV.8 are for general reference and judgment only. The impedance of tantalytic and aluminum electrolytic capacitors varies considerably with the manufacturer and model.

The data are for capacitors with very short leads. The longer leads necessary in a practical circuit greatly degrade the high-frequency

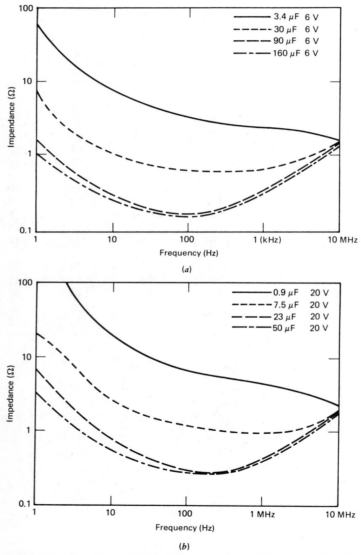

FIGURE IV.8   Impedance of tantalytic capacitors. (Courtesy of Mallory.)

impedance. If the use of the capacitor is intended to extend to moderately high frequencies, the series-resonant frequency should be determined as outlined in Section 7.1.7. This test *must* be made with the intended lead length. Normal polarized capacitors are bipolar for voltages less than 5–10% of their rated value and can be tested and used in this manner. The manufacturer should always be consulted on this matter before proceeding with a final application.

For quick reference, we have

$$0.025 \text{ in. } D \text{ (lead wire)} = 0.2 \text{ } \mu\text{H/in.} = 1.3 \text{ } \Omega/\text{in. at 10 MHz}$$

Table IV.1 contains some series-resonant data on dipped mica and ceramic capacitor.

TABLE IV.1
Series Resonant Data

Dipped Mica $\frac{1}{4}$ in. Leads		Ceramic $\frac{1}{4}$ in. Leads		
100 pF	156 MHz	0.1 in. $D \times \frac{5}{32}$ in. long	0.001 μF	64 MHz
470 pF	71 MHz		0.01 μF	18 MHz
1,000 pF	48 MHz			
7,500 pF	15 MHz	$\frac{1}{4} \times \frac{1}{4}$ in.	0.1 μF	5.5 MHz
39,000 pF	6 MHz		1.0 μF	2.0 MHz

(Reprinted with permission from *Radio Engineers Handbook* by F. E. Terman. Copyright © 1943 McGraw-Hill Company.)

IV.5 COPPER WIRE

This section contains information on copper wire that is of importance in designing transformers and inductors.

Table IV.2 is a standard copper wire table. This and Fig. IV.10 are reprinted through the courtesy of F. E. Terman [1].

Table IV.3 contains insulated copper wire diameters which must be used in determining the space required for a given coil, as shown in Fig. IV.9.

TABLE IV.2
Copper-Wire Table, Standard Annealed Copper, American Wire Gauge (B & S)

Gauge No.	Diameter (mils at 20°C)	Cross Section at 20°C		Ω/1000 ft at 20°C (=68°F)	lb/1000 ft	ft/lb	ft/Ω at 20°C (=68°F)	Ω/lb at 20°C (=68°F)	Gauge No.
		Circular mils	in.²						
0000	460.0	211,600.0	0.1662	0.04901	640.5	1.561	20,400.0	0.00007652	0000
000	409.6	167,800.0	0.1318	0.06180	507.9	1.968	16,180.0	0.0001217	000
00	364.8	133,100.0	0.1045	0.07793	402.8	2.482	12,830.0	0.0001935	00
0	324.9	105,500.0	0.08289	0.09827	319.5	3.130	10,180.0	0.0003076	0
1	289.3	83,690.0	0.06573	0.1239	253.3	3.947	8,070.0	0.0004891	1
2	257.6	66,370.0	0.05213	0.1563	200.9	4.977	6,400.0	0.0007778	2
3	229.4	52,640.0	0.04134	0.1970	159.3	6.276	5,075.0	0.001237	3
4	204.3	41,740.0	0.03278	0.2485	126.4	7.914	4,025.0	0.001966	4
5	181.9	33,100.0	0.02600	0.3133	100.2	9.980	3,192.0	0.003127	5
6	162.0	26,250.0	0.02062	0.3951	79.46	12.58	2,531.0	0.004972	6
7	144.3	20,820.0	0.01635	0.4982	63.02	15.87	2,007.0	0.007905	7
8	128.5	16,510.0	0.01297	0.6282	49.98	20.01	1,592.0	0.01257	8
9	114.4	13,090.0	0.01028	0.7921	39.63	25.23	1,262.0	0.01999	9
10	101.9	10,380.0	0.008155	0.9989	31.43	31.82	1,001.0	0.03178	10
11	90.74	8,234.0	0.006467	1.260	24.92	40.12	794.0	0.05053	11
12	80.81	6,530.0	0.005129	1.588	19.77	50.59	629.6	0.08035	12
13	71.96	5,178.0	0.004067	2.003	15.68	63.80	499.3	0.1278	13
14	64.08	4,107.0	0.003225	2.525	12.43	80.44	396.0	0.2032	14

15	0.3230	314.0	101.4	9.858	3.184	0.002558	3,257.0	57.07	15
16	0.5136	249.0	127.9	7.818	4.016	0.002028	2,583.0	50.82	16
17	0.8167	197.5	161.3	6.200	5.064	0.001609	2,048.0	45.26	17
18	1.299	156.6	203.4	4.917	6.385	0.001276	1,624.0	40.30	18
19	2.065	124.2	256.5	3.899	8.051	0.001012	1,288.0	35.89	19
20	3.283	98.50	323.4	3.092	10.15	0.0008023	1,022.0	31.96	20
21	5.221	78.11	407.8	2.452	12.80	0.0006363	810.1	28.46	21
22	8.301	61.95	514.2	1.945	16.14	0.0005046	642.4	25.35	22
23	13.20	49.13	648.4	1.542	20.36	0.0004002	509.5	22.57	23
24	20.99	38.96	817.7	1.223	25.67	0.0003173	404.0	20.10	24
25	33.37	30.90	1,031.0	0.9699	32.27	0.0002517	320.4	17.90	25
26	53.06	24.50	1,300.0	0.7692	40.81	0.0001996	254.1	15.94	26
27	84.37	19.43	1,639.0	0.6100	51.47	0.0001583	201.5	14.20	27
28	134.2	15.41	2,067.0	0.4837	64.90	0.0001255	159.8	12.64	28
29	213.3	12.22	2,607.0	0.3836	81.83	0.00009953	126.7	11.26	29
30	339.2	9.691	3,287.0	0.3042	103.2	0.00007894	100.5	10.03	30
31	539.3	7.685	4,145.0	0.2413	130.1	0.00006260	79.70	8.928	31
32	857.6	6.095	5,227.0	0.1913	164.1	0.00004964	63.21	7.950	32
33	1,364.0	4.833	6,591.0	0.1517	206.9	0.00003937	50.13	7.080	33
34	2,168.0	3.833	8,310.0	0.1203	260.9	0.00003122	39.75	6.305	34
35	3,448.0	3.040	10,480.0	0.09542	329.0	0.00002496	31.52	5.615	35
36	5,482.0	2.411	13,210.0	0.07568	414.8	0.00001964	25.00	5.000	36
37	8,717.0	1.912	16,660.0	0.06001	523.1	0.00001557	19.83	4.453	37
38	13,860.0	1.516	21,010.0	0.04759	659.6	0.00001235	15.72	3.965	38
39	22,040.0	1.202	26,500.0	0.03774	831.8	0.000009793	12.47	3.531	39
40	35,040.0	0.9534	33,410.0	0.02993	1,049.0	0.000007766	9.888	3.145	40

TABLE IV.3
Insulated Wire Diameter

Nos. B. and S. Gauge	Diameter Bare (in.)	Average Diameter over Enamel	Nos. B and S Gauge	Diameter Bare (in.)	Average Diameter over Enamel
13	0.0720	0.0740	28	0.0126	0.0136
14	0.0641	0.0661	29	0.0112	0.0121
15	0.0571	0.0591	30	0.0100	0.0108
16	0.0508	0.0528	31	0.0089	0.0097
17	0.0452	0.0470	32	0.0079	0.0086
18	0.0403	0.0421	33	0.0071	0.0078
19	0.0359	0.0377	34	0.0063	0.0069
20	0.0320	0.0338	35	0.0056	0.0062
21	0.0284	0.0301	36	0.0050	0.0055
22	0.0253	0.0269	37	0.0044	0.0049
23	0.0225	0.0240	38	0.0040	0.0044
24	0.0201	0.0215	39	0.0034	0.0039
25	0.0179	0.0192	40	0.0031	0.0035
26	0.0159	0.0171			
27	0.0142	0.0153			

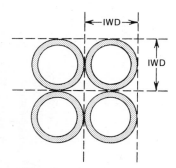

FIGURE IV.9 Conductor stacking.

This space-factor allowance is suitable only for coils with a small number of layers that are carefully wound and contain no taps. Larger coils, especially with taps, must employ smaller wire.

Figure IV.10 shows the inductance of a straight conductor. This is of value in estimating the effect of lead length in circuit layouts, and is particularly important for filter capacitors.

Figure IV.11 gives the increase in resistance of an isolated straight conductor due to the high-frequency skin effect.

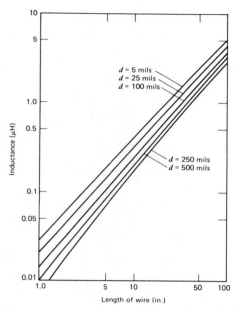

FIGURE IV.10 Inductance of a straight conductor. (Reprinted with permission from *Radio Engineers Handbook* by F. E. Terman. Copyright © 1943 McGraw-Hill Book Company.)

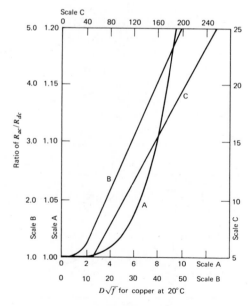

FIGURE IV.11 R_{AC}/R_{DC} of a straight conductor; D = diameter (in.). (From *Reference Data for Radio Engineers*, 6th Edition; copyright © 1977, Indianapolis, IN 46268.)

Unfortunately, this is only an approximation for a conductor wound as a coil. The closeness of the turns to each other increase the losses. The graph does, however, serve the purpose of alerting the designer that parallel conductors or possibly Litz wire should be considered.

REFERENCES

[1] F. E. Terman, *Radio Engineers Handbook*, McGraw-Hill, New York, 1943.
[2] *Reference Data for Engineers*, 5th ed., ITT, New York.

IV.6 T-PADS

T-pads are used to attenuate signals in a matched line without disturbing the existing impedance levels. Figure IV.12 shows their application, while Fig. IV.13 shows that of π-pads. A π-pad is a T-pad adapted for a balanced line.

An accurate T-pad can also be used to improve the accuracy of a source where the impedance level is not well defined or reliable. The greater the attenuation of the pad, the more the resulting output source impedance depends on the pad instead of the original source. Figure IV.14 shows an application for a 6 dB T-pad.

If the resulting attenuation is desired, it must be calculated from the total network with R_L as the load. If the T-pad were terminated with 500 Ω, R_L would see 250 Ω and the resulting attenuation would still have to be calculated. Tables IV.4 and IV.5 contain design values for T-pads of selected values of attenuation.

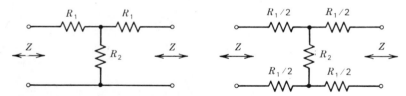

FIGURE IV.12   (*a*) Unbalanced and (*b*) balanced T-pads.

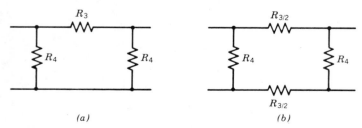

(*a*)   (*b*)

FIGURE IV.13   (*a*) Unbalanced and (*b*) balanced π-pads.

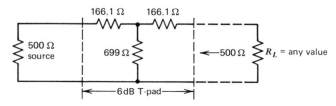

FIGURE IV.14 Source stabilization.

TABLE IV.4

Resistor Values for 50-Ω Attenuators

Atten. (dB)	R_1 Ω R_2	R_3 Ω R_4	Atten. (dB).	R_1 Ω R_2	R_3 Ω R_4
1.0	2.88 433.0	5.77 870.0	11.0	28.0 30.6	81.7 89.2
2.0	5.73 215.0	11.6 436.0	12.0	29.9 26.8	93.2 83.5
3.0	8.55 142.0	17.6 292.0	13.0	31.7 23.6	106.0 78.8
4.0	11.3 105.0	23.8 221.0	14.0	33.4 20.8	120.0 74.9
5.0	14.0 82.2	30.4 178.0	15.0	34.9 18.4	136.0 71.6
6.0	16.6 66.9	37.4 150.0	16.0	36.3 16.3	154.0 68.8
7.0	19.1 55.8	44.8 131.0	17.0	37.6 14.4	173.0 66.4
8.0	21.5 47.3	52.8 116.0	18.0	38.8 12.8	195.0 64.4
9.0	23.8 40.6	61.6 105.0	19.0	39.9 11.4	220.0 62.6
10.0	26.0 35.1	71.2 96.2	20.0	40.9 10.1	248.0 61.1

How to use the 50 Ω attenuator design table:
  (a) For a 50 Ω impedance level:
    1. Select one of the network configurations shown in Figs. IV.12 and 13.
    2. From Table IV.4 read the resistor values corresponding to the desired attenuation and the selected network.
    For example, the R_1 and R_2 values for a 10 dB T network are 26.0 and 35.1 Ω, respectively.
  (b) For impedance levels other than 50 Ω:
    1. Calculate the ratio of the desired impedance relative to 50 Ω.
    2. Multiply the tabulated resistor values associated with the desired attenuation by the calculated impedance ratio.
    For example, the R_1 and R_2 values for a 75 Ω 10 dB T network are 1.5(26.0) = 39 Ω and 1.5(35.1) = 52.7 Ω, respectively.

Note: The VSWR (voltage standing wave ratio) smoothing effect of these attenuators (or any resistive attenuator) is found from Fig. IV.15. For example, if the 50 Ω RF output of a signal source (such as the H-P Model 8444A tracking generator) has an unpadded VSWR of 2.3, a 10 dB pad placed between the generator output and a load will reduce the VSWR to about 1.08. Reducing an excessive VSWR of a signal generator is especially important when measuring the response of a filter.

TABLE IV.5
Values For Minimum-Loss Matching Pads Shown in Figure IV.16

R_S Ω	R_L Ω	R_3 Ω	R_4 Ω	Atten. (dB)	Figure No.	V Drop (dB) (V_{out} re V_{in})
50	75	43	87	5.7	16a	4.0
50	93	63	74	7.2	16a	4.5
50	125	97	65	9.0	16a	5.0
50	150	122	61	10.0	16a	5.2
50	300	274	55	13.4	16a	5.6
50	500	474	53	15.8	16a	5.8
50	600	574	52	16.6	16a	5.8
75	50	43	87	5.7	16b	7.5
75	93	41	170	4.1	16a	3.2
75	125	79	119	6.5	16a	4.3
75	150	106	106	7.7	16a	4.6
75	300	260	87	11.4	16a	5.4
75	500	461	81	13.9	16a	5.7
75	600	561	80	14.8	16a	5.7
93	50	63	74	7.2	16b	9.9
93	75	41	170	4.1	16b	5.0
93	125	63	184	4.8	16a	3.6
93	150	92	151	6.2	16a	4.2
150	50	122	61	10.0	16b	14.7
150	75	106	106	7.7	16b	10.7
150	93	92	151	6.2	16b	8.3
150	125	61	306	3.8	16b	4.6
150	300	212	212	7.7	16a	4.6
150	500	418	179	10.5	16a	5.3
150	600	520	173	11.4	16a	5.4
300	50	274	55	13.4	16b	21.2
300	75	260	87	11.4	16b	17.5
300	93	249	112	10.3	16b	15.4
300	125	229	164	8.7	16b	12.5
300	150	212	212	7.7	16b	10.7
300	500	316	474	6.5	16a	4.3
300	600	424	424	7.7	16a	4.6
500	50	474	53	15.8	16b	25.8
500	75	461	81	13.9	16b	22.2
500	125	451	103	12.9	16b	20.2
500	150	433	144	11.4	16b	17.5

93	300	249	112	10.3	16a	5.3	500	150	418	179	10.5	16b	15.7
93	500	451	103	12.9	16a	5.6	500	300	316	474	6.5	16b	8.7
93	600	552	101	13.8	16a	5.7	500	600	245	1225	3.8	16a	3.0
125	50	97	65	9.0	16b	12.9	600	50	574	52	16.6	16b	27.4
125	75	79	119	6.5	16b	8.7	600	75	561	80	14.8	16b	23.8
125	93	63	184	4.8	16b	6.1	600	93	552	101	13.8	16b	21.9
125	150	61	306	3.8	16a	3.0	600	125	534	140	12.3	16b	19.2
125	300	229	164	8.7	16a	4.9	600	150	520	173	11.4	16b	17.5
125	500	433	144	11.4	16a	5.4	600	300	424	424	7.7	16b	10.7
125	600	534	140	12.3	16a	5.5	600	500	245	1225	3.8	16b	4.6

How to use the minimum-loss matching pad design table:

1. From Table IV.5 find the values of R_3 and R_4 corresponding to the source R_S and load R_L impedances to be matched.
2. Connect resistors R_3 and R_4 between the source and load as shown in Fig. IV.16, depending on whether R_S is smaller or larger than R_L.

For example, to obtain a match with minimum loss between a 50 Ω source and a 75 Ω load, connect R_3 and R_4 (43 and 87 Ω, respectively) between the source and load using Fig. IV.16 as specified in the table listing for the 50/75 Ω combination.

Note: Explanation of the Atten. parameter listed in Table IV.4: This is the signal loss that results from the use of a minimum-loss resistive matching pad instead of a matching transformer. The VSWR smoothing effect caused by the attenuation of these minimum-loss pads can be found by matching the value in the Atten. (dB) column with the corresponding attenuation curve in Fig. IV.16. Interpolation may be required. For example, the 50/75 Ω 5.7 dB pad reduces a VSWR of 2.0 to about 1.2.

The voltage drop in decibels from the pad input to the pad output is given in the V-drop column of Table IV.5. This is not the same as the pad attenuation.

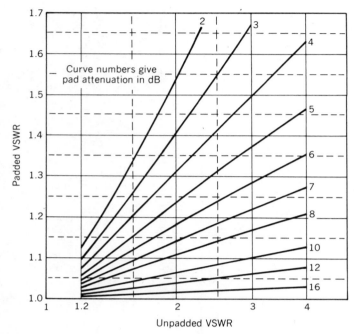

FIGURE IV.15   Padded VSWR vs. VSWR for various pad attenuations.

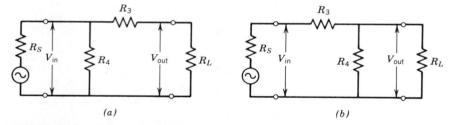

FIGURE IV.16   Networks for resistive minimum-loss matching pads: (a) $R_S < R_L$; (b) $R_S > R_L$.

The following are design equations used in calculating the 50 Ω and minimum-loss matching pads (∗, multiplication; ∧, exponent):

(a) 50 Ω Pads:

   A = Attenuation (dB)

   K = $10\wedge(A/20)$

   Z = Impedance (ohms)

   $R_1 = Z*(K - 1)/(K + 1)$

   $R_2 = Z*2*K/(K\wedge2 - 1)$

   $R_3 = Z*(K\wedge2 - 1)/(2*K)$

   $R_4 = Z*(K + 1)/(K - 1)$

(b) Minimum-Loss Pads:

   A = Attenuation (dB)

   R_S = Source impedance (Ω)

   R_L = Load impedance (Ω)

   $R = R_S/R_L$

      when $R_S > R_L$

   $R = R_L/R_S$

      when $R_L > R_S$

   $M = (1 - 1/R)\wedge0.5$

   $K = [(1 + M)/(1 - M)]\wedge0.5$

   $X = (K\wedge4 - 1)/(4* K\wedge2)$

   $Y = (K\wedge2 + 1)/(K\wedge2 - 1)$

   If $R_S < R_L$:

      $R_3 = R_S*X, R_4 = R_S*Y$

   If $R_L < R_S$: $R_3 = R_L*X,$

      $R_4 = R_L*Y$

   $A = 20*0.434295*LOG(K)$

V Drop $= 20*0.434295*LOG(V_{in}/V_{out})$ where LOG is to base e.

(c) VSWR smoothing curves of Fig. IV.15:

   A = Attenuation

   T = Unpadded VSWR

   V = Padded (smoothed) VSWR

   $K = 10\wedge(A/2)$

   $X = (K\wedge2 + 1)/(K\wedge2 - 1)$

   $V = (1 + T*X)/(T + X)$

REFERENCES

[1] E. E. Wetherhold, Annapolis, MD, private communication.
[2] P. R. Geffe, Comprehensive Tables for Resistive Attenuator Design, *EEE Mag.*, Nov. 1964.
[3] Attenuator Network Design, *Reference Data for Radio Engineers*, 6th ed., Howard W. Sams, Indianapolis, IN, 1981, Chapt. 11.

APPENDIX
V

Symbols

The symbols used in this book are, to the best of the author's knowledge, the preferred standards in the industry. These standards are set up by the IEEE. However, since there are various classifications of these symbols, usually no single publication covers a unique requirement.

Reference [1] by the IEEE contains a large number of the symbols used in this book. Additional symbols are available from other publications by the IEEE.

Reference [2] has a very large collection of symbols and is convenient as a guide. However, since symbols are frequently changed and new ones are constantly being defined, a publication of this sort should not be considered as an absolute reference.

V.1 GENERAL SYMBOLS

Name	Symbol
Admittance	y, Y
Alternating current	AC
Ampere	A
Amplification factor	μ
Amplitude modulation	AM
Audiofrequency	AF
Automatic frequency control	AFC
Automatic gain control	AGC
Beat frequency oscillator	BFO
Binary coded decimal	BCD
Bit	b

Name	Symbol
Capacitive reactance	X_c
Charge	Q
Conductance	
Previous unit	G (mhos)
Present unit	S (siemens)
Conductivity	σ
Continuous wave	cw
Current	I
Current (instantaneous value)	i
Cycle per second	Hz
Deci (1×10^{-1})	d
Decibel	dB
Decibel relative to 1 mW	dBm
Decibel relative to 1 W	dBW
Degrees (Celsius)	°C
Degrees (Fahrenheit)	°F
Degrees (Kelvins, not degrees Kelvin)	K
Digital voltmeter	DVM
Double pole, double throw	DPDT
Double pole, single throw	DPST
Electromotive force	EMF
Farad (unit of capacitance)	F
Field effect transistor	FET
Frequency	f
Frequency (angular)	ω
Frequency modulation	FM
Giga (1×10^9)	G
Gigahertz	GHz
Henry (unit of inductance)	H
Hertz	Hz
High frequency	HF
Impedance	Z
Inductance (mutual)	M
Inductance (self)	L
Inductive reactance	X_l
Integrated circuit	IC
Kelvin	K (no degree symbol)
Kilo (1×10^3)	k
Kilogram	kg
Kilohertz	kHz
Kilohm	kΩ
Kilometer	km
Kilovolt	kV

Name	Symbol
Kilowatt	kW
Large-scale integrated circuit	LSI
Light-emitting diode	LED
Low frequency	LF
Magnetic flux (Maxwell)	φ
Medium-scale integrated circuit	MSI
Mega (1×10^6)	M
Megahertz	MHz
Megohm	MΩ
Metal oxide semiconductor	MOS
Metal oxide semiconductor field effect transistor	MOSFET
MHO (*see* conductance)	
Micro (1×10^{-6})	μ
Microampere	μA
Microfarad	μF
Microhenry	μH
Microsecond	μs
Microvolt	μV
Microwatt	μW
Milli (1×10^{-3})	m
Millihenry	mH
Milliampere	mA
Millisecond	ms
Millivolt	mV
Milliwatt	mW
Nano (1×10^{-9})	n
Nanoampere	nA
Nanofarad	nF
Nanohenry	nH
Nanosecond	ns
Nanowatt	nW
Ohm (unit of resistance)	Ω
Pico (1×10^{-12})	p
Picoampere	pA
Picofarad	pF
Picosecond	ps
Picowatt	pW
Quality factor	Q (relates to the sharpness of a resonant circuit, also a figure of merit)

Name	Symbol
Radio frequency	RF
Reactance	X
Resistance	R
Primary resistance, parallel resistance	R_p
Secondary resistance, serial resistance	R_s
Root mean square	rms
Second (time)	s
Single pole, double throw	SPDT
Single pole, single throw	SPST
Single sideband	SSB
Silicon-controlled rectifier	SCR
Standing-wave ratio	SWR
Transconductance	g_m
Transistor–transistor logic	TTL
Turns (number)	N
Ultrahigh frequency	UHF
Very high frequency	VHF
Very low frequency	VLF
Voltage-controlled oscillator	VCO

V.2 GREEK SYMBOLS

Letter	Uppercase	Lowercase	Application
Alpha		α	Amplification factor, current gain (common base)
Beta		β	Feedback gain, current gain (common emitter)
Gamma		γ	Propagation constant
Delta	Δ		Increment
Epsilon		ϵ	Dielectric constant, electrical intensity
Zeta	Z		Impedance
Eta		η	Hysteresis coefficient, efficiency
Theta		θ	Phase angle
Lambda		λ	Wavelength
Mu		μ	Micro, amplification factor, permeability

Letter	Uppercase	Lowercase	Application
Pi		π	Ratio of circumference to diameter = 3.1416
Rho		ρ	Reflection coefficient (magnitude), resistivity
Sigma	Σ		Sign of summation
Tau		τ	Time constant
Phi		φ	Magnetic flux, phase angles
Omega	Ω		Ohms
		ω	Normalized frequency, angular velocity

V.3 TRANSISTOR SYMBOLS

Transistor symbols are less consistently organized and more complex than some of the other symbols. In using data sheets it is usually better to look for the manufacturer's definitions if they are given.

Normally, and in this book, lowercase letters are used for the intrinsic transistor and uppercase letters for the supporting circuit. For example, r_e is the emitter resistance of the transistor and R_e is the external resistor that is in series with the transistor emitter.

For operating conditions such as current, lowercase letters represent the dynamic or signal value and uppercase letters the quiescent or DC value. Again, i_c and I_c.

In general, subscripts are used to describe a parameter in a specific manner. For example, BV_{CEO} is the breakdown voltage between the collector and the emitter with the base open, while BV_{CES} is the breakdown voltage with the base shorted to the emitter.

In addition to this general guide, Chapters 1 and 2, which deal specifically with transistors, carefully define the symbols and parameters that are used.

REFERENCES

[1] *IEEE Standard Letter Symbols for Units of Measurement (ANSI/IEEE Std. 260-1978),* New York, 10017.
[2] R. H. Ludwig, *Illustrated Handbook of Electronic Symbols and Measurements,* Parker, Englewood Cliffs, NJ.

Index